A HOLE
IN THE BOTTOM
OF THE SEA

A HOLE
IN THE BOTTOM
OF THE SEA

THE STORY OF THE MOHOLE PROJECT

by *Willard Bascom*

ILLUSTRATED BY THE AUTHOR
AND RUSSELL F. PETERSON

GARDEN CITY, NEW YORK
Doubleday & Company, Inc.

The author alone is responsible for any errors of fact or interpretation that may be found within this book. However, he wishes to acknowledge the assistance of the following persons who reviewed all or part of the original manuscript and made helpful suggestions: Gordon Lill, Harry Ladd, Harry Hess, John Isaacs, J. B. Hersey, Gustaf Arrhenius, Jack McLelland, Edward Horton, Francois Lampietti, Hatten Yoder, A. J. Field, Ralph Lapp, Richard Winslow, Howard Lewis.

FOR RHODA

Contents

Illustrations

PLATES

LIST OF TABLES

NOTE TO READER

This book will follow the practice of using the units that are customary in the subject being discussed.

The geophysical measurements are in the international metric system—meters, kilograms, and degrees Centigrade; the engineering units are in feet, pounds, and degrees Fahrenheit; the geological and oceanographic units are those of the original investigator and may be in either. Where the systems overlap and it is practicable to do so, both kinds of units are used.

The relationships between the most commonly used units are given on page 327.

A HOLE
IN THE BOTTOM
OF THE SEA

I

Introduction

"Look! That's not basalt; it's the mantle! We're through the Moho! We've made it!"

A dozen men are clustered around the end of a grimy piece of pipe. From its end a rod-shaped piece of rock about two inches in diameter is slowly emerging. Their words are jumbled and blown away by the wind but there can be no doubt that this is a great moment. They pound each other exuberantly on the back like the winners of a long-shot bet.

The scene is the drilling floor of a huge derrick which is a lot like the ones that prickle the skyline above oil country. The draw works, the elevators, the pumps, all look the same as usual, but where is the stand of drill pipe? It is stretched full length on the ground—no, the deck. For this is a ship; the whole huge machine is gently swaying as it rolls with the swell. The horizon? Clouds and water.

There is a quiet throbbing of engines deep in the hold, the low whistling of the wind in the rigging, and the hum of a fast-running cable, but over them all is the exciting sound of conquest. A few moments ago a piece of rock about a foot long fell with a clunk from the end of the pipe into a shallow half-round tray. When it did, a sunburned fellow standing alongside the tray suddenly dropped to his knees on the muddy platform of the great derrick, snatched the fragment of core up, and dunked it in a bucket of water, scrubbing the mud off it with his hands.

When the rock is clean enough so that its details are visible he peers at it closely. Two heads close in, effectively screening this fascinating object from the others who crowd closer. One offers a geologist's magnifying glass.

"What is it? What have we got?"

"It looks like . . ." but the last word is indistinct.

A man who has been firing questions and jotting notes on a folded scrap of paper breaks away and heads for the typewriter in the ship's radio shack to pound out the news for the world.

THE MOHO, LOWER BOUNDARY OF THE EARTH'S CRUST, HAS BEEN REACHED. AT 10:45 THIS MORNING, SAMPLES OF THE BASIC MATERIAL THAT COMPOSES MOST OF THE EARTH WERE SEEN BY MAN FOR THE FIRST TIME. SCIENTISTS, DRILLING IN THE DEEP OCEAN A THOUSAND MILES OFF THE MEXICAN COAST, TODAY BROUGHT UP CORES OF THE EARTH'S MANTLE. "NOW WE KNOW WHAT THE EARTH IS MADE OF," SAYS THEIR JUBILANT LEADER. . . .

One of the roughnecks on the rig, unable to contain his curiosity any longer, stands on tiptoes to lean over the scientists' backs and take a look at the splendid thing that has caused all this excitement. When he sees it he is astonished and says, half to himself, "That's what we've been after?" He backs off a little and mutters incredulously, "Ten million bucks for that—and they're happy?"

Suddenly he is unsure of his values and turns to his boss for understanding. "Did you see what they got? It's just a plain piece of rock."

But the driller shrugs without looking away from his dials or the wire that's spinning out. He's thinking, "Thank God we got their core—whatever it is. They'll never know how close we came to losing this hole. Wonder how long this job will last now."

In the background is a bulky fellow, the drilling contractor, studded with sweat but with a grin of obvious relief on his face. He calls to the elated scientists, "Congratulations fellows, the celebration starts in my cabin any time now."

That's the way the Mohole story may end.

A Geological Study

What kind of men are these that can get so excited about a piece of seemingly barren rock? They are some of the top earth scientists of our time, who will have worked and waited a long time for that dramatic instant to come. For them the moment of truth is in sight after years of study and planning and struggling for support, because when that chunk of rock has been thoroughly analyzed, many important secrets of our earth will be unlocked. It is a geological key, a thousand times more valuable than gold.

That little story is a preview of one of the great moments in science that will arrive within the next few years. Probably you are greatly mystified about why and where and what was going on in that curious scene. The answer is simple—in a complicated sort of way. Scientists want to know exactly what the interior of the earth is made of, so they plan to drill a hole where the crust is thin to get a sample. The structure of the earth's crust being what it is, the thinnest place is under the ocean.

This book traces the history of geological thought and attempts to explain how early theories of the earth developed into those presently in fashion by the slow accumulation of data and the testing of ideas over many years. It shows how geological work has expanded and subdivided, tending to become more quantitative and tending toward a closer relationship with the basic sciences of physics, biology, and chemistry, so that now this widened field of effort is called the earth sciences.

In this new grouping of earth sciences, astronomy and oceanography are brought into intimate contact with geophysics and radiochemistry and each of these has been given equal status with traditional geology in the determined effort to unravel the mysteries of the earth. The result is that the evidence that each subscience is accumulating is constantly being re-evaluated in terms of the new evidence found by the others. For in the understanding of the earth the assembled knowledge is far greater than the sum of its parts. As a result of pooling this knowledge, a unified concept of the earth and its history has been formulated which meets with general agreement among scientists.

Even so, many of its parts rest on indirect evidence and it is necessary to distinguish between the things which are "known" with a 95 per cent certainty from those that are "known" with a 50 per cent certainty. The objective of continuing these scientific studies is to produce more evidence that will confirm or deny existing ideas but will continually increase man's confidence in his concept of the earth. Drilling to obtain direct evidence is one of the best ways of doing that. Scientists will, in effect, go and see for themselves what the earth's interior is like. This direct exploration is another expression of man's present intensive desire to fully understand the nature of the earth—and he should, for it's home.

So this book first describes how these indirect investigations are carried out today; how man looks deep inside the earth and backward in time. It then describes how the size and mass and structure of the earth have been worked out, how the composition of the unseen rocks can be estimated, and how the history of the earth has been assembled. It explains how the thickness of the crust is measured and how the best place to drill through it will be located. The final chapters are devoted to modern deep-drilling techniques on land, in shallow water offshore, and in the deep ocean, ending in a description of what the ultimate deep-sea drilling equipment may be like.

The history of scientific explorations has repeatedly demonstrated that unpredicted discoveries which upset accepted theories are the most valuable result of new work. For example, an early bathyscaphe dive by the French off the African coast sighted a shark on the bottom of the deep ocean. This animal was apparently living happily in abyssal darkness two miles below the level that was believed to contain his food supply—a circumstance previously regarded as impossible. This single sighting opened the door to a host of new biological theories.

The first rocket probes beyond the atmosphere surprised the theorists by finding the Van Allen radiation belts, yet these were almost missed because the Geiger counters which were set to measure the anticipated small amount of radiation were overwhelmed. From this unexpected discovery has come a host of new explanations and ideas about the influence of the earth's magnetic field on cosmic particles. Almost certainly a deep hole into the rocks beneath the ocean will find something we do not now anticipate; at least it will be a great stimulant to geological thinking.

The Structure of the Earth

Man is a curious animal who rides a spinning sphere on its endless track about the sun. For thousands of years he directed his questions outward into a vastness of space spangled with fixed stars and crossed by wandering planets. For not much more than a hundred has he had the means to look inward at his own vehicle. The science of physics had to develop first; then the new knowledge had to be employed in the study of the earth. The combination of the two was naturally called geophysics.

The geophysicist works with causes and effects. He observes that something happens; he uses physical laws to explain how such an effect can be produced; he proposes a structure for the earth that would supply the cause. For example, he observes that a compass needle points north; that a pendulum swings more slowly in the high mountains; that earthquake waves are recorded in some places and not in others. A physical explanation of these curious happenings must come first. He says, "The earth has a magnetic field; the force of gravity is not everywhere the same; something creates a shadow zone for earthquakes." But these statements do not explain how it is possible for the earth to have a magnetic field or why the force of gravity varies or what could cast a seismic shadow.

So he invents hypotheses of how the earth can produce such phenomena. He suggests: The magnetic field may be created by a dynamo-like action in the earth's nickel-iron core; mountains must be extra-thick masses of lightweight rocks which are interposed between the pendulum and the main attractive mass of the earth; the core of the earth must act like a liquid to prevent certain kinds of earthquake waves from passing through it.

Having proposed these ideas, he seeks supporting evidence. For it the geophysicist draws heavily on related work in astronomy, chemistry, mathematics, and the physics of structures and materials. But mainly he relies on his own techniques, making repeated measurements at many places on earth, charting the small variations from the normal that he calls anomalies. With magnetometers towed by ships and aircraft; with gravity meters that are temporarily set up in out of the way places, he "runs a line of stations"; with permanent seismographs to listen for the rumble of distant earthquakes; and with hydrophones to listen to the sound of his own explosives, he probes the deep and unseen rocks. Then he takes all the data and ponders what it means in terms of geology. How can the structure beneath which he sees only as a pattern of sound measurements be fitted to the real rocks that are seen at the surface?

Slowly, by combining all the pieces of evidence, a working hypothesis has been developed—a concept of the structure of the earth. Figure I-1 shows its main parts: solid inner core, molten outer core, mantle, and crust. By far the largest part of the earth—about 85 per cent by volume—is mantle, whereas the crust is merely a slaglike veneer on the outside, much thinner than the drawing indicates. This explains why scientists are so anxious to find out more about the mantle and, at the same time, why it is reasonable to believe that the crust can be penetrated.

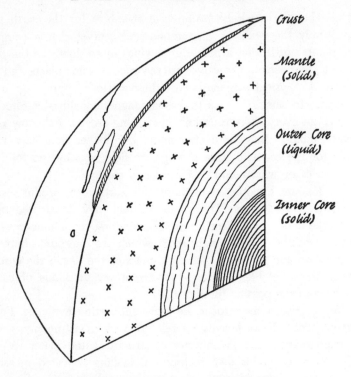

Crust

Mantle (solid)

Outer Core (liquid)

Inner Core (solid)

Fig. I-1 The Structure of the Earth

Figure I-2 illustrates the essential differences between the crust of the continents and that of the ocean basins. The continents are thick blocks of relatively light granitic rock and the ocean basins seem to be floored with thinner, heavier basaltic rock. Both types of crust act as though they are floating on the much denser rock of the mantle.

Floating does not necessarily mean that the continents move about sidewise on the earth's surface—it is not certain whether they do or not. Rather it is a loose description of isostasy, a concept which regards the continents as being something like icebergs, which in order to rise a little above the surface of the sea, must extend far below it. The continental blocks of rock make a similar vertical adjustment but the rate is very slow because the material of the mantle is enormously viscous. If a mass of rock stands high, whether it be a large island, a mountain chain, or an entire continent, it must be compensated by an extra thickness of rock below. This means that there is very slow but constant adjustment. If new lava flows or thick sedimentation add weight to the surface, the crust will sink; if erosion of the rocks or

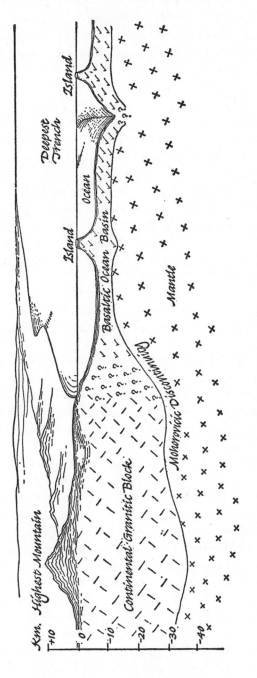

Fig. I-2 The Crust of the Earth

the melting of very thick ice sheets removes some of the weight, the crust will rise. The result of this is that the bottom surface of the crust tends to be maintained in a rough mirror image of the major features of the earth's surface. "Mountains" project downward under mountain ranges; "valleys" rise up under wide troughs on the surface.

The first piece of evidence that led to this theory was unearthed in 1740 by an expedition of French scientists who were surveying in the high Andes. Much to their surprise they found that the earth's gravitational attraction amid this great mass of rock was much less than in the surrounding lowlands. The leader correctly deduced that the rocks of the mountains were relatively light and that their roots extended far downward, displacing denser deep rocks beneath. The lowlands, which did not have deep projections beneath, permitted the dense rocks with their greater gravitational attraction to come closer to the surface. Measurements of small variations in gravity at a great many places on the surface of the earth have confirmed this opinion and given us the concept of the crust that we now have: Under mountains and continents the crust is thick, under the oceans the crust is thin. This explains why it will be much easier to reach the earth's interior by drilling from a ship at sea rather than on land or from an island, which is, of course, an oceanic mountain top.

Thus it appears that the continents and the ocean basins have always maintained a relationship something like the present one. The continents apparently have grown with time and changed their outlines; their positions may have shifted. But still they are thick rafts of a relatively light granitic rock whose surface rises high above the thinner, heavier oceanic basalt.

Few scientists now believe that any great proportion of the waters of the oceans originally fell as rain from primordial steam. It simply does not seem possible for such a large amount of water to have been stored above the earth. It seems much more likely that since the formation of the earth, readjustments in the interior have permitted trapped internal waters to move outward, largely in the form of volcanic steam, and be released on the surface over a period of many years. Other water was chemically released as original rocks disintegrated. Naturally this water ran downhill and collected in the low spots—the ocean basins. Gradually the basins began to fill as the puddles joined to make lakes and the lakes joined to form oceans. Chemicals from the disintegration of rocks which arrived with the waters made them salty—and the saltiness of sea water appears to have been unchanged for at least half a billion years. The early rocks were eroded as the down-running waters carried the first grains of volcanic sand to the low spots, where they formed the first sediments.

In a few billion years the ocean basins became full and now the water has overflowed and is covering the continental shelves. If one defines the edge of the continent as the place at which there is an abrupt break in the rocky topography, then the continental margins are already six hundred feet underwater. Since water continues to be squeezed out of the deep rocks and vented in volcanoes, it is only a question of time before the ocean will completely cover the earth. But if any geophysicist survives to that day—which may be another billion years away—he will probably still talk about ocean basins and continents. For to him the water does not make an ocean nor dry land a continent; rather it is the difference in composition and depth of the rock masses. The position of the shoreline at any time is merely a detail which concerns geographers.

Do not be too impressed by all this water, for even though it covers two-thirds of the surface to a depth of four kilometers it is only a thin film on the earth. Our planet and its ocean are in about the same proportion as a damp basketball.

An astonishing number of clues about the nature of the interior of the earth have come from the study of the earth's relation to its fellow inhabitants of space. It is evident that the members of our solar system had a common origin. Therefore, knowledge about the composition and characteristics of the sun or any of the other planets is of value in working out the origin and internal composition of the earth. Conversely, anything learned about the earth's interior is helpful to those who wish to know about the moon and Mars and the other planets and their moons. In fact, our ideas about the earth's composition have been greatly influenced by the theory that a planet once existed beyond Mars and was somehow destroyed in the distant past. That ex-planet is now the belt of asteroids and the samples are called meteorites.

Meteorites vary in composition from "stony" to nickel-iron and include all gradations between the two. An analysis of a considerable number of specimens representing an over-all average of those reaching the earth indicates that about 87 per cent of this ex-planet was composed of a basic rock called peridotite and 13 per cent of it was nickel-iron. These are about the same materials in the same proportion as has been proposed for the earth's mantle and core by reasoning from other kinds of evidence. To go a step further, small glassy fragments called tektites, which occasionally shower down from space, may even represent the crust of the broken planet.

Astronomers, also very much interested in all the problems of the earth's composition—but from the opposite point of view—have worked out the total mass, the average density, and the inertia of the earth, all of which must be taken into account by any hypothesis of the internal composition.

Man's first ideas about the nature of the material beneath the surface were derived from watching volcanoes spew out molten rocks which obviously rose from the depths. He concluded that the earth was a liquid except for the crust. This seemed to be substantiated by measurements in mines and drill holes which showed that the observed increase in temperature with depth would give a temperature sufficient to melt any known rock at less than 100 kilometers below the surface. This was where the original idea of a crust came from. It was believed that a once-molten earth had cooled, creating a surface crust similar to that which forms on a molten metal after it has been removed from a smelter furnace.

This concept was generally accepted until Lord Kelvin's studies of the resistance of the earth to being pulled out of shape by the gravitational attraction of the sun and moon (earth tides) convinced him that the earth does not have a molten interior but is in fact more rigid than if it were made of steel. He proposed instead that the interior was solid, having cooled from a molten state. This was apparently borne out by the increase in density with depth and the probable existence of a heavy metal core, as though gravity had segregated materials while they were in liquid form.

Now that theory is in turn challenged by recent measurements of heat flow and radioactivity. It is possible that there is an excess if radioactive heat which must be accounted for. If so, this means that the earth is still heating up, having originally condensed from a cloud of gases and small particles which contributed relatively little primordial heat. In other words, the gravity segregation could have taken place first, followed by internal heating due to the rise in pressure. Then the disintegration of radioactive elements spread throughout the mantle would slowly have heated the deep rocks to their present temperature.

We do not know, but it is evident that the question of the origin of the heat is far from settled. Undoubtedly it is some combination of original heat of formation plus the heat which is continually added by radioactivity; the proportions are uncertain.

The study of volcanic eruptions has revealed a good deal about both the composition and the conditions within the deep crust and mantle. In the Hawaiian Islands, where the most intensive studies of volcanoes are being made, seismographs indicate that eruptions are preceded by earthquakes which begin at a depth of as much as 30 kilometers. Over a period of several days these disturbances approach the surface, releasing the pressure that keeps the deep rock solid and opening fissures which the lava can follow upward. The lava that finally flows out on the surface is a dark-colored dense material called basalt, containing occasional lumps of an even heavier greenish rock named dunite. Since independent seismic evidence indicates that the thickness of the crust at Hawaii is only 16 kilometers, this could be interpreted as meaning that the lavas actually came from the mantle. If that were true there would be no need to drill a hole to obtain samples. However the concensus of scientific opinion is that the lavas reaching the surface are not representative of the mantle but rather are only a partial sample of material that has been segregated by unknown processes. Because the dunite meets the density requirement for the mantle and conducts seismic waves at the proper velocity (the basalt does not), some scientists believe that dunite is a principal component of the mantle. Moreover, it is much like the material of which stony meteorites are made. Why so little of it reaches the surface in these eruptions which seem to originate within the mantle is something of a mystery.

The existence of the earth's magnetic field suggests that there must be conducting materials in motion at great depth. This has been explained as a convection in a nickel-iron core which acts something like a dynamo to create a magnetic field with local variations. The constant westward drift of the field at the rate of one revolution every 1600 years suggests that the core rotates somewhat more slowly than the rest of the earth.

The largest share of man's information about the interior of the earth has come from the study of earthquake waves. Earthquakes are the result of rocks fracturing under stress. Pressures within the earth gradually build up over a period of years; when the rock suddenly breaks, seismic waves of several kinds radiate outward in all directions. Since the velocity of these shock waves is greater in more rigid rocks, by measuring the time for them to travel to distant seismographs it is possible to work out their pathways and to determine the characteristics of the rocks through which they traveled. Incidentally, the fact that earthquakes may originate at all depths from the surface down to as much as 700 kilometers is very good evidence that the rock acts like a rigid solid to that depth. Otherwise the forces would cause the rocks to flow like a plastic instead of breaking abruptly.

Of the many kinds of seismic waves, two have been used most successfully to probe the interior of the earth. These are P waves or compression waves, which travel with the speed of sound through all media, and S waves or shear waves which travel by the same pathway but at about half the speed of the P waves. The time that it takes for these two waves to travel from an earthquake to a series of seismograph stations gives us a means of investigating the deep rocks. Shear waves do not travel through liquids and since there is a large zone on the side of the earth opposite an earthquake in which S waves are not recorded, the earth is believed to have a liquid core. In other words, the liquid nature of the core causes it to cast a seismic S-wave shadow; the low rigidity and great density of the core causes it to slow the compression waves. By the careful analyses of the travel time of these waves in a great many seismograms, the diameter of the core has been determined to be 2740 kilometers and the density (at its outer edge) to be 9.7 grams per cubic centimeter.

While studying the seismic waves caused by the earthquake of October 8, 1909, a professor at the University of Zagreb named Andrija Mohorovičić (pronounced Moe-hoe-roe-veéch-ic) made a momentous discovery. He noticed that seismograph stations less than 800 kilometers from the quake recorded two sets of P and S waves. At any one station it looked as though there had been two separate shocks but when records from stations at different distances were compared, he observed that the separation between the two pairs of waves increased with distance. This could only mean that all the waves started out at the same instant but that they had followed two pathways, one much faster than the other. He reasoned that the earth must be layered in such a way that low velocity rocks rest on top of higher velocity rocks. Even though the waves had to travel farther to reach the lower layer, they quickly overtook and passed the slower waves in the upper one.

With this hypothesis Professor Mohorovičić gave the world a specific definition of the crust of the earth, and the depth at which the seismic waves abruptly increase in velocity is now called the Mohorovičić discontinuity. Beneath it is the mantle; above it is the crust. For the sake of convenience, this boundary has generally become known as the Moho.

Since natural earthquakes are very unreliable generators of seismic waves, scientists investigating details of the crust prefer to generate their own waves by means of explosives. The time and size of the shocks can be regulated by convenience and comparatively simple geophones or hydrophones can be used to detect the waves. By repeated shooting and listening the structure of the layers beneath the ocean bottom has been worked out.

So it is that small diverse pieces of information such as the variations in the swinging of a pendulum, a few seconds difference in the arrival of earthquake waves, and the existence of small lumps of heavier rock in volcanic outpourings form the basis of man's concept of his earth. Uncounted years of scientific time have gone into reasoning from such meager evidence to a grand hypothesis of earth structure. We "know" what the earth must be like and yet this uncertain knowledge needs to be verified by direct observation. Therefore, earth scientists are eager to drill a hole to the Moho—a Mohole, of course. The Mohole will completely penetrate the crust and touch the edge of the mantle, obtaining rock samples all the way. It may confirm ideas that are already accepted, enhance the value of the indirect evidence we already have, find out things about the deep rocks which cannot be learned by indirect methods, and discover the unexpected.

The Mohole project is under the direction of the AMSOC Committee of the U. S. National Academy of Sciences. This committee had its origin as the deep drilling group in a whimsical, near-mythical, near-scientific society which originated the idea of drilling to the mantle. The society itself requires a little explanation.

The American Miscellaneous Society

The Office of Naval Research, whose mission is to guide the Navy's basic-research program and to make research contracts with universities and private laboratories, has its offices in a "temporary" wooden office building on Washington's Constitution Avenue. There, in the sweltering summer of 1952, Gordon Lill and Carl Alexis of the

Geophysics branch attempted to organize a large pile of incoming proposals and suggestions for research. Their intention was to arrange the papers into a few neat piles, each of which would contain related ideas. This seemed like a good idea but when they were finished, desks and floors were covered with neat little piles—each one paper deep. Each scheme had come from a scientific individualist and dealt with a different subject; the papers refused to be fitted into any reasonable system of classification. Everything was miscellaneous.

As they gathered the papers into a single pile again, the thought struck them that there should be a catch-all group which would be appropriate to grapple with such a diverse array of subjects. It was christened on the spot: the American Miscellaneous Society. The first step was to have the stationery printed which has so successfully dignified the Society's written transactions; in its upper right-hand corner is the cable address from which the deep-drilling committee takes its name: AMSOC, Washington, D.C. The AMSOC coat of arms shows the geophysicist rampant on his fields of action amid the ancient elements, earth, air, fire, and water.

Any scientist who has business with ONR's Geophysics Branch is likely to claim membership in the American Miscellaneous Society since there are no official membership rolls. In fact, there are no by-laws, officers, publications, or formal meetings. Nor are there any dues, for funds are a source of controversy. The membership is largely composed of university professors or scientific researchers but the rumor that only persons can be admitted whose research proposals to ONR have been turned down because they are too far-fetched is completely false—it is merely a coincidence.

It was, of course, necessary to organize the Society so that it could properly fulfill its functions, and in this the time-honored pattern of successful scientific groups was followed. Five divisions were established: Etceterology, Phenomenology, Calamitology, Generalogy, and Triviology. If a new member feels that his own particular competence lies outside these restrictive categories, he may establish a division of his own. Or, he can take advantage of the affiliations that the Society maintains with the Committee for Cooperation with Visitors from Outer Space and the Society for Informing Animals of Their Taxonomic Positions. Moreover, the members are permitted to "enter into any entanglements normal to professional societies." On only one point are the unwritten rules strict. Copies of all correspondence involving the Society must be sent to the CENTRAL FILES in Washington—where the filing cabinets look suspiciously like incinerators!

Although the things said about AMSOC indicate that some people regard it as a spoof of more formal scientific societies, its gatherings are by no means given over to foolishness or trivia. Rather they are proving grounds for new ideas that are not well enough developed to be presented formally. Besides, these casual meetings provide an excellent means for exchanging information on new research between scientists of different disciplines. A great advantage is that one's reputation is not at stake as in a formal presentation and it is possible to propose ideas that in other circumstances would be regarded as wild or flighty.

In a few minutes a group of critical, free-swinging AMSOC scientists will find the flaws and tear an idea to pieces if it is unsound. However, the same group can, with equal speed, appreciate the implications of important new ideas or findings and develop them with a series of suggestions. When an AMSOC meeting breaks up it is often late and the participants physically exhausted; the table may be littered with napkins and envelopes covered with a jumble of "order-of-magnitude" calculations—but the scientific batteries of the participants are recharged with the excitement of new ideas.

There are great advantages in pooling the ideas of scientists from many disciplines in an informal session. Opportunities for free exchange between such varied disciplines as geology, engineering, seismology, atmospheric physics, and biology are, unfortunately, rare. The organization of science in universities and in specialized societies tends to prevent contact between men who work in unrelated fields but a miscellaneous group solves that problem.

Of course similar informal scientific meetings went on in Washington long before the American Miscellaneous Society was formed; probably there are other such groups throughout the land. But somehow AMSOC meetings have the atmosphere of a national university seminar in geophysics.

There have been unkind rumors that AMSOC deals only with crazy ideas. That is not so. Imaginative or bizarre they may be, but not crazy. The development of the Great Iceberg Scheme of John Isaacs is a good example of the sort of scientific stream-of-consciousness that characterizes AMSOC meetings.

About 1952 some would-be inventor wrote a letter to the Scripps Institution of Oceanography suggesting that the problem of supplying water to Southern California could be solved by the construction of a great plastic pipe which would lie on the ocean bottom and lead the fresh waters of the Sacramento River across San Francisco Bay, out the Golden Gate, south along the coast, and ashore near Santa Barbara. This scheme is of course hopelessly impractical, but it started John Isaacs, scientific man-of-parts on one of his favorite topics: how to pipe the vast water resources of the Columbia River Basin to Southern California. He decided that a pipe was needed which was large enough so that frictional losses would approach zero; as the conversation progressed, his imaginary pipe got bigger and bigger until it was a half mile in diameter.

A quick computation showed that ten miles of this pipe would hold a year's supply of water by itself—no flow was needed. Why not tow the pipe to California like an old-time log raft? But the pipe makes it difficult; how about a big plastic bag full of fresh water. Better still, if the water is frozen, even the bag won't be needed. Where can you find a lump of ice that size? Let's see, Arctic icebergs are made of salt water and rarely over a few dozen feet thick; besides, the shallow sill of the Bering Sea would prevent taking large bergs out of the Arctic Ocean. Antarctic bergs, however, are all fresh-water and ones 10 miles long, 600 feet thick, and a half mile across are occasionally sighted. So Isaacs proposed towing an Antarctic berg to California. He skipped through a series of calculations which showed that this was within the realm of possibility if it were possible to take advantage of ocean currents. The plan was as follows: Three Navy fleet tugs would put lines on one end of a big berg and guide it into the Humboldt Current which flows northward along the west coast of South America. The tugs would have to pull for a week to bring the berg up to a speed of one-third knot and a month to get it up to two knots.

With judicious maneuvering, the tug and the Humboldt Current would lead the berg to the equatorial countercurrent, which would carry it west to the Hawaiian Islands then north almost to the west winddrift toward Canada, and eventually into the California current. In about a year the berg would arrive at its Los Angeles destination from the north, having made a loop around the Hawaiian Islands. Eventually, if it were possible to get it stopped, the ice would be moored in the lee of one of the Channel Islands and fenced in with a floating dam extending downward perhaps twenty feet (the light fresh water would float, without mixing, on the heavier salt water). Then pipes would be run along the bottom to the mainland.

In the course of Professor Isaacs' subsequent investigations it developed that melting during towing would give the ice a good ship-like form so that it could move faster as it went but would not greatly reduce its size. Moreover, when the berg was in the equatorial regions it could, theoretically, generate enough power to tow itself by means of a thermoelectric plant which could make use of the temperature difference between the warm sea water and the cold surface waters on the ice (melted by dusting carbon-black on the surface to absorb the sun's heat).

After the berg is at anchor the effect of its low temperature would be to cool passing air and precipitate the moisture as dew—probably producing as much water as the melting of the ice.

From the beginning all admitted it was unlikely that the Great Iceberg Scheme would ever actually be carried out for California—although as the calculations developed everyone was surprised how much more practical the scheme was than was at first apparent. Indeed, it appears to be wholly feasible for Australia, South Africa and South America. In fact, the most serious objection was that it might have changed the climate in Los Angeles.

Against such whimsical ideas do the scientists of AMSOC flex their intellects, for perhaps the real advantage of the American Miscellaneous Society is that it affords an opportunity for a group of scientists to relax by toying with unusual ideas—including that of drilling a hole in the bottom of the sea.

II

Origin of the Mohole Idea

Where did the idea of digging or drilling a hole into the earth for scientific purposes come from? There is no simple answer; it seems to have been thought of by a great many people, each with a particular point of view.

The idea of drilling in the ocean basins did not come to AMSOC in a sudden burst of inspiration. Rather it was the other way around; some of the members of the American Miscellaneous Society had a long history of interest and experience in scientific drilling which had made it a frequent topic of discussion for years. The Mohole project is a logical extension of those thoughts and since it exists because of those scientists, it may be well to begin by introducing them and describing their experiences with geological drilling. Some of them originally found a common interest in the search for proof of the origin of coral atolls.

Drilling and Coral Atolls

Many scientists have, at one time or another, suggested that exploratory holes be drilled into the earth for scientific purposes. Among the first of these proposals was that made by Charles Darwin in 1881. In a letter to Alexander Agassiz, the famous Swiss-American naturalist, he wrote, "I wish that some doubly-rich millionaire would take it into his head to have borings made in some of the Pacific and Indian Ocean atolls and bring home cores for examination from a depth of 500 or 600 feet." Eventually the Royal Society of London acted on this suggestion and in 1897 a hole was drilled 1140 feet deep at Funafuti in the Ellice Islands. The purpose of the hole was, of course, to verify Darwin's theories about the origin and development of coral atolls. Darwin wanted to prove that coral atolls are built up, layer by layer, on top of a volcanic mountain which is slowly subsiding beneath the ocean.

But the Funafuti hole did not settle this point and more holes were drilled. In 1934–36 the Japanese cored to a depth of 1416 feet on a small island south of Japan; the results were indefinite. In 1947 during resurvey of Bikini atoll (the year after the first A-bomb test) several holes were drilled in Bikini Island—one to 2556 feet. It was a step downward but it too bottomed in coral and so was short of the objective. This hole, with its attendant frustrations, served mainly to whet the scientific drilling appetite of the three American geologists who reported on it in *Science*, Harry Ladd, Joshua Tracey, and Gordon Lill.

In 1951 another hole was drilled in the Marshall Islands, this time on one of the islets of Eniwetok atoll; again the results were tantalizing, for at 1285 feet the hole was still in loosely-consolidated coral fragments. The question to be settled was still the same: Is Darwin's theory correct? Do coral atolls have basalt basements?

Darwin believed that the coral atoll structure was founded when minute coral polyps freely drifting in the tropical sea found and attached themselves to the newly hardened basalt in the shallow waters around a conical volcanic island. As the coral colonies grew, a fringing reef was formed. Millions of years passed; the water level rose and the volcanic base slowly settled. The corals built vertically upward, each apartment-like colony being built on the wreckage of the ancestral skeletons so that the reef was maintained just below the waves in the warm, nutritious surface waters. The reef now encircled a dark-colored steep-sided island which was all that could be seen of the old volcano; between the reef and the ancient volcano was a shallow lagoon. More eons passed and the water level continued to rise, but the circular shape of the original reef was maintained. The volcano's snout which had once hurled fiery debris into the skies became completely submerged and all that remained was the great flat ring of living coral which had kept even with the rise of the ocean. It surrounded a lagoon which was rarely over 180 feet deep and from two to twenty miles across.

Here and there on the broad hard surface of the shallow reef, coral fragments were piled by the winds and currents into low islets whose highest point was not a dozen feet above the sea. Cocoanut palms took root, as well as vines and low bushes; people landed, found living easy, and stayed.

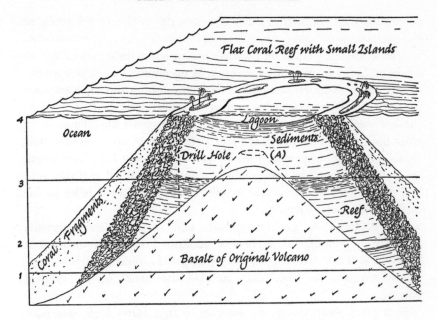

Fig. II-1 The Growth of a Coral Atoll
1 Corals (shown dark) start to grow in the shallow waters around a new volcano (A).
2 As sea level rises and/or volcano sinks, coral builds upward.
3 As process continues, volcano wears down and is surrounded by a lagoon ringed by a coral reef.
4 Eventually, only a ring of coral which we call an atoll can be seen.

Darwin, as a young geologist voyaging around the world on the *Beagle* in the 1830's, observed coral reefs and atolls in all stages of development and worked out their life story. He saw new volcanoes rise; Tahiti represented the fringing reef stage; Bora Bora that of the offshore reef ringing a volcanic summit; atolls like those of the Marshalls were the final stage. The sequence he described sounded plausible but there were other possibilities to be considered, and scientists, being the kind of people they are, wanted to check up. It took considerable imagination to believe that an almost microscopic animal could build a structure the size of an atoll—many of which have a volume of 200 cubic miles. But the supporting evidence continued to accumulate.

Soundings made by deep-sea geologist Harry Hess and others during and after World War II established that the bottom of the Pacific basin is pimpled with sea mounts many of which rise within about a mile of the surface. Some have rugged topography on top; others are flat-topped as though planed off by wave action when their surface was at sea level. Deep-sea rock dredges brought up chunks of basalt from the tops of these undersea mountains, thus establishing their volcanic origin, and fossils were found on them of small mollusks that lived in shallow water in Cretaceous time—100 million years ago. These were clear indications that (1) there had been a lot of volcanic pedestals available as atoll foundations in the remote past, (2) the water which is now a mile deep had been shallow at that time, and (3) if the coral had grown upward for nearly a mile, none of the drill holes so far could have reached basalt.

The evidence of gravity, seismic, and magnetic measurements made from scientific ships further confirmed Darwin's theory but scientists still insisted that the only real proof would be a hole completely through the coral that sampled the basalt of the original volcano.

So it came about that in the summer of 1952 Harry Ladd was once more "sitting on a rig" (trade slang meaning that a geologist is watching the drilling of a hole so closely that he practically lives on it). This hole was being drilled on Elugelab Islet at Eniwetok Atoll in the Marshall Islands. Someone had painted "Basalt or Bust" on the side of the geologist's shack.

There are plenty of problems in drilling through old coral reefs and this hole encountered just about all of them. The drill would encounter great voids or cracks in the rock and drop suddenly; circulation of the drilling fluid could not be maintained because these cracks were open to the ocean; and sometimes the material was so fragmented that cores could not be taken at all.

However, there were compensations. When I visited the site in July of 1952, during periodic respites from the arduous task of watching Harry Ladd examine the fossil corals that were brought up, we would swim in the shallow waters of the adjoining reef. The water was as clear as any in the world, for the trade winds constantly supplied deep Pacific water to the reef—there was no land upwind for thousands of miles to muddy it. The coral castles and painted fishes quickly made one forget the problems of drilling until the sound of the drill would signal Harry back to work.

At a depth of 4630 feet drilling progress slowed markedly, indicating that hard rock, presumably basalt, had been reached, and the core barrel was sent into the hole to get a sample. At this critical moment the hole collapsed and only with great luck was it possible to salvage most of the drill pipe. There was no time to bypass the cave-in since this exact point was about to become the site of the first H-bomb explosion. In November "Mike," as the explosive device was called, was exploded, erasing the reef and the drill hole—replacing it with another hole a mile across and several hundred feet deep.

Undaunted, and with tired equipment and crew, Harry began another hole on another of the atoll's islets. The core barrel finally brought up altered olivine basalt from 4222 feet. Darwin's theory of general subsidence of volcanoes beneath the sea had finally been checked by drilling.

At the time I was project engineer in charge of measuring the waves produced by "Mike." Not long after the shot, our ship *Horizon* was joined at Kwajalein by another University of California research vessel, the *Spencer F. Baird,* which had crossed the Pacific under chief scientist Arthur Maxwell. Dr. Roger Revelle flew in to take command and as Expedition Capricorn the two ships sailed on a voyage that was to cut a scientific swath through the island groups of the tropical Pacific.

Shortly after New Year's Day 1953 the Capricorn Expedition was passing through the Tonga Islands and our ships visited Falcon "Island." At least, we visited a reef that marked the spot where it had been, for Falcon is one of the volcanic up-again down-again islands of the world. In 1929, only twenty-four years before, Harry Ladd had visited the place and climbed a smoking cinder cone 600 feet high to watch Prince Tungi plant the Tongan flag on his new territory. In 1938 a passing British ship noted volcanic activity on a "good-sized" island. But by the time our expedition reached the spot in 1953, Falcon Island had disappeared. The waves had worn it down to a series of submarine knolls and pinnacles whose steep sides dropped away into deep water. The captain, who had carefully navigated us to the position of the island shown on the charts, was on the bridge scanning the horizon for land when the echo sounder showed the rock rising almost vertically toward the keel. He leaped to ring the engine room telegraph for full astern. Unmarked rocky pinnacles hundreds of miles from land are enough to scare anyone and the R.V. *Baird* churned to a stop, throwing a turbulent foam out over water less than twenty feet deep. The ship then retreated to an ultrasafe distance, where it sulked and the scientists who wanted to have a close look had to row a long way to see Falcon.

Using self-contained diving equipment for the first time in the Tongas, we dove down to have a look. The fresh dark basalt of the recent volcano was studded with little coral colonies just getting their start in life and already tiny angel fish swam through their branches. Walter Munk even jammed a thermometer into the soft volcanic rubble to see if there was any trace of volcanic warmth remaining.

Although no one had really doubted that corals do attach themselves to volcanoes and grow in this way, it is a sight that few men have actually seen. We were a little awed to be present at the birth of an atoll, the greatest structure ever built by any animal, including man. For that is what Falcon will be some day when its volcanic period is finally over.

To Drill for Science

Most ideas evolve or are compounded from previous ideas and the idea of drill holes for various scientific purposes is no exception, having been repeatedly proposed since, and probably before, Darwin. Thus the Mohole has its roots deep in scientific history.

Few holes are drilled purely to obtain geological information where there is no prospect of finding natural wealth. There are thousands of holes drilled every year by companies prospecting for oil, however, and it is from the data on stratigraphy so obtained that virtually all our direct subsurface knowledge comes. Since only one in eight of the holes in previously unexplored areas will produce oil, most of them are reluctantly admitted to produce only geological knowledge. Mining companies also prospect for ore deposits by probing into unknown rocks with core drills but these are relatively short holes drilled into special kinds of rock and only on rare occasions would they produce generally useful geological data.

One of the earliest proposals for a purely geological hole was made in November 1902 by G. K. Gilbert, director of the Carnegie Institution of Washington, who suggested to the trustees that "an investigation of subterranean temperature be made by means of a deep boring into plutonic rock." The trustees appropriated one thousand dollars for the preparation of preliminary plans.

Two years later Gilbert reported back on the results of his study of sites and of costs. "The Lithonia district, Georgia, both appears preferable to all other districts and satisfies the conditions requisite for a successful boring. No effort has been made to choose a precise spot but the natural conditions are there favorable over so large an area that the selection of a particular spot can be made in view of local economic conditions.

"The cost of boring in granite to the depth of 10,000 feet would be very large—so large as to be prohibitory. However, the Sullivan Machinery Company estimates the cost of boring to the depth of 6000 feet at $110,000, and is willing to enter into a contract on the basis of that estimate" (the world's record depth at that time was 2800 feet).

"I recommend that the making of such a deep boring be undertaken by the Carnegie Institution and I submit herewith a discussion of the value to science of the proposed boring."

In his discussion of the value of the deep boring, Dr. Gilbert had some things to say which are as valid now as in 1902.

"Theories of the origin of the earth are intimately related to the constitution and condition of the interior. In the field of geophysics there is probably no problem which does not involve the distribution of internal heat. For the purpose of testing our theories of the origin of the earth's heat it is important to know not only the temperature gradient but the variation of gradient with depth.

"In the planning of the boring, no other instrument has been considered than the diamond drill. The rock could probably be penetrated by a churn drill at less cost, but the churn drill, by grinding rock to sand destroys its structure. The diamond drill, on the other hand, by removing part of the rock in the form of a core, preserves a continuous record of the character of the rock traversed. The core, moreover, permits the prosecution of investigations other than thermal which may prove of great importance to geophysics.

"It is at least worthy of suggestion that the boring could be utilized for the subterranean swinging of a specially constructed pendulum and that the earth's weight could be measured by means of gravity determinations. The rock samples brought up would be peculiarly favorable for the determination of the crust layer."

Apparently the cost of this drilling project was too high for the Carnegie Institution and in 1906 Gilbert reluctantly returned the balance of the funds appropriated by their board of trustees for his feasibility study. The only expense was $80.69—cost of his trip to Georgia to examine the site.

The first of the recent proposals for a major scientific drilling effort seems to have come from a remarkably imaginative and controversial fellow, Dr. T. A. Jaggar. The mention of his name to the old-timers around the U. S. Geological Survey is, to this day, sure to start a chain of anecdotes. Jaggar was far-sighted and enthusiastic about the future of geological research; he founded and directed the famous Volcano Observatory on Hawaii; he was a research associate of the Geological Survey; he was president of the Hawaiian Academy of Sciences. But he was a fellow whose far-ranging ideas made his associates a little wary; he was regarded as too futuristic and grandiose.

Dr. Jaggar toyed with numerous ideas for drilling to get geological information and in the 1920's actually succeeded in getting some holes drilled to explore the underground workings of the Kiluea fire pit of Moana Loa volcano on the island of Hawaii.

His insistence on large ocean "observatories" goes back at least to 1939 when the Honolulu *Advertiser* ran a story entitled "Dr. Jaggar Looks to the Future," which quoted him as saying,

"We have just scratched the surface of this world on which we live. Nearly 75 per cent of it is covered with water. Mountains and deserts occupy a good deal of the remaining area. Let's take two or three of those old warships which are rusting in idleness at the wharves. Let's put the best brains of the oil industry to work on the development of a new kind of drill for boring beneath the ocean's floor. Send them to deep water and tie the boats together. Then we can put down drills to get samples of the rock beneath the mud. That's what we want! We'll have a start, then, for solving what still is an unanswered geophysical problem. . . .

"We spend millions for an observatory to study the craters on the sun and moon. That's very commendable. But we have studied only a small number of the craters on the earth. We know very little about the world we live on.

"We must strike the imagination of some capitalist who could finance an expedition of this type. Perhaps a syndicate will be convinced yet that oil deposits lie beneath the sea; maybe greater fields than those they have found on the tidelands."

In 1943, when he was seventy-two, Jaggar sent a proposal entitled "Core Drilling under the Ocean" to Professor R. M. Field of Princeton University, who was then chairman of a committee on Continental and Oceanic Structure of the International Union of Geodesy and Geophysics. To make sure that it was noticed, Jaggar had it mimeographed and sent out hundreds of copies, including one to Dr. Ray Fosberg, botanist of the Pacific Science Board. Upon hearing of AMSOC's proposal Fosberg recalled Jaggar's scheme and dug it out of his cavernous files. This remarkable document, he said, proved that we were "pikers" by comparison.

The following is Jaggar's proposal:

CORE DRILLING UNDER THE OCEANS

It is proposed that Geological Societies, Petroleum Geologists, American Institute of Mining Engineers, American Geophysical Union, and the wealthy retired geological engineers of Tulsa, Florida, Los Angeles and New York organize

To drill one thousand core-producing holes in the deep ocean bottoms each one thousand feet deep and preserve the cores for specialist study, with worldwide drill-hole distribution.

That the wealthy industrialists be told about it. That its object is to begin to know the crust of the earth for the first time. That its object is to place laboratories of drilling on any Armstrong seadromes that may be built. That its object is to expend twenty million dollars as a starter.

ITS ACTUATING MOTIVE: That dynamic geology following Lyell must know the whole earth crust, its thermal gradient, its rock specimens, its inner waters, its physical variables, its resources for future labor, its stimulus for future invention, its topography in comparison with the moon, and its economic minerals in relation to the trivial area of surface that today yields power, iron, copper, oil and aluminum.

GEOLOGY HAS STOOD RELATIVELY STILL without enterprise for earth exploration, earth sampling, great instruments or new inventions; its young men keep secrets for mining and oil companies entirely within continents, or work for glass and steel industries that seem to care nothing about the greater science of the globe. The geophysical unions have been pushed by engineers for economic needs, but how many geologists devote all their time as astronomers do, to observing the earth?

THE OIL INDUSTRY ALONE is intelligent enough and wealthy enough to carry and man the whole proposal, doing the diplomacy, laying out the blueprints, finding the engineers, and prospecting world

43

oceans for beginning shallow and ending deep. The oil geologists are enterprising enough to swing their companies and see the vision.

THE WAR'S ENDING will be the time, with thousands of ships and engineers and government unemployment problems, with Americans in every land and on every ocean from Bering Sea to New Zealand, from Iceland to Martinique, and from the Cape of Good Hope to the Caspian oil fields.

ALL THAT IS NEEDED is for young geologists, engineers, physicists, geochemists, inventors, oil industrialists, navy officers and fliers to pull together and bring to bear all the war geography and oceanography.

WHY CORE-DRILLING ONLY? The problem is that geographic knowledge is needed instead of guesses. It may be that explosion quarrying or submarine amphibians or twenty other inventions will develop and spread out among the nations. But one thousand cores over the ocean bottoms where not one rock core exists today will make a big enough enterprise. The products will furnish a century of scientific specialists with materials for chemical, physical and biological analyses in the laboratory.

It must not be permitted to fail for that would leave geology a speculative science as before, surviving by continental anatomy, when its real function is global exploration of the two-thirds of the surface that is under the sea.

T. A. JAGGAR

There is no record that Jaggar's memo had any great impact on the "wealthy retired geological engineers" of the country but his general theme was taken up by others. Notable among these was Maurice Ewing, professor of geophysics at Columbia and director of the Lamont Geological Observatory, who has often referred to the drilling of a hole to sample the ocean sediments from top to bottom as "the dream of my life." His dream began in the questions raised by seismic surveys in the Atlantic Ocean basin such as: Why doesn't sound reflect from the tops of some of the dense layer below the soft sediments? And it developed as every additional foot that Lamont's coring devices penetrated the sea bottom yielded valuable new data. "We must have longer cores," he would say, "the seismological data indicate that the thickness of the sediment on the sea floor is only about 2000 feet and they also show that this sediment is unconsolidated—no firmer than a fine clay. We have every reason to believe that in that 2000 feet of unconsolidated sediment, the whole history of the earth is preserved better than it is in continental rocks which have been subjected to heat, folding and mineral changes. As we punch deeper into the ocean sediments, we may reach levels holding traces of the first animals that concentrated calcium carbonate, then evidence of atmospheric oxygen from the earliest green plants, and ultimately the primeval sediment of the earliest erosion marking the advent of the water in the sea. The entire record of terrestrial conditions from the beginning of the ocean is there in the most undisturbed form it is possible to find anywhere—and the dream of my life is to punch that hole 2000 feet deep and bring the contents back to the lab to study them."

In 1953 Professor Ewing traveled about the country as Distinguished Lecturer for the American Association of Petroleum Geologists and the Society of Economic Geologists. Over and over he spoke of the need for drilling a hole through the sediments and tried to obtain support for such a project. He suggested that the drilling could be done from a vessel such as the research ship *Vema* and that a million dollars would drill the first sediment hole; subsequent ones would cost one-fifth that much. The support never materialized even though in February 1954 the New York *Herald Tribune* quoted him as wistfully hoping that someone with $500,000 and a spirit of scientific adventure would help do this job and make his life complete.

Three years later while passing through the Cosmos Club, Maurice Ewing accidentally came upon the AMSOC group while it was discussing deep drilling and was invited to become involved in the Mohole project.

The first specific suggestion for sampling below the Moho seems to have been made in a letter from Dr. Frank B. Estabrook of the Basic Research Branch of the U. S. Army (with a credit line for Dr. James Garvey) which was published by *Science*, under the title "A Geophysical Research Shaft," on October 12, 1956. The idea of digging a very deep hole was used as an example of the basic philosphical point that "massive financial backing can with increasing ease be obtained for organized group attacks on basic problems."

One paragraph from that letter sets forth the objectives that such a hole would have in words quite similar to the ones later used by AMSOC.

"There appear to be many geophysical problems that could be profitably investigated by a physical penetration of the earth's crust and by an examination of the composition, properties, and physical condition of the mantle below the Mohorovičić discontinuity. Among these are the following: (i) Knowledge of the variation of the earth's magnetic field below the surface could show whether its origin is in the crust or, alternatively, is the result of magnetohydro-dynamic mechanisms in the core. (ii) Knowledge of the temperature variation below the surface is important for discussions of the earth's heat balance, radioactivity, and evolution. (iii) Knowledge of pressure, temperature, and density conditions at the outer boundary of the mantle are required for the numerical integrations in geophysical theories of Earth, Venus, and Mars. (iv) Geophysical theories of continent building require knowledge of the ultrabasic mantle material and of its relation to the basalt layer and to the granitic continental basement. (v) Penetration of the crust could shed light on the validity of the iostasy concept; this in turn has important and practical geodetic consequences. (vi) The earth's crust apparently has an unusually high radioactive content; it is important to determine whether this is actually so, and whether the radioactive elements have been fractionated out of the mantle. (vii) Knowledge of the composition of the mantle, and hence, of by far the largest part of the earth's mass is of great interest for astrophysical discussions of cosmic abundances. Furthermore, as in any scientific exploration, one cannot estimate in advance the importance of the new and unexpected phenomena and conditions that would be encountered; for example, it was suggested to me, not necessarily in jest, that the mantle might prove diamondiferous."

Estabrook suggested that an oceanic island be used for a drilling site, and that the most ancient rocks known might be a good place to start. Feeling that present well-drilling technology would be inadequate to achieve the required vertical depth of ten miles, he suggested that "a small bore (perhaps 12" in diameter, and 30° down-slant) shaft be drilled by remote-controlled equipment. The power transmission from surface to drill could be by electric cable; rock removal, by belt or hydraulic means." Costs, he estimated, might be less than those of near-surface tunneling, which are around a million dollars a mile.

The letter evoked interest but not action, for ideas have no momentum. In order to bring an idea to fruition, organization and determination are required.

AMSOC and the Mohole

The National Science Foundation is responsible for managing the federal government's basic-research program. As a part of this it contributes to the financial support of scientific projects in universities and laboratories by means of grants and research contracts. In order to make sure that this money is utilized most effectively, panels of experts review the proposed research projects and recommend which ones should be supported.

In the spring of 1957 after two days of sitting around a table in Washington discussing requests for grants, the Earth Sciences review panel adjourned with an air of mild discouragement. They had reviewed some sixty-five proposals, most of which were for small, desirable pieces of research. The projects were worthwhile and well thought out; each was proposed by a scientist of some stature in the field of geology-geophysics.

Why the discouragement? None of these attempted to courageously break through to new ground on any of the most important problems of the earth sciences. While the proposals were by no means trivia, it did not appear likely that any major advance would be produced even if each were carried out to the complete satisfaction of its proponent. Two of the panel members, whom we met before while they were exploring the Pacific, were especially bothered by this. They were geologist Harry Hess and geophysicist Walter Munk and they asked themselves, "How could the earth sciences take a great stride forward?" Munk suggested that they should consider what project, regardless of cost, would do the most to open up new avenues of thought and research. He thought that the taking of a sample of the earth's mantle would be most significant.

They talked it over: "How do you sample the mantle? You drill a hole where it's closest to the surface. Like a deep oil-well hole. Perhaps on an island. Or under the ocean, if that is possible. This would be the perfect antianalogue of a space probe. Think of the attention it would attract to the earth sciences. Maybe we would get some support from the big oil companies."

These were brave bold words. The scope could not then be imag-

47

ined but obviously such a project would be a heroic undertaking costing a large sum of money and requiring new techniques and
monumental equipment. Their own grand ideas, so far from realization, made them a little self-conscious. Hess suggested that it be
referred to the American Miscellaneous Society for action.

The following month, April of 1957, on a sunny Saturday morning
in La Jolla, California, there was an informal breakfast meeting of
the Society at Walter Munk's house. The agenda was, as always,
diverse, but in time the talk turned to the suggestion for drilling to
obtain a sample of the mantle. Curiously enough, none of those
present were aware of the previous proposals by Jaggar, Ewing, or
Estabrook, but oceanic drilling seemed like a fine idea. They talked
of drilling to the Moho from an island—essentially a deepening of
the old Eniwetok holes—and of the possibility of using a new technique, drilling from a floating vessel. They were not certain about the
minimum depths to the Moho or of the maximum depths that had
been reached in the search for oil, so they could not even make a good
guess whether or not such a hole was possible. What they could do
was talk about past experiences and who should be consulted and
what such a hole might find.

Then they reviewed the history of scientific drilling on atolls and
they thought about the men who had been involved in getting those
holes drilled. The idea of a major effort to directly explore the deep
rocks was appealing; maybe it would reach the mantle and revolu-
tionize geological thinking about the nature of the deep rocks.
The thing to do was to form a committee of the experienced scientists
to look into the matter and see if such a hole were possible.

Gordon Lill, founder of AMSOC and head of the Geophysics
Branch of ONR, was acclaimed chairman on the spot. In the best
tradition of AMSOC Lill is able to see the lighter side of heavier
problems but he took this assignment seriously. The rest of the group
helped him pick the other members. They nominated those whose
names have already been mentioned: Dr. Roger Revelle, Director
of the Scripps Institution of Oceanography, who had worked to get
the first holes drilled at Bikini; Drs. Joshua Tracey and Harry
Ladd, geologist and paleontologist, respectively, with the U. S. Geological Survey who had supervised the Marshall Islands drilling.
Dr. Walter Munk, Professor of Geophysics at the University of
California, and Dr. Harry Hess, Professor of Geology at Princeton,
originators of this version of Moho-drilling, were of course included.

48

This was the special deep-drilling committee of AMSOC. In a way the formation of such a group was a meaningless gesture since there was no means of support in sight. Nevertheless the enthusiasm was great and the thought never occurred to those present that the proposed committee members might not want to participate—they were all personal friends; as soon as they heard the idea they would become enthusiasts. The question of where the money would come from to bring them together and make preliminary studies never arose; somehow it would be provided. The project sounded so simple and logical at a breakfast meeting on a sunny patio. The members lazily looked down a desert canyon at the sparkling Pacific below and felt pleased with the morning's work. The American Miscellaneous Society had its first "formal" committee: the Committee on Deep Drilling. That afternoon a delegation called on Roger Revelle to inform him about the grand new idea that had blossomed on his campus.

On April 27, back in Washington, the first meeting of the new committee was held at the Cosmos Club. By this time Dr. William Rubey of the U. S. Geological Survey, an expert on the history of the oceans, had been added; Dr. Maurice Ewing, who chanced to be passing by, was invited to join in the discussion and thus became a member. At a later meeting in 1957 Dr. Arthur Maxwell, Chief of Oceanography for the Office of Naval Research and expert on heat flow through the floor of the ocean, was added to the committee.

It was decided to ask the National Science Foundation for funds to make a feasibility study. With genteel horror that august organization declined, politely suggesting that such a distinguished group of scientists might be able to attach themselves to a more reliable organization than the American Miscellaneous Society.

While this exchange was going on, the IUGG (International Union of Geodesy and Geophysics) met at Toronto, Canada. There, in several of the discussion groups, the subject of deep drilling arose again, prodded by AMSOC members and by Dr. Tom Gaskell, a British geophysicist. Finally on September 14, 1957, resolution number eleven was adopted:

The I.U.G.G.
Considering that the composition of the earth's mantle below the Mohorovičić discontinuity is one of the most important unsolved problems of geophysics,

And that, although seismic, gravity and magnetic observations have given significant indications of the nature of this material, actual samples that could be examined petrographically, physically and chemically are essential,

And that modern techniques of drilling deep wells are rapidly developing to the point where drilling a hole ten to fifteen kilometers deep on an oceanic island may well be feasible,

And that the crustal material above the Mohorovičić discontinuity is also of prime interest

Urges the nations of the world and especially those experienced in deep drilling to study the feasibility and cost of an attempt to drill to the Mohorovicic discontinuity at a place where it approaches the surface.

During the discussion from the floor of the Toronto resolution, a Soviet scientist arose and said, "We already have the equipment to drill such a hole, we are now looking for the place." By the following September the Soviet Academy of Sciences was rumored to have appointed its equivalent of a deep-drilling committee.

The IUGG resolution made everybody feel better because once the idea had received the stamp of international approval there were fewer snickers when the subject of drilling to the Moho was mentioned. It was also useful because the Russian's remark had pricked the pride of the U.S. oil industry. "Anything they can do we can do better" was the instant reply and before long a group of Texas oilmen held a meeting to ask themselves critically, "What are the limits on deep drilling?"

On December 6, 1957, the next meeting of the AMSOC Committee was held at Dr. William Rubey's house in Washington. One government agency, jittery in the uproar over the recent Russian success in launching the first satellite and sensitive to the remarks at Toronto about their deep-drilling abilities, actually stationed a security guard around the house, presumably to protect whatever advantage the United States might have in a drilling race. However, since that time no AMSOC meeting has been so honored and no part of the project has ever had a security classification.

At this meeting there were some new faces present, including Texas oil operator John Mecom, who was then co-holder of the world's record for deep drilling, with a hole called the LL & E which had reached 22,570 feet in a Louisiana bayou. Those present decided that the problem of drilling to the mantle should be broken down into three parts: (1) a "practice" hole on the continent to 35,000 feet (an idea that was soon discarded), (2) a "sedimentary-section" hole in the deep ocean basin, (3) a mantle hole beneath the ocean.

No one was sure whether or not some form of the floating platforms that were used for offshore oil drilling could be used in deep water but all felt that if they could the Moho was within reach—somehow, somewhere. For by then the geophysicists had located sites where the Moho was only 30 per cent deeper than the LL & E. Two days later Harry Hess, chairman of the Earth Sciences Division of the National Academy of Sciences, appeared before the Academy's governing board to ask that the Academy take the deep-drilling committee under its wing. As he put it:

"The American Miscellaneous Society has no officers, no constitution, no bylaws and consequently can act expeditiously when action is appropriate. It is an organization which warrants respect; note that five of its nine-man committee are members of the Academy [Ewing, Rubey, Revelle, Munk, Hess]. Its present organization is not such that it can accept funds from the National Science Foundation and therefore it comes to the Academy-Research Council for sponsorship. Our division strongly recommends that the Academy take over the entire committee as is and accept up to $50,000 in funds to study the feasibility of the project."

Professor I. I. Rabi, Nobel laureate on the board, remarked dryly, "Thank God we're finally talking about something besides space." And with that the American Miscellaneous Society's deep-drilling committee became the AMSOC Committee of the National Academy of Sciences, the letters no longer representing anything but a memory as far as the Academy is concerned.

The National Academy of Sciences is a private organization of distinguished scientists dedicated to the furtherance of science for human welfare. Election to membership in the Academy is considered to be one of the highest honors that can be visited on a scientist, for it is awarded solely on the basis of distinguished achievement in original research. The Academy was established in 1863 under a Congressional charter signed by President Lincoln and is required by that charter to act as an advisor to the federal government on scientific matters. It receives funds from both public and private sources to stimulate and promote the interests of science. In order to enable scientists generally

86620

to associate themselves with the work of the Academy, a working organization known as the National Research Council was set up by means of which thousands of scientists and engineers can participate in the Academy's work by serving on its various boards and committees. The AMSOC committee is one such committee in the NAS-NRC division of Earth Sciences. It was a big step upward for AMSOC's committee to be taken into the Academy-Research Council organization for it gave formal recognition to the idea of drilling deep into the earth for scientific purposes.

The year 1957 was the International Geophysical year and I had spent most of it in Tahiti and the South Seas installing ocean-wave measuring instruments. But luckily, I had returned to the Academy the week before it accepted the AMSOC Committee and, on hearing what had happened while I was away, became an enthusiastic advocate of oceanic drilling. I vowed to become associated with the project somehow and before long was invited to become its part-time executive secretary.

In April of 1958 a form letter was sent out by Dr. William R. Thurston, executive secretary of the Earth Sciences Division of the National Academy of Sciences to nearly two hundred scientists who were planning to be in Washington for the annual meeting of the American Geophysical Union. It invited "knowledgeable friends of the division —to a meeting in the Academy's Great Hall—preparatory to conducting a study to determine the feasibility of drilling to the Mohorovicic discontinuity." The meeting was intended to lay the idea before the men who would be most interested in the scientific results and to develop a broad base of support.

So it was that on the afternooon of April 26, 1958, many of the leaders of geophysics in the United States were arrayed around a square of tables that had been set up in the Great Hall. Presiding was Harry Hess, sponsor, AMSOC founder, and chairman of the Earth Sciences Division. AMSOC chairman Gordon Lill began by describing the plan as it was then conceived, but he barely was able to enumerate the main advantages of the Mohole project to geophysics before unexpected opposition developed and a three-point salvo was fired. The objectors said, in effect: You won't prove anything! You shouldn't do it! You can't do it! But the proponents were ready and a scientific battle began which went something like this:

"What good will it do to get a single sample of the mantle? The material beneath the Moho is probably not homogeneous and one sample cannot be expected to be representative. It might throw us off the track for years; ten or even a hundred holes may be needed before we will know what the mantle is made of."

To which Harry Hess answered, "Perhaps it is true that we won't find out as much about the earth's interior from one hole as we hope. To those who raise that objection I say, If there is not a first hole, there cannot be a second or a tenth or a hundredth hole. We must make a beginning."

The second objection dealt with money: "This project will cost many millions of dollars—you cannot even estimate how much. If it is paid for out of geophysical research money it will strip all other projects of funds for years. If that amount of money were divided up among the existing institutions, we would all be able to do more and better geophysics."

Now the fact is that most large new scientific projects are carried on essentially independently of previously existing efforts. They do not strip established laboratories of funds; on the contrary they attract students and money to the particular field of endeavor so that in the end all the scientists in it are benefited. But Roger Revelle gave a much better answer when he said, "I imagine that an argument like that was used against Columbus when he asked Queen Isabella for funds for his adventurous project. One of the Queen's advisors probably stepped forward and said, 'Your Majesty, it won't be important even if this crazy Italian does reach India by sailing west. Why not put the same amount of money into new sails and better rigging on all the other ships? Then the whole fleet will be able to sail half a knot faster!'" This devastating analogy silenced that part of the opposition.

The third objection was: "It's impossible to drill a hole in the bottom of the ocean in the foreseeable future. Nobody has any idea how it can be done. Why doesn't AMSOC forget about oceanic drilling until it has done some research on deep-drilling techniques on land? Perhaps after a few years work on metallurgical and mechanical developments, better machines and materials will be available that that will be capable of drilling to the Moho on land through miles of hot rocks."

The answer to this was given by A. J. Field, an engineer from the Union Oil Company, who showed movies of the ship *Cuss I* (a name compounded from the initials of the oil companies who owned it: Continental, Union, Shell, Superior) drilling an oil well at sea off the California coast in two hundred feet of water with a full-sized oil-

53

drilling rig. Admittedly the ship was a long way from being capable of drilling to the Moho, but it demonstrated new possibilities to every man present. Almost until that moment the capabilities of floating drilling platforms had been kept closely guarded commercial secrets and virtually no one present had seen or even heard of such equipment before. But now they could see a new sort of tool which looked as though it could be developed into the first deep-sea drilling rig. A wave of enthusiasm went through the audience and they saw the project in a new light. If American technology could go this far it could drill to the Moho. Why not? In fact the *Cuss* itself looked as if it could be used without major changes to drill shallow holes and sample the upper part of the sedimentary layers of the sea floor.

By this time most of those who had been on the fence were persuaded that the deep-drilling project was a better idea than it had at first seemed and a vote was taken on the resolution "The project as outlined by Gordon Lill is approved." It carried unanimously.

Under the aegis of the Academy and with the support of geophysicists generally it was not long before a grant of $15,000 was received from the National Science Foundation as a down payment on a feasibility study. Thus it was that the idea, the scientists, the Academy, and the money all came together.

The feasibility study began at once. We looked into various possible sites in both Atlantic and Pacific; we persuaded the office of Naval Research to sponsor site surveys; we examined nearly all the floating drilling vessels in the world. Behind the scenes things were proceeding nicely, but by October the committee was becoming disturbed about the misinformation reaching the public. Rumors were flying which made it sound more like science fiction than science: The hole would have to be at least ten miles deep; the rock at the bottom would be too hot to permit any ordinary kind of drilling; the project would cost hundreds of millions of dollars, and so on.

It was decided to scotch these wild rumors with a complete public statement, for by then possibilities had narrowed and thoughts on how the work should proceed were more orderly. At least the committee could say with reasonable certainty what the scientific objectives were, which drilling sites seemed the most promising, and what kind of equipment might be used. The result was an article in the *Scientific American* (April 1959) entitled "The Mohole," which summarized our thinking.

The Mohole story—which first used that word—was treated as news and the material in it was widely reprinted. It triggered an outburst of comment and reaction.

Industrial interest was immediate and widespread. Oil companies became worried that we might find oil beneath the sea and upset the economics of that business. Drilling companies wanted contracts. Tool and machinery companies called to explain how their equipment would solve our problems. But for each company who wanted something from us there were two others who wanted to give us something just so they could become involved in the project.

The fame of the Mohole spread abroad and before long a letter was received from Stjepan Mohorovičić, a retired professor of geophysics at the University of Zagreb and son of the discoverer of the seismic discontinuity. He had heard about the project on the Voice of America and sent us some photos and personal data on his father.

At this time the implications of the undertaking just began to be understood by the remainder of the scientific community outside the geological sciences. The workers in these other fields had adjusted to satellites—and gladly accepted the boost the Russian Sputnik gave to public interest in all forms of American science. The Mohole project might achieve a similiar result.

Most scientists hoped that AMSOC was right and that it would be able to sample the earth's history and interior with a hole in the sea floor—yet they retained their normal skepticism. Few could refrain from making jokes—both erudite and crude—about what would happen when the crust was penetrated. Our friends were sarcastic but fascinated, snide but envious. The 1960 Pick and Hammer show— an annual musical mockery of the Washington Geological Society— was entitled "Mo-Ho-Ho and a Barrel of Funds." Its hero, Glib Bunkum, uses a posthole digger in the bottom of the ocean while the chorus sings about drilling to the Moho.

In the many informal discussions where we were exposed to this ribbing there were few in which the converstion did not turn briefly to science fiction and some of the curious and crackpot ideas about the interior of the earth.

III

Science Fiction and Pseudo Science
inside the Earth

It would be possible to accumulate a ten-foot shelf of books all dealing with fictional travels into the "bowels," or at least below the surface, of the earth. And although inner space has not been quite as attractive to imaginative writers as outer space, they have bored and burrowed like literary termites. The favorite plot—which makes use of a hollow earth, usually lighted and inhabited, that can be reached by means of caves, tunnels, volcanoes, or submarines—has been used over and over again. Some of these fictional ideas about the earth appear to have been taken from crank theories—or perhaps it was the other way around.

Three of the world's best-known storytellers, Jules Verne, Sir Arthur Conan Doyle, and Edgar Rice Burroughs, dispatched heroes to the underworld. Each found a very different sort of arrangement. In fact, these three sets of adventures represent the major ideas about the inside of the earth which have been used so often by less prominent science-fiction authors.

Science Fiction

Jules Verne set forth his version in *Voyage au Centre de la Terre* (*Journey to the Center of the Earth*), first published in 1864. The story is told by Axel, the relatively timid young man who serves as a perfect foil for his uncle, Professor Liedenbrock, the paragon and prototype of all science-fiction professors. At fifty the professor is vigorous, tall and strong—a fountain of knowledge who "concentrated so as to exclude the outside world for days on end" and "knew a fair share of the thousand languages of the world."

One day the professor brings home an old manuscript. As he leafs through it, a scrap of parchment flutters to the floor; on it are several columns of ancient Icelandic runic writing. The professor is intrigued and when he translates it finds a cryptogram in Latin written backward. He manages to work it out, eventually getting an English version which reads as follows:

Descend into the crater of Snaeffels Jokull that lies under Scartaris' shadow just before the calends of July, bold traveller, and you will reach the center of the earth as I have.*

ARNE SAKNUSSEMM

Within two days of the deciphering, the Professor and Axel have outfitted themselves to follow the trail into Snaeffels and are on their way to Iceland. There they find that Arne Saknussemm, a famous alchemist and naturalist, had been burned at the stake for heresy on a fire made of his own books. The cipher is his only surviving piece of writing.

The reluctant nephew tries to delay the trip by raising objections and these serve as a wonderful opportunity for the professor to explain his ideas about the earth.

When the Professor's first answers are not entirely satisfactory, Axel persists: "It is generally acknowledged that the heat increases about one degree centigrade with every hundred feet below the surface. If this ratio remains constant for 1500 leagues until the center of the earth is reached, the temperature there is more than two million degrees."

Professor Liedenbrock's answer shows how well Jules Verne appreciated the ways of science: "Neither you nor anyone else knows for certain what goes on in the interior of the globe considering that we are familiar with scarcely a twelve-thousandth-part of its radius. My answer is that science can always be improved and that every new theory is always overthrown by a newer one. But we shall see for ourselves and then, like Saknussemm, we shall know where to stand on this great question."

With Hans, a guide of remarkable strength and resourcefulness, they

---

* Even this needs a little translation. Jokull, so the professor explains, means glacier in Icelandic and since virtually every volcano there has thrust its way upward through an ice field, all the names of Icelandic volcanic mountains, like Snaeffels, are paired with the word *jokull*. Scartaris is one of the peaks; calends means beginning. Thus the last days of June are "just before the calends of July."

use ropes to descend a perpendicular volcanic chimney for nearly three thousand feet to make a beginning. Continuing down an inclined corridor in the lava they overcome numerous difficulties to reach at last a great internal sea. It stretches away beyond the limits of sight, illuminated by a peculiar light. "The power of this light, brilliant but completely diffused so that there were no shadows, plainly indicated an electrical origin. It was like a continuous aurora borealis filling a cavern large enough to contain an ocean; the vault above, or sky if you will, seemed to consist of mobile and shifting vapors."

Hans builds a raft and they set sail toward the southeast, continuously beset by dangers. Two great antediluvian monsters (an ichthyosaurus and a plesiosaurus) battle, nearly upsetting the raft; a great geyser is sighted; a hurricane tosses the raft for many days. Eventually the raft is flung on the far shore near a prehistoric forest in which they come unexpectedly upon a herd of mastadons being tended by a human giant more than twelve feet tall.

Arne Saknussemm's trail of initials show the way to the center of the earth but a rockfall in the intervening three hundred years has blocked the passage. With a powerful explosive (gun cotton) the adventurers blast the obstruction away, fortunately taking the precaution of waiting on the raft. The explosion opens a great crack and the inland sea starts to drain toward the center of the earth. For hours the raft is carried downward in the blackness on a rushing torrent. Then suddenly it starts to rise again as the abyss fills with water; the water turns hot and finally they are borne upward on molten lava.

"Fortunately," says the Professor, "we are in the chimney of an active volcano. It is the only chance we have of returning to the surface of the earth." He was right as always and soon the raft is spewed out of Stromboli in the Mediterranean, 1200 leagues from the starting point.

When he returns to Germany, Professor Otto Liedenbrock is showered with honors and "made a corresponding member of all scientific, all geographical and all mineralogical societies in all corners of the world."

Sir Arthur Conan Doyle had quite different ideas about the interior of the earth and how it could be examined in *When the World Screamed*, which was first published in 1922.

Professor Challenger, a huge, black-bearded, and irrascible scientist (who previously had found the Lost World) is, as Mr. Peerless Jones puts it, "clearly a lunatic." He tells Jones his ideas about the earth.

"Having obtained your promise of inviolable secrecy, I come down to the essential point. It is this—that the world upon which we live is itself a living organism, endowed, as I believe, with a circulation, a respiration, and a nervous system.

"You will recall how a moor or heath resembles the hairy side of a giant animal. You will then consider the secular rise and fall of land which indicates the slow respiration of the creature. Finally you will note the fidgetings and scratchings which appear to our Lilliputian perceptions as earthquakes."

Jones is astonished. "Is it not a fact that the temperature rises rapidly as one descends?"

Professor Challenger waves this aside. "You are probably aware, sir, that the earth is flattened at the poles. This means that the pole is nearer to the center of the earth than any other point and would therefore be most affected by the heat of which you spoke. Perhaps you have noticed that the conditions of the poles are not tropical."

The professor holds up a sea urchin. "Nature repeats itself in many forms regardless of size. This echinus is a model of the world. You see, it is roughly circular but flattened at the poles. And how is it nourished? Why the earth browses upon a circular path in the fields of space and as it moves the ether is continually pouring through and providing the vitality—the same as Mars and Venus and the others.

"Suppose now that on this hard outer rind there were infinitely small insects which crawled upon the surface. Would the echinus be aware of their existence? No? Nor does the earth have the least idea of the way in which it is utilized by the human race. It is quite unaware of this fungus growth of vegetations and tiny animacules which has collected upon it. That is what I propose to alter."

Jones is amazed. "You propose to alter?"

"I propose to let the earth know that there is at least one person, George Edward Challenger, who calls for attention. Like the mosquito who explores the surface of the human body, we are unaware of its presence until it sinks its proboscis through the skin, which is our crust, then we are reminded that we are not altogether alone."

"Good Heavens, you propose to sink a shaft?"

"It is now eight miles deep. The last stage has been reached and you, Mr. Peerless Jones, represent the mosquito. Your artesian drill, a hundred feet in length and as sharp as possible, will be my stinging proboscis."

Jones is leaving the study when his curiosity leads him to turn and unwisely interrupt the professor's new train of thought. "What can be the object of so extraordinary an experiment?"

"Away, sir, away!" is the irritated response. "Raise your mind above the base utilitarian needs of commerce. Science seeks new knowledge. Let that knowledge lead us where it will, we still seek it. To know what we are, why we are, where we are, is that not in itself the greatest of human aspirations? Away, sir, away."

Later Jones gets a letter from the professor, with "writing that looks like a barbed-wire fence," which informs him that the time has come to set up the pointed drill in the bottom of the shaft. However, he is particularly warned not to tamper with the "sensitive inner cuticle of the earth" which is exposed beneath the crustal rock. On direct inspection the shaft floor is found to consist of grayish material glazed and shiny that ripples and bubbles. A smell, hardly fit for human lungs, fills the air. "Does look rather like a skinned animal," Jones says in an awed whisper as he makes the final adjustments. Then he races for the surface.

Before a multitude of celebrities assembled for the occasion, Professor Challenger presses the button that releases the harpoon-like drill.

"There was a cyclone, an earthquake, a volcano. Our ears were assailed by the most terrible cry ever heard. It was a howl in which anger, pain, menace and the outraged majesty of nature all blended into one hideous shriek. No sound in history has ever equalled that cry of the injured earth. A spout of vile treacly substance shot into the air and the pit closed like a wound.

"Professor Challenger smiled with satisfaction and posed for the photographers. It has been the common ambition of mankind to set the whole world talking. To set the whole world screaming was the privilege of Challenger alone."

A few years after Conan Doyle's hero had found that the crust of the earth was the shell of a great animal, Edgar Rice Burroughs discovered that a hollow shell of rock gave more room for adventuring. In *Tarzan at the Earth's Core* (1929) the hollow inner earth was named Pellucidar. Far from being the mere collection of great caves and passages that Jules Verne had written of, this was a sphere nearly as large as the outside of the earth. Entrance could be gained by means of a great opening near the North Pole. As a matter of fact, it was a sort of inside-out world with oceans beneath our continents and continents beneath our oceans—all only five hundred miles down. Pellucidar was lighted by a central sun so that it was always noon, but once Tarzan found jungles there just about like the ones he left on the outside earth (but populated with prehistoric animals), he adjusted rapidly and found his usual form of adventures. This wildly fictional story seems to have been taken from theories that were actually proposed by pseudo scientists not many years before.

Crank Ideas

Most science-fiction stories are contrived to entertain by stimulating the imagination; nobody is expected to believe them. It is said that Jules Verne often consulted with scientists of his time, not about whether his adventurous schemes were technologically possible, but whether the basic ideas violated any laws of physics. For his story about the projectile to the moon he engaged a well-known mathematician to compute its trajectory and the travel time so that the writing would sound authentic. In his story about the interior of the earth he inserted as much geological knowledge as was possible at the time; certainly there was no attempt to mislead.

However, there are at least three other forms that "science misinformation" may take and although none of these are presented with malicious intent, an uninformed public may believe them in preference to the unfamiliar facts. These are "theories" by scientific cranks, hoaxes that get out of hand, and speculations by well-intentioned but untrained people. Often the sponsors take themselves too seriously and become so trapped in the maze of their own statements that they cannot retreat.

The craziest schemes about the earth have usually originated in minds which were least inhibited by facts. For the less one knows about a subject, the freer is his mind to roam. This by itself is not necessarily bad, for new advances can come only from imagination. The difficulty arises when the author becomes aware of facts which make his idea impossible but stubbornly refuses to change his mind. This man is a crank. He will make a last-ditch defense of an idea stranger than those deliberately contrived as fiction, insisting that he is right to his dying breath. Some of the more bizarre schemes are fun to look over.

There is a long chain of hollow-earth theories which seems to have begun with the famous astronomer Edmund Halley—after whom the comet of 1692 was named. Halley was a very imaginative fellow who made both sensible and bizarre suggestions. He thought the outer shell of the earth was five hundred miles thick and that there were three inner spheres comparable in size to Mars, Venus, and Mercury—each capable of supporting life. His suggestion that the inner spheres and outer sphere did not rotate at the same speed and thus caused the westward drift of the magnetic field was remarkably close to the present theory, as we shall see later. As Burroughs was to picture it in the Tarzan story, Halley thought that the flattening of the earth thinned the shell at the poles, allowing the inner gas to escape. Inside the earth there was the perpetual light of a luminous atmosphere—this light, shining on the escaping gas, created the northern lights.

This general scheme was resurrected by Captain John Symmes, a U.S. hero of the war of 1812. The idea seems to have come to him in a dream—or perhaps while he was looking at Jupiter through a telescope. Anyway, on April 10, 1818, he wrote a letter which was printed and distributed to all Congressmen as well as to leading scientists throughout the world. It read:

To all the World:

I declare the earth is hollow and habitable within; containing a number of solid concentric spheres; one within the other and that it is open at the poles twelve or sixteen degrees. I pledge my life in support of this truth and am ready to explore the hollow, if the World will support and aid me in the undertaking.

I ask 100 brave companions well equipped to start from Siberia, in the fall season, with reindeer and sleighs on the ice of the frozen sea. I engage that we will find a warm and rich land, stocked with thrifty vegetables and animals, if not men, on reaching one degree northward of latitude 82; we will return in the succeeding spring.

JNO. C. SYMMES

The hole at the pole became known as the Symmes' hole and until his death he energetically searched for evidence to support his idea and for money to go and investigate. The theory improved with time. The outer shell was about a thousand miles thick; there were curious races of men and monsters; it was possible for the inhabitants of each one to walk on the inside as well as the outside of their own particular sphere. His son later suggested that the Lost Ten Tribes of Israel had probably gone underground via the hole. The best reason that the son managed to muster in support of the whole scheme was that "A hollow earth, habitable within, would result in a great saving of stuff" and a logical Creator would make it that way—like the stalks of plants or the bones of animals.

In 1823 Symmes asked the U. S. Congress to finance the trip and actually managed to muster twenty-five votes in support. The scientists of the time of course opposed it and nothing ever came of the project. When the North Pole was finally reached seventy years after his death, the hole had been forgotten.

Nevertheless, the hollow earth was repeatedly reinvented; if the earlier schemes were remembered, the later authors gave no credit. There were changes in the number and thickness of shells and in the size of the openings. One would-be scientist suggested that the Eskimos and the frozen hairy mammoths of Siberia came from the interior surface of "the only sphere definitely known to exist." This gentleman's book expounding these ideas in considerable detail was published in 1920, long after the Arctic had been crossed—apparently his objective was to prove that Perry and his successors had never really reached the North Pole.

In Germany during the 1930's a "Hollow Earth Doctrine" devised by Karl Neupert became fashionable. It held that we are already living on the inside of a spherical void and that the antipode is above our heads instead of on the opposite side of the earth beneath our feet. This theory holds that the shape and dimensions given for the earth are correct except that they apply to the hollow that is filled with the sky; out away from this internal heaven is an infinity of rock. In the center of this "earth" is a sun, a moon, and a blue sphere which eclipses the sun one-half of the time to give us night. It is hard to believe that anyone in the twentieth century would give such an idea a second thought, but according to G. P. Kuiper, Professor of Astronomy at the University of Chicago, the German Navy actually conducted experiments on it in World War II. A scientific party under an infrared expert, Kuiper wrote, was sent to the Isle of Rugen to try and photograph the British fleet by pointing the cameras upward at 45°. (If you believe the theory, every other point on earth is above the horizon.)

One of the best-known of the modern religious crackpots with a theory of the earth was Wilbur Glen Voliva, a go-getting minister who by a legal coup in 1905 took over the super-puritanical town of Zion, Illinois, from an equally fanatical predecessor. Voliva believed that the earth was saucer-shaped, with the North Pole on a mound in the center; his South Pole was a continuous high wall of ice around the outer edge. As late as the 1930's he offered a prize of $5000 to anyone who could prove to him that the earth is spherical. Of course nobody could, for his mind was thoroughly made up; probably one good look at him dressed like a seventeenth-century preacher in a frock coat and lace cuffs immediately discouraged some of those who arrived with proofs. Voliva actually traveled around the world several times lecturing on its flatness. As for what surrounded or supported the earth, he felt that it was not necessary to know; his sermons indicated that he believed that somewhere below was Hell, quite warm and populated by a race of bad spirits.

Voliva insisted that the moon furnished its own light, that the stars were really tiny and revolved around the earth, and that the sun was only 32 miles across and 3000 miles away. His reasoning for the latter was simple: If God made the sun to light the earth, why would he be so silly as to make it a million miles in diameter and place it 93 million miles away? Voliva repeatedly predicted the end of the world—the last time he set was in 1935. As of this writing his forecast appears to have been wrong. However, in November 1959 the International Flat Earth Society of Dover, England, which seems to follow Voliva's views, began a new membership drive (four shillings the subscription) to "keep alive the spirit of doubt."

The MOLE

In mid-1958, about the same time that AMSOC formally became a deep-drilling committee under the National Academy of Sciences and the word *Mohole* had been coined, rumors of a project with a similar-sounding name and destination began to circulate around Washington. There is no direct evidence that there was confusion between the two but it is possible that after the story of the MOLE became known, some of those who might have supported AMSOC in its early days held back for fear of being taken in by another elaborate hoax.

The story of MOLE is told by a series of excerpts from pseudo press releases in electronics trade journals which printed Washington date-line stories above the very tiny word *adv*.

May 19, 1958

An undisclosed source deep in the Pentagon today admitted that the Department is "becoming heavily committed to a radically new weapons system known as Project MOLE (Molecular Orbiting Low-Level Explorer)."

The MOLE should put an end to the threat of war. No place on earth will be secure from the MOLE.

June 2

Dr. Talpa, chief of SEA (Subterranean Exploration Agency) outlined the basic premise of the MOLE. Because conventional missiles are in danger of burning up when the missile reenters the atmosphere, the MOLE is conceived to avoid that problem. It is to be launched downward. Since its orbit is below ground, re-entry at high velocity is no problem. To avoid high temperatures the MOLE will travel near the earth's crust.

Aug 4

The MOLE which was successfully fired a few days ago is now in orbit at depths variously reported as from a few inches to 60,000 feet. Scientists have their ears to the ground listening to the steady "crunch, crunch" signals from the new missile.

Aug 18

A senatorial security committee today declared there has been altogether too much publicity on the vital MOLE project and clamped on it the megasecret classification of DBR (Destroy Before Reading).

This signaled the end of an advertising campaign with phony news stories for a real company that makes potentiometers. It effectively accomplished its objective of spreading the company name through the electronics industry, but, to the surprise of the originators, it left a trail of people who actually believed the fantastic story. Letters and phone calls arrived from people wanting jobs and from companies seeking subcontracts to build parts and launching bases.

The increasingly frequent appearance and mushroom-like growth of new and secret government agencies with large sums to spend on "Buck Rogers" projects had made industry jittery. Who knew which way science would go and what funds might follow?

Speculations and Theories

A remarkable number of people untrained in science have their own theories about the earth, its origin, composition, and phenomena. Most of them seem to be kindly inclined toward the Mohole project and are unstinting of the time it takes to explain their ideas. Long and detailed letters describe why societies are being formed to abolish gravity or what has happened to the lost "fourth magnetic pole" which causes the earth to slant on its axis. Several of our new-found friends are disturbed about the accumulation of ice on Antarctica, which they feel will start the earth wobbling on its axis and eventually fling civilization off into space or deluge it in a great flood. Others have unified hypotheses of magnetism, atomic energy, tidal radiation, and rocket ionization which they stoutly insist are the result of months of mathematical computation.

One man assured us that there was a hole already through the earth and that we could find the opening to it by digging under the northwest corner of the Great Pyramid. A number have warned against drilling into the earth at all, suggesting that if the crust is pierced our globe will pop like a toy balloon or that a hole in the ocean floor will permit all the water to drain out. AMSOC can hardly make use of such suggestions but it can at least assure the authors that it will not be reckless with the future of humanity and that the results of the new findings will be available to everyone.

By far the largest number of letters come from people who are genuinely worried that a volcano will be released, as, for example, the following: "When molten lava from the earth's interior seeks an outlet, it naturally breaks through at the weakest points. Therefore if you want a thin place to drill to the Moho you should look around volcanic areas—although the weakest places are not necessarily the thinnest ones. However there is the danger that just as a hole in a dam may set off a disastrous flood, a tiny hole in the crust may set off a full scale volcano. The thing would soon be beyond man's control so you had better drill in a useless area where, if a volcano should erupt, it would do as little damage as possible."

The ideas are logical but the basis for reasoning is inadequate. The fact is that there is not the slightest danger of releasing a volcano. But how is the public to know? How can science fiction, hoaxes, and crank ideas be distinguished from real scientific projects? To those who have not studied the subject under discussion the impossible suggestions may sound just as sensible as a bona fide project which is unusually imaginative.

Even scientifically trained men cannot always separate the two. As a result there are nearly as many examples of scientists being rejected by their fellows for proposing radically different ideas as there are of cranks who have been honored by the public for pseudo-scientific schemes that have sounded plausible. In fact, the man who promotes the crackpot idea may look and talk more like the public's preconceived idea of a scientist than a real scientist does.

Can you tell which of the following subjects are being actively discussed by scientists today because it may lead to an acceptable theory? The drifting of continents; the moon coming out of the Pacific Ocean; the visits of flying objects from outer space; the possibility that the earth stood still for a time; the finding of the lost Atlantis; the use of dowsing rods to find water; the shifting of the ice cap at the South Pole; the possibility that the Arctic Ocean was much warmer only a few thousand years ago.

Only the first and the last of these are considered worthy of scientific debate today but the others either have been the subjects of recent books or have been repeated so often that the public places credence in them. For example, the hypothesis that the moon came out of the Pacific Ocean was scientifically discredited over thirty years ago but it is still retold in popular books as though it were a generally accepted theory.

One result of this confusion is that the public has hazy ideas about the structure of the earth and how well it is known. The impression seems to have been created that scientists themselves are not sure. This is not quite correct. Actually, earth scientists are in close agreement on nearly all major points. Any arguments that may be overheard by the public are concerned with relative details. But arguments on all points are permitted, for the very essence of science is that no faith is required. Anyone who is skeptical can repeat any observation or experiment himself. He can see the outcome and retrace the reasoning that led to the accepted conclusion. Then, if he has reason to disagree, he will be listened to. The scientific theory that survives the tests of such constant re-examination is very likely to be correct. As this constant culling and modification of ideas proceeds, man's ideas about the interior of the earth become increasingly clear and well documented. In the study of the earth, science begins at the top with geology and works downward.

IV

Evidence in the Rocks

The idea of drilling a deep hole beneath the sea floor to explore the crustal layers and to reach the earth's interior may sound simple, yet it is based on some very sophisticated concepts. The Mohole would not be a worthwhile project if a great deal of scientific work had not already gone into the direct examination of the surface rocks by geologists and into the indirect study of the subsurface rocks by geophysicists. Therefore this chapter and several of the succeeding ones will try to explain the evolution of scientific thought in the earth sciences. They will try to answer the questions: What do we know about the earth now? How was it discovered? What remains to be learned by means of the Mohole project?

Geologists

Most of what is known about the crust of the earth has been extorted from the rocks over a period of years by a persistent breed of men called geologists. Geologists come in assorted varieties, including stratigraphers and paleontologists, who study the sedimentary strata and the evidences of ancient life they contain; vulcanologists, who examine volcanoes and eruptive rocks; structural geologists, who map warped rocky structures and try to determine what forces caused them; and petrologists, who examine rocks to see what they are made of. Their methods are different but the basic questions they ask are much the same.

They want to know: How did the rocks come into being? How old are they? How did they get into their present positions?

They work mostly outdoors "in the field," where they apply the tools of their trade—meticulous examination of the rocks, careful mapping, orderly thought. The geologist needs X-ray eyes to look both deep into the earth and far back in time. Unfortunately he is only human and cannot do this directly, but by virtue of his training his mind can almost see beneath the surface and into the past. To him the seeming confusion of the rocks may represent a clear and sensible record of a sequence of events long past. A true geologist does not feel quite comfortable when confronted by warped and crumpled rocks; immediately his mind sets about smoothing them out and trying to reconstruct the conditions under which they formed. The folded coal seam in the highway cut becomes the floor of a jungle swamp again and the dinosaur tracks up the side of the cliff move across a sandy tidal flat.

Geologists can be deadly serious about the discovery of a tiny fossil or hilariously happy about an earthquake. They are, in the words of Gordon Lill, "as independent as pigs in a peach orchard."

For all these reasons, plus some indefinable ones, they are inexorably attracted to any scheme for obtaining unique evidence about the earth's history, even if they have to go to the extreme of drilling beneath the ocean to get it. Moreover, each of the varieties of geologists feels that deep ocean drilling will be particularly valuable to the work of his own specialty and each longs to have first chance at new evidence. Paleontologists and stratigraphers pretend that it is hardly worthwhile to continue drilling after the sediments have been passed; the vulcanologists and petrologists are anxious for the drill to get through the sediments and deep into the igneous rocks below.

Present geological theories are based on fundamental ideas that have taken hundreds of years to develop and to become generally accepted. These are ideas about how rocks form and how they get into their present position, about how animals evolve, and about the length of geologic time.

Looking Backward in Time

Anyone who carefully examines the rocks of the earth soon concludes that they represent evidence of many complicated events. It is clear that in order for these events to have taken place a great deal of time was required.

Probably no concept of geology has caused so much debate as the length of geologic time. In the 1600's many people held the earth was only a few thousand years old. Some believed it was created at nine o'clock in the morning on October 23, 4004 B.C. Since then, estimates based on rates of erosion and deposition of rocks, on the amount of salt in the ocean, and finally on the decay of radioactive minerals have steadily lengthened the amount of time available, until now the concensus is that the earth has existed for about five billion years. Now the estimation of the length of geologic time has passed from conventional geology into astronomy and radiochemistry. But geologists do look backward, down the last billion years or so, at rocks which give a reasonably intelligible picture of past events. By piecing together bits of information discovered in rocks of many lands, they are able to create a picture of the events that took place on various parts of the earth in ages past. One big question about each event is always, How long ago did it happen?

There are two ways of answering this question. One is to get the events in their correct relative order without being concerned over how many years have elapsed. This is usually best accomplished by stratigraphy, which reasonably assumes that the oldest layers of sedimentary rocks were laid down first and that successively younger rocks were deposited on top. This means the information contained in the rocks remains in correct chronological order from bottom to top. Sometimes it is poetically called the story in the book of rocks. Unfortunately, so many of the pages are dog-eared or missing that the book is not always easy reading.

If you store old newspapers in the cellar, adding one to the top of the pile every day, you can easily understand the essence of stratigraphy. Each paper is in sequence with the oldest on the bottom, the most recent on top. If some are lost or if you go on a week's vacation, the papers for those days will be missing from the stack but the order is still correct. Perhaps a neighbor also saves papers but takes his vacation at a different time. It would be possible to assemble a complete set of papers for the year from the two piles *without looking at the dates* just by reading the headlines and filling the gaps in one pile with papers from the other. Then, if you memorized all the headlines in sequence so that you always knew each one's position relative to the others, you could answer the question "How long ago?" for any important news event by saying, "That happened the same day that Eisenhower was elected President" or "the day the *Andrea Doria* sunk," without specifying the day or month or year. This is the time-honored method of geologists. The left-hand column of Table IV-1

71

lists the geologic periods that are used, the headlines. If you were
to ask when the first land animals appeared on earth the answer
would be: "In Devonian time."

TABLE IV-1

The Geologic Time Scale

| | | | MILLIONS OF YEARS | |
| | | | | radioactive methods + stratigraphy |
Eras	Periods	Epochs	Years ago	Duration
Cenozoic	Quatenary	Recent Pleistocene		1
			— 1 —	
	Tertiary	Pliocene Miocene Oligocene Eocene Paleocene		11 16 12 20 } 59
			— 60 —	
Mesozoic	Cretaceous Jurassic Triassic			65 25 } 120 30
			— 180 —	
Paleozoic	Permian Carboniferous Devonian Silurian Ordovician Cambrian			25 50 60 } 330 35 80 80
			— 510 —	
Precambrian	Precambrian			at least 2,500
Cosmic Time		Birth of the earth	5,000±	

The other kind of response to the question "How long ago?" is to
state the number of years that have passed since the event in question;
such dates can be obtained by the use of radioactive dating methods.

To return to the newspaper analogy, if the papers had not been stacked but were strewn about the cellar, it would be necessary to refer to the dates to assemble a set. With radioactive dating techniques, the actual age of a rock in years may be determined. The procedure is not a simple one, however, and cannot be used on many rocks for reasons that will presently be discussed. The right-hand column of Table I lists the dates of the geologic periods that have been determined by the radioactive dating of key rocks.

Like the newspapers, the rocks of the crust are jumbled and strewn about. Parts of the record of the sediments are in one place, parts in another. Some of the rocks are buried deep and samples of them can be obtained only by drilling; others have been warped into ragged mountain ranges and partly carried away by erosion. Some of the rocky evidence is covered with rain forests, some with thick deposits of gravel, some with water.

The geologist's job is to take the best parts of the record wherever he can find them and assemble a complete history of the major events on earth. Then, using this reconstructed order of events as a scale, he can assign a position in time and an age to any new rock that is discovered if he can correlate its position with that of the rocks on the scale.

This order of events is the geologic time scale; a geologist can recite it, always from bottom to top, as fast as you can say the alphabet. The assembly of that scale began in the early 1800's with Cuvier, a Frenchman who found elephant fossils beneath the city of Paris, and William Smith, an engineer who studied fish fossils in the Old Red Sandstone of England. These two men laid the foundations of paleontology and stratigraphy at a time when the origins of fossils and of rocks were in doubt.

Fossils are any evidence of life in a previous geologic period. Most people think of fossils as being the shells of marine animals or dinosaur bones but there are many other forms including coal deposits, worm burrows, and footprints. Actually they are very common and can be found almost anywhere on earth. But at the beginning of the nineteenth century scientific opinion was divided about fossils because two even more important geological ideas had not yet been accepted. One of these was the vastness of geologic time. The other was the realization that on many occasions shallow seas have covered parts of the continents and that sediments deposited in these seas had hardened into rocks and been raised up into mountains. For those who believed, as many did, that fossils were the remains of plants and animals that died in the Biblical flood, these two ideas were not necessary.

Most of the theories about the flood were proposed by men who had never made any field investigations; however, when the most ardent proponents of the flood theory ventured into the Alps, they were taken aback by the scale of things. It was obvious that no simple flood had created such structures. The huge folds and faults in the towering mountains on all sides looked like the "wreckage of a ruined earth." Then there was the troublesome question of how a flood, only a few dozen feet deep, could have buried skeletons hundreds of feet beneath the surface of the ground thousands of feet above sea level.

Until the end of the eighteenth century sedimentary rocks still had not been distinguished from igneous rocks and few people believed that granites or basalts had ever been molten. Nor was anything much known of the sea bottom. Consequently in the late 1700's there existed for a time a school of thought called the Neptunists, who believed *all* rocks had formed in a great "original" ocean. The proponents had not troubled to observe and compare the layered rocks with those around active and ancient volcanoes. Volcanoes, they held, were burning mountains produced by accidental ignition of underlying coal beds.

The Neptunists were opposed by the Vulcanists, led by a redoubtable naturalist named Nicholas Desmarest, on the specific question of the origin of basalt. Although the Vulcanists were able to point out flows of basalt leading from volcanic craters in Auvergne, France, and elsewhere, most Neptunists refused to look; they stayed inside their laboratories and insisted that basalt was "aqueous," formed by chemical precipitation under water. Desmarest declined to discuss the matter in a theoretical way. He answered all geological arguments with the same remark, "Go and see." Those who did were quickly converted.

As a result of this argument one point became clear; observations would have to come before theories. In order to understand the history of the earth, direct examination of rocks as they exist in nature was necessary. Georges Cuvier, a French naturalist, believed this implicitly.

In 1796 Cuvier found fossil elephants of an unknown species in a gypsum quarry in Montmartre, near the center of Paris, and tremendous public interest was aroused. An explanation was needed but Cuvier was not a man to make wild speculations about how the bones came to be there; he thought about the matter for a long time before expressing an opinion. By applying his knowledge of comparative anatomy to the jumble of bones dug out of the gypsum, he was able to reconstruct many kinds of reptiles, birds, and mammals. In fact, he seems to have been the first to recreate whole animals which had never been seen by man from the evidence of a few scattered bones. Ultimately the Montmartre quarry yielded hundreds of species and Cuvier realized that these animals had lived in a completely different geologic period. Naturally, he asked himself, "How long ago did these animals die? How were they buried and preserved? How could marine plants and animals be interbedded with terrestrial ones? How does this fit in with the scriptural concept of one great flood?"

After a lifetime of study and observation Cuvier could enunciate the principles which form the basis of paleontology: (1) There are great differences in the conditions under which the fossil-containing beds were laid down. Some formed in lakes and some in salty seas; some were deposited in cold conditions, others in a tropical climate. (2) Fossils of similar animals in different strata are systematically different, suggesting that animals gradually adapt themselves to changes in environment. The older forms, from the lowest beds, are least similar to living animals. This was the first clear evidence of evolution. (3) Quarries many miles apart exhibit the same succession of rocks. This means that it is possible to recognize the same strata over a wide area both by means of their ordered sequence and by the fossils they contain.

It was clear that the seas had invaded the land and retreated several times, so Cuvier searched for present-day evidence of cataclysmic events that would cause such invasions. He could not find these and so felt forced to conclude that a series of divine creations and floods had occurred, one for each layer of different fossils.

This fitted the flood theory closely enough to satisfy the churchmen and the direct evidence well enough to satisfy many scientists. Cuvier's theory was wrong but his observations and methods marked the beginning of a renaissance in geological thinking. He died in 1832, the same year a remarkable book was published in England.

Principles of Geology by Charles Lyell summarized the views previously expressed by James Hutton and others on another aspect of geology. Its central thesis was that natural forces such as wind, moving ice, running water, and waves act slowly but inexorably over a period of many years to erode and shape the surface of the earth into the forms and features we see about us. Lyell held that the erosional forces which degrade the mountains and supply the materials for the fossil-bearing strata are offset by internal forces in the earth which raise the mountains and cause the rocks to bend and fault and crumble.

By following Lyell's logic, one reasoned that cataclysmic events of short duration were not necessary to cause major crustal changes but that these could take place slowly over many years. This eliminated the need for floods or divine intervention; the earth was much older than a few thousand years. In fact the changes are going on around us now, slowly and almost imperceptibly. He often quoted the famous words of his own teacher, James Hutton: "The present is the key to the past. Look at the processes going on today and see how the great changes occurred." A great barrier had finally been crossed; unlimited quantities of time could now be hypothesized to form the physical features of the earth.

Lyell's book was written in a popular style so that the layman could understand the arguments. Its eloquent and convincing summary of the revolutionary ideas about how changes in the earth were accomplished finally dealt a mortal blow to the Diluvialists, as the flood-theory supporters called themselves, to which Lyell's good friend Charles Darwin later administered the *coup de grâce*. Geology became a science based largely on the new concepts of evolution, stratigraphy, and the length of geologic time.

Stratigraphy

The eras and periods of geologic time represent major cycles of change in the earth's crust—rhythmic repetitions of mountain-building and invasion by the sea accompanied by erosion and deposition. Mountains are heaved up and eroded; sediments from them are carried by rivers to the sea where they are deposited in horizontal layers. Eventually the mountains are worn down and the basins are filled in; then a new upheaval raises the former sedimentary basins into mountains to complete the cycle.

These upheavals and the resulting abrupt changes from depositional to erosional conditions mark the beginning and the end of each geologic period. Within each period differences in rock character make it possible to identify formations—natural groupings of strata with some common characteristic. And within the formations are fossil keys.

The existence of fossils had, of course, been known for thousands of years before Cuvier and Smith. Cave men made primitive jewelry from them and the pyramids are built out of a limestone which contains easily recognizable fossils. The new thing these early stratigraphers discovered was that fossils could be used, in accordance with the principles Cuvier had set forth, to identify the rocks containing them with a specific time in the earth's history.

These were exciting new scientific ideas in the early 1800's and a new subscience formed around them: paleontology, literally the science of ancient life. Its objectives were to identify the fossils, classify them, date them (relatively), and determine their geographic extent, their environment, and their relationship with other forms of life. Once the systematic development of fossils in sequential beds was acknowledged, the importance of fossils in dating strata was recognized and a vigorous search for fossiliferous rocks began. The big question then became: Over how wide an area can a time correlation be made with fossils? By mid-century parallel lines of fossils had been found in the rocks of all continents. Therefore, a standard geologic column, usable around the world, could be constructed. Since there were times when no deposition took place on any continent and no fossil record can be found on land, it is possible that the missing record will be found beneath the deep-sea floor.

In the early days of paleontology no one realized what a monumental undertaking it would be to sort and classify all the forms of life found as fossils. A recent estimate places the total number of plant and animal species that have ever lived at 350 million, of which only a small fraction have been discovered to date.

As the study of fossils progressed and the volume of stratigraphic data grew, the estimates of the over-all time required for evolution became longer and longer. Until radioactive dating give us a means of telling how old rocks really are, the paleontologists were hard put to see how evolution could have been accomplished in the time permitted by the previous estimates. But now they have plenty of time, for traces of organic carbon have been identified in rocks dated at 2.7 billion years, five times as ancient as the first fossil record of the Cambrian. Plants must have developed before animals, for the only source of energy on earth, aside from radioactivity, is that of the sun, and only plants through photosynthesis can use the sun's energy.

A number of other ways have been suggested for determining how long geological processes have been going on. Some of these use the rates of erosion and deposition.

Most of the material eroded from highland areas are deposited as layers of sediment beneath shallow seas and on continental shelves. If one measures the rate at which sediment is being deposited and the thickness of the layer being formed, one can establish by simple division how long it took for that layer to accumulate. This sounds easy but there are many difficulties, particularly that of measuring the sedimentation rate.

It is readily apparent that this rate changes. During periods when the rocks in certain mountain belts stand high, erosion and sedimentation are rapid. As the rocks become worn down, the rate decreases. Moreover, careful studies of sedimentation rates checked against radioactivity measurements show that continental sediments were deposited three times as fast in recent geological periods as in earlier periods. This indicates that geologic processes are moving more rapidly and that the earth's crust is becoming more restless. The reason for this is not known.

It is important to distinguish between continental marine sediments and oceanic sediments. Most geologists believe, as noted previously, that continents are blocks of light rock that stand high, that ocean basins are composed of a denser rock relatively low, and that the two have never traded places. This means that continental processes, including the deposition of sediments on the bottom of shallow salt-water seas, take place on a high platform well above the ocean bottom. Probably these shallow waters of ancient seas were connected to the ocean but they were no more a part of it than the Gulf of Mexico is of the Atlantic Ocean.

No epeiric seas, as these are called, exist on our continent today like the ones we think existed in the past. However, the shoal waters of the Gulf of Mexico and the Yellow Sea are similar to them in many respects. There, sedimentation is going on rapidly and animals are dying and being buried to form the fossils of the future. It is in such shallow seas, which probably were never over a few hundred feet deep, that the tremendous thicknesses of sediments were formed which later became the Appalachians, the Rockies, and the California coast range. In Louisiana, drill holes that penetrate 20,000 feet of shale are apparently still far above the bottom of the original basin floor, estimated to be 50,000 feet down. This does not mean that a very deep basin was filled to the brim with sediment. Rather, it is believed that the weight of the sands and clays, added over many years from the erosion of a nearby mountain range, caused the whole structure to settle gradually. Since the basin sunk at the same rate as the new sediments were added, the water depth never changed appreciably. The pressure of the material above and the curious chemistry of time eventually caused the sediments to be compacted into rock.

The transfer of material from a mountainous land mass, which rises as the load is removed, to a sedimentary basin, which sinks as weight is added, is part of the preliminaries in the building of a new mountain range. The process is not clearly understood but apparently the added thermal insulation of the new sediments causes the temperature to rise in the rocks beneath. The noted geophysicist Sir Harold Jeffreys once calculated that a ten kilometer thickness of sediment would cause a 250° C rise in 100 million years. Perhaps as the deep rocks get hot, they are more easily deformed and create a zone of weakness which permits the sediments above to be heaved up into mountains. When this happens, all the material that was deposited in the shallow sea, including the fossils, rises well above sea level. These are uplifted marine sediments but they are not at all like oceanic sediments.

The two most widely distributed forms of deep-sea sediment are the red clays and the calcareous or siliceous oozes which consist largely of the skeletons of tiny sea animals.

Only in isolated circumstances have sediments believed to have originated in the deep sea been found on land. In Indonesia layers of deep-sea oozes and red clays have been found alternating with land formations, and at Barbados in the West Indies oceanic ooze deposits lie on top of sediments which include coal seams. Although these examples may indicate that the ocean floor can be uplifted to form land, this rarely occurs. If oceanic fossils are needed to complete the geologic record they must be brought up from the strata beneath the deep sea. This is one of the objectives of the Mohole project; another is to examine the deep volcanic rocks.

Volcanic Rocks

Much information about the rocks beneath the surface comes from the study of volcanoes and the lavas they bring to the surface. It is reasonable to expect that volcanoes occasionally would spew up samples of the deep crustal layers and of the material beneath the

Moho, and this evidence of the depths should be as valid as the samples obtained by drilling. Volcanoes do display samples of deep rocks; the problem is to decide what these rocks represent. This is complicated since each volcano has its own personality and composition. Paracutin, for example, was born in Mexico on February 20, 1943. An account of the circumstances was given by J. Gonzales and W. Foshag in the 1946 report of the Smithsonian Institution:

From the little town of Parangaricutira the group gathered in front of the church could see a thin column of smoke rising above the trees. There had been disturbing earthquakes for several days and news had already arrived that a crack had opened in Dionisio Pulido's cornfield. The populace was worried and it was decided that someone should go and investigate. Five men volunteered, and since the mission was believed to be a dangerous one in which they might lose their lives, the Cura gave them his benediction.

They went by horse, riding rapidly, and very soon came to the spot, the first two to arrive being Jesus Anguiano and Jesus Martinez. They found that the earth had opened, forming a kind of fissure, at the extreme southern end of which was a hole about half a meter across, from which issued smoke, and red-hot stones were thrown into the air a short distance. Anguiano, desirous to see what was taking place in the hole, approached the spot, when Solorio cried out to come back, the side was about to collapse. Scarcely had he leapt back when the wall fell in, widening the orifice to two meters across, and the column of smoke increased in size.

According to Anguiano, the orifice was pear-shaped and from this cavity arose a fine gray dust like ashes and "sparks", and stones were thrown out without much force to a height of five meters. A choking odor pervaded the spot. In the vent the sand was "boiling" like the bubbling sand in a rising spring, with a noise like a large jug of water, boiling vigorously, or boulders dragged along a stream bed by a river in flood. About the vent small mounds of fine dust half a meter high gathered. This fine ash was very hot but Anguiano collected some in his handkerchief as well as two of the hot stones.

The ground shook violently, jumping up and down, not with the swaying motion they had experienced in town.

They decided then to return and report what they had seen, and they carried with them the ash and the two stones. The stones were delivered to the Cura, and being still hot, they were placed in a dish, and the Cura exorcised them, that the volcano might cease. The Cura and others then consulted a book on Vesuvius in the library of the church, and it was decided that what they had seen was a volcano, which greatly astonished the gathered people.

Between six and nine o'clock the volcano began to throw out large stones, and at ten o'clock, one could see clearly from Parangaricutiro, through the pine trees, incandescent rocks hurled out, but without any thunderous noises. Between eleven o'clock and midnight the volcano began to roar, huge incandescent bombs were hurled into the air, and flashes of lightning appeared in the heavy ash column.

Eventually Paracutin built a cinder cone 1500 feet high and destroyed the fields and forests for miles around. This volcano, which became quiescent in 1952, is remarkable chiefly because this is only the sixth time in recorded history when the birth of a volcano has been observed in a previously nonvolcanic area. There had been many experiences with erupting volcanoes, however. Mostly these had been unhappy, as at Pompeii, and it is not surprising that the ancients believed the interior of the earth to be a place where boiling rock in constant turmoil is ever seeking for a crack to escape to the surface.

The fact that each volcano has its own personality makes volcanic activity puzzling. Some explode with great violence, others flow gently; some are steep-sided, others have gentle slopes; some produce acidic rocks, others give out basic lavas. But several main types and intensities of eruption have been recognized.

The volcanoes whose crests form the Hawaiian Islands have furnished the most evidence about the suboceanic crust and mantle because they have been intensively studied by the Volcano Observatory on the slope of Moana Loa. These volcanoes were built up by countless small lava flows rather than by explosive ejections; consequently they are quite different from Paracutin in action, appearance, and material.

A Hawaiian eruption is foretold by earthquakes that begin at considerable depth and, over a period of days or weeks, migrate surfaceward. Rising lavas cause the surface above to bulge slightly; a crack forms and molten rock of low viscosity wells out and runs riverlike down the mountainside. There is little of the violence which often marks the eruption of other volcanoes.

About every five years a new eruption sends a lava stream down the gently sloping flank to add another small segment of a lamination. In this manner, layer on layer, Moana Loa has risen from the Pacific Ocean until now it towers 28,000 feet above the sea floor. This makes it a higher peak than Mount Everest, which rises only about 22,000 feet from the hills around its base.

As the summit of the volcano rises, the newly added material imposes an additional load on the oceanic crust supporting the whole structure. As a result the crust sags, tending to restore isostatic balance. Harry Hess has calculated that an island made of basalt which has achieved this equilibrium will have depressed the bottom of the crust—the Moho—to a depth of 22 kilometers.

Volcanic eruptions furnish important evidence about the nature of the earth's interior by displaying fresh samples of the deep rocks, perhaps even the mantle. But if we are to attach any great significance to these rocky specimens, we must know something about the depth at which they originated and the temperatures and pressures that exist there.

First the mechanism of volcanoes must be understood. Because of the differences in the type of volcanic activity it was sometime before geologists had enough consistent data to come to any conclusions about these mechanisms. There were apparent contradictions in the evidence. For example, measurements in deep mines and drill holes showed that the temperature of the earth increases about 30° C for each kilometer of depth. If this increase were constant, at depths of 40 kilometers the temperature would be about 1200° C and the rock would be liquid. However, the evidence of the seismograph is contradictory. An earthquake occurs when rocks subjected to great stresses suddenly break. It is hard to see how a liquid rock could "break"— that is, to withstand a force up to an instant and then suddenly rupture. One would expect it to deform like a plastic. Yet earthquakes occur at depths of as much as 700 kilometers, well below the depth where the rocks were expected to be molten.

The vulcanologists were forced to conclude that the deep rocks are kept solid by the pressure of the rocks above. As solids, the rocks occupy minimum space. In order to become liquid they would have to expand and in order to expand they would have to lift the weight of the rocks above. So the rock at depth remains solid even though it may have a temperature higher than that required to melt it at the surface. With each kilometer of depth the increase in pressure due to the weight of rock above is sufficent to raise the necessary melting point by approximately 3° C. Thus for the solid rock at depth to become liquid there must be either a substantial rise in temperature or a considerable decrease in pressure.

An earthquake furnishes both. When the rock faults (breaks), much of the elastic energy is converted to heat along the fault zone and the temperature rises. This is a minor effect, however, compared to the sudden release of pressure, which permits the rock to become molten almost instantaneously. Moreover, since these magmas, as the deep molten rocks are called, contain great quantities of water and gases, the reduction in rock pressure permits these gases to expand explosively. It is like removing the cork from a champagne bottle; the expanding gas carries the liquid upward with it. As the lava moves upward, it may start to freeze in the volcano's throat, but often, as the pressure from below builds up, a new passage is opened. The rupturing of these temporary barriers apparently accounts for the audible deep rumblings and the secondary shocks used to trace the progress of the rising lava. At the Volcano Observatory at Moana Loa, where this method of tracking the upward motion of lava was developed, the position and time of an eruption can be predicted several days in advance.

The eruption brings up samples. Then the petrologist must go to work on them to try to determine what they mean.

The Deep Rocks

Because there is so much mantle rock and because the thin crust which covers it is constantly being broken by earthquakes and pierced by volcanic upheavals, it would indeed be remarkable if fragments of the mantle were not exposed somewhere on the surface. But there are so many kinds of volcanic rocks exposed that the geologist must have some idea of the mantle rock's characteristics if he is to distinguish it from the crustal rocks. Fortunately he knows the mantle's approximate density, its most likely mineral and chemical composition, and the speed with which it conducts sound. Guided by this information he begins looking for outcroppings of the deep rock in the most likely places.

His chances are better in an ocean basin because the crust is thinner there, and best where zones of seismic and volcanic disturbances intersect the basins. So he starts the search on islands or along the oceanic rim where seismic evidence shows that the volcanoes are active and the faults reach deep. Walking and climbing over the rough lava surface, he occasionally stops to look more closely at some unusual chunk of rock. He breaks off a corner that is unaltered by weathering so he will have a fresh surface to look at. He hefts a piece to see if it feels unusually dense, for high density is perhaps the simplest clue to deep origin. Then he examines it under a small magnifying glass to see if he can find indentifiable mineral crystals. If the rock feels heavy and if it contains the minerals olivine or pyroxene, the geologist is hot on the trail of the mantle. Very likely he will use the pick which he always carries to whittle out a hand-sized sample to take back to the laboratory, where more definitive studies can be made. Let us see why he believes that olivine and pyroxene would be likely to be found in mantle rock—rock that no man can be certain he has ever seen.

TABLE IV-2

Mineral Composition of Igneous Rocks

	Rocks	*Minerals*
crustal rocks	granite	quartz orthoclase feldspar mica
	basalt	plagioclase feldspar pyroxene
likely mantle rocks	dunite	olivine
	peridotite	olivine pyroxene
	eclogite	garnet pyroxene

A mineral is a naturally occurring substance with definite composition, crystal structure, and physical characteristics. Rocks are made up of combinations of minerals whose proportions for any species are only approximate. The composition of basalt, the most widely distributed lava and the one which formed the Hawaiian Islands, varies greatly from place to place. To be classified as a basalt, a rock must be composed mainly of the minerals pyroxene and plagioclase.

Igneous rocks can be classified in a general way according to the amounts of silica (SiO_2) they contain. This silica is the material generally recognized as quartz, the clear constituent of beach sand. Once the approximate chemical composition of a rock is known, the mineral possibilities are greatly narrowed.

Continental granitic rocks are likely to be composed of about 60 per cent silica but the igneous rock of the ocean basin, traditionally referred to as oceanic basalt, contains only about 50 per cent silica. Beneath them both, below the Moho, is the mantle, from which both oceanic and continental rocks appear to have originated. The scientific concensus is that the rock of the mantle contains only 40 per cent silica, in addition to large amounts of magnesium oxide, iron oxide, aluminum oxide, and water as shown in Table IV-3.

TABLE IV-3

Chemical Similarity of Mantle-Like Rocks

Reported by	Brought up by Volcanoes olivine nodules (Wager et al.)	Brought up by deep faults St. Paul's Rocks (Tilley & Vincent)	Arriving from space stony meteorites (Urey & Craig)
SiO_2	41.9%	44.0%	47.0%
MgO	46.2	41.1	29.5
FeO Fe_2O_3	7.4	7.9	15.4
Al_2O_3	1.1	2.9	3.1
CaO	1.1	2.4	2.4
Na_2O	0.1	—	1.2
H_2O	0.5	0.4	—
Plus small amounts of other minerals	1.7	1.3	1.4
About	100.0%	100.0%	100.0%

As this hypothesis has become better established by the addition of supporting data, the number of rocks and minerals meeting the density and compositional requirements of the mantle have been reduced until only a few remain as likely candidates for sub-Moho material. These are (1) dunite, made up almost entirely of a mineral called olivine; (2) periodotite, a combination of olivine and pyroxene; and (3) eclogite, composed of garnet and pyroxene. Specimens of these rocks have been found at widely separated places on the earth's surface including Hawaii, Japan, and California on the Pacific rim, and St. Paul's Rocks in the mid-Atlantic.

Particularly interesting are St. Paul's Rocks, barren islets that lie a few hundred miles from the eastern tip of Brazil (0°-58′N 29°-15′W). Very active seismically, they are the scene of continual small earthquakes as well as intermittent underwater volcanoes. The Rocks are a high point on the mid-Atlantic ridge, a great seam in the sea floor thousands of miles long, and they are maintained above water by the continual motion of a great fault that thrusts new materials up to replace the rocks eroded away by the waves.

Although St. Paul's Rocks are not far off the main shipping lanes and occasionally have been visited by ships, including Darwin's *Beagle,* it is not easy to land on them and obtain samples. The USN hydrographic vessel *Atka* stopped there in 1955 and attemped to send a geologist ashore in a whaleboat. When the boat crew tried to take soundings, sharks, visible in the clear waters, ate the sounding leads. On the other hand, the waves broke against the Rocks so violently that it would have been suicide to attempt a landing. The boat returned to the ship and a helicopter was used to put a man on the largest islet and to photograph the Rocks from the air. Unfortunately, as Charles Darwin had pointed out long before, a glossy incrustation of hardened bird dung on the Rocks is easily mistaken for volcanic rock and this was the predominant material of the *Atka*'s samples. However, small pieces of the Rocks were obtained and these were identified as peridotite. The combination of structure and rock composition leads some geologists to believe that St. Paul's Rocks are an outcropping of the mantle.

Another possible place where the materials of the mantle may reach the surface is in the diamondiferous rocks of South Africa. This is a tantalizing idea which was mentioned in the Estabrook letter that first proposed Moho-digging. Comparatively little is known about the origin of the rock in which diamonds are mined, but kimberlite, as it is called, occurs in vertical pipe-shaped masses that extend deep into the crust. Diamonds are formed from pure carbon under conditions of heat and pressure much greater than are likely to have existed at the depth where they are now found. Thus it has been suggested the kimberlite has risen from the mantle and the carbon is original material—a residue from the formation of the earth.

This hypothesis is supported by the finding of an eclogite boulder studded with diamonds in one of the deep mines—remember that eclogite is one of the rocks of which the mantle may be composed. Moreover, tiny diamonds have been found in the peridotite-like rock of stony meteorites, another material that is apparently similar to the mantle. A diamondiferous mantle would be a very pleasant place to terminate the Mohole but it is, unfortunately, less likely to be encountered than dunite, which is found in the Hawaiian lavas.

The basaltic lavas that flow from the Hawaiian volcanoes sometimes bring up lumps of dunite a foot or more in diameter. Since the earthquakes which are the preliminaries of the Hawaiian eruptions begin at depths of as much as 30 kilometers and since independent seismic surveys show that the depth to the Moho beneath the islands is only about 20 kilometers, it is reasonable to suppose that the lavas come from the mantle. Perhaps they do begin in the mantle but most of the rock that comes up is certainly not representative of it. Only the dunite is dense enough to be mantle material; the basalt seems to be a segregation product, a light material representing only a small fraction of the deep rocks. Probably when the basalt separated from the main mass of mantle rock and started to move upward, it accidentally carried with it small lumps of the heavier materials of which the deep rocks are principally composed. Table IV-3 shows the remarkable similarity between mantle-like rocks from three very different sources—a vivid demonstration of how the jigsaw puzzle of geology fits together.

How this separation into groups of minerals takes place is one of the great problems of geology. The geologist starts with the rocks that come to the surface at a place like Hawaii and reasons backward to try to determine the conditions under which they formed. The greatest puzzle of all is that the apparently uniform materials of the mantle seem to have given rise to the many varieties of rock which are seen at the surface. Some complicated process of differentiation must take place which releases one kind of rock at one time and different kinds of rock later on.

How can it be that one deep parent rock produces such diverse offspring as the granites of the continents and the basalts of the oceans? This is the question to which N. L. Bowen of the Geophysical Laboratory of the Carnegie Institution of Washington addressed himself. In the 1930's, after many years of experimentation in which he cooled small quantities of synthetic rock melts under closely controlled conditions, Bowen proposed that deep basaltic magmas are really the parents of all igneous rocks and that the many varieties we see at the surface have been produced by differential crystallization.

As a molten rock cools, some minerals crystallize first. If heavier than the constituents which remain liquid, these crystals will settle out; this is differentiation by gravity. The remaining molten mixture is then composed of slightly different materials and has a new chemistry. As it cools further another mineral will form. Bowen and his associates worked out the "order of crystallization"—that is, the order in which the different minerals appear. Olivine is first, along with calcium plagioclase; then comes pyroxene, biotite, orthoclase, and quartz. If the new olivine crystals do not immediately sink to the bottom of the magma chamber, they will react with the surrounding liquid to produce pyroxene. The resulting mixture of plagioclase, pyroxene, and the leftover olivine forms basalt. If, however, the crystals of olivine and plagioclase do settle to the floor of the magma chamber the remaining material near the top of the chamber will be composed largely of quartz and orthoclase. Then the rock produced will be granitic.

When the basaltic magmas rise to the surface, they form lava flows like those in Hawaii. It is easy to imagine that in the turbulent deep chamber where the magma originated, small lumps of the olivine (dunite) could be picked up and carried along by the viscous magma it moved surfaceward. If the theory is correct, we have in the dunite a sample of one more constituent of the mantle.

Bowen's simple explanation of the origin of the great diversity of rocks implies that the kind of rock which emerges at the surface depends on the history of its magma chamber and the time and level at which that chamber was broached by an earthquake. This suggests that no rock brought up by a volcano can be a fair sample of the mantle. To be sure what that rock is, it will be necessary to drill and to sample it in its natural unmelted state. Then the question of the age of the igneous rocks will arise.

Radioactive Dating

The unchanging rate of disintegration of radioactive elements gives a time clock which has superseded all others for absolute geological dating. The principle of the method is simple. A mineral in the rock to be dated is selected which contains a radioisotope with a half-life of appropriate length. Since the isotope's rate of decay into various products is known, geochemists can calculate the time since the rock formed by comparing the precise amount of newly-created elements with the remaining amount of original element. Often they use techniques which involve counting alpha particles.

Alpha particles are simply helium nuclei which have been stripped of their two electrons and consequently have a positive charge. Although they are ejected from the nucleus of the isotope at a high velocity, they are stopped almost immediately by collisions with other atoms from which they attract two new electrons and become normal helium again.

Obviously an atom of a radioactive element cannot give off an alpha particle—a helium nucleus with an atomic weight of four—and still remain the same. It becomes an atom of an element whose atomic weight is lower by four. Uranium with a mass of 238, for example, decays in steps to ionium, to radium, and finally to lead of mass 206 by losing eight alpha particles. In a similar way uranium 235 decays to lead 207 and thorium decays to lead 208. Each of these radioactive decay series starts out with a long-lived isotope, becomes a radioactive gaseous isotope, and ends in an isotope of lead. The ordinary lead as used in storage batteries is a mixture of all of these final lead products.

This rate of expulsion of alpha particles and consequent disintegration of the parent element is constant and measurable for each isotope. It is described as the element's half-life and for various elements it ranges from fractional seconds to millions of years. Half-life is governed by the laws of chance which state that after a certain length of time only half of the original atoms will have survived. When that amount of time has elapsed again, half of the remaining ones will survive, and so on.

The isotopes that were present at the origin of the earth and were not long-lived have long since vanished from the earth, as some isotopes apparently have, for it is apparent that the disintegration started at the moment of the element's creation. But the longer-lived ones such as uranium 238 have a half-life of 4.5 billion years and are very useful to the geologist. Since this is approximately the age of the earth, half of the original supply is still around. Uranium 235's half-life is 0.7 billion years and thorium's is 1.4 billion years so there is quite a range of long half-lives to choose from.

Radioactivity was discovered by Henri Becquerel in 1896 and by 1907 Lord Rutherford and his associates had proven that lead and helium were stable products derived from the radioactive decay of uranium and thorium. In that same year B. B. Boltwood published the first absolute age determinations of rocks and minerals based on these methods. But even after fifty years of experience with the uranium-thorium methods, the age-dating of rocks is far from routine. The experts agree that great pains must be taken in selecting samples, analyzing them, and evaluating the results.

A major problem is to select a rock that can be dated and is worth dating. Since most of our knowledge of geologic events comes from sedimentary rocks, it would be nice if it were easy to give these rocks absolute geochemical dates. Unfortunately, although sediments do contain small grains of suitably radioactive minerals, these were derived from the destruction of earlier igneous rocks. Any date obtained would be that of the original rock, not of the sediment.

This means that in order to date a sedimentary rock and connect the age determined by fossils to the absolute age determined by radioactivity, it is necessary to find a place where igneous rocks have some clear time-relationship to the sedimentary strata.

A specific example makes this easier to understand. Suppose that a series of layers of sandstone and clays containing fossils have been deposited in a shallow sea. Nearby a crack opens in the earth and molten lava flows out covering some of the sediments. After a while the volcanic activity ceases and the sedimentation resumes. If the lava can be dated, limits can be put on the age of the adjacent strata and on the fossils they contain.

Having found the right kind of a rock in the right kind of a place, it is then necessary to ascertain if it contains the right kind of minerals in the right kind of state. The datable rocks are composed of crystals of individual minerals that formed when the rock cooled. At the moment they "froze" into their present shapes, the disintegration products could no longer escape and the accumulation began which the radiochemists measure. So, if they are unaffected by physical or chemical weathering, all the necessary constituents are still locked inside—the lead, the helium, and the remaining part of the original radioactive isotope. Therefore, it is desirable to have a "fresh" unweathered specimen for dating from deep within the rock.

By using the mass spectrometer, it is possible to determine the amounts of each of the four isotopes of lead in the sample. The standard counting techniques employed to analyze radioactive materials can determine the remaining amount of the parent element (uranium 238, uranium 235, or thorium). Then, with a little fancy arithmetic, it may be possible to obtain three independent dates on the same sample. If they all agree, the measurement is reasonably reliable. However, many things may have happened to the rock which would produce an erroneous result. For example, part of the intermediate gaseous isotope may have escaped by slow diffusion over the long life of the rock, or substantial amounts of lead may have been present originally in the rock. Either of these could cause age variations of many millions of years in these delicate measurements. The oldest rock yet dated by the lead method is a granite from Rhodesia. Its age is 2.7 billion years, about half the age of that estimated for the earth's origin through the study of meteorites.

For unique rock specimens of meteorites or boulders dredged from the deep sea the helium method may be used. If the amount of helium can be determined and compared with the remaining amount of its parent element, an age estimate can be made. But gaseous products such as helium are likely to escape through very tiny cracks in a mineral crystal that may open over a period of millions of years, especially if there is enough uranium generating it so that considerable pressure is built up. Because of the likelihood of such losses, helium ages are generally considered to be too low. However, it may be the only possible way of getting an approximate age and one must make use of the samples that nature provides.

Amid the long chain of radioactive decay products between uranium and lead are ionium and radium. Radium is found in surprisingly large quantities in the red clays beneath the deep sea. Since sea water contains five times as much uranium as is necessary to account for the radium in the water, it was at first thought that in some way the radium was selectively precipitated out of the water. If this were true, then by measuring the amount of radium in the layers of the sea bottom it would be possible to tell how long ago the radium had been deposited and thereby calculate the rate of deposition of the sediments.

The top of the sediments should contain the maximum amount of radium and the radioactivity should decrease with depth.

However, when the first deep-sea cores were analyzed it was discovered that the maximum radium content was not at the surface but a short distance below. To explain the slower decrease in radioactivity actually found in the sediments, Prof. Hans Petterson of the Oceanographiska Institutet of Sweden suggested that not radium but its longer-lived parent ionium was being precipitated. Thus the radioactivity of the sediments was found to come not only from directly precipitated radium but also from the radium produced by the ionium. Although the radium method of dating oceanic sediments is not as simple as had been hoped, it has a useful range of about 6000 years.

One of the most generally useful means of rock age determination is based on the decay of the potassium isotope with mass 40 to the gas argon. This is the result of the capture by the nucleus of one of the orbital electrons and here, as with the helium method, the sample must be gas-tight. However the potassium-argon method, as it is called, has a great practical range since it is usable upon the oldest rocks as well as on those formed as recently as 100,000 years ago.

This brief look at some of the geological and geochemical dating methods indicates that they are not simple procedures that can be routinely applied to any rock. They offer a spectrum of possibilities, a range of times and techniques, on which the earth scientist can draw. In order to assign any rock or event to its proper position in the long column of geologic time, he must carefully select a method and support it with logical reasoning.

In order to date a rock, the geochemist has to have a sample of it. The Mohole cores will provide such samples of the deep remote rocks. But before drilling, the earth's structure, particularly that of its crust, must be investigated in detail by the remote methods of geophysics: geodesy, seismology, magnetism, and heat flow. Evidence from each one is important in selecting a drilling site.

V

Exploring the Crust with Gravity

Man's earliest effort in the earth sciences was the attempt to discover the size and shape of the earth. This work, which began at least 2500 years ago, is still going on. Without a knowledge of the proportions of our space platform, it would be difficult to fit together the information about the earth. Every year the measurements become more precise and detailed, but on the main points the ancients were correct.

Socrates, the great Greek philosopher, is quoted by Plato as having said in 400 B.C., "My conviction is that the earth is a round body in the center of the heavens and therefore has no need of air or any similar force to be a support. . . ."

The Size of the Earth

Not long afterward the size of the earth was first measured and although the tale of how it was done has been recounted many times, it is worth retelling as a charming example of clever reasoning which solved a big problem with a small amount of evidence. Ask yourself how you would measure the size of the earth, even with modern equipment, before you read on.

In the third century B.C. a refugee Greek scientist named Eratosthenes was in charge of the great library of the Ptolemies at Alexandria. Like other well-educated men, he believed that the earth was round and he may even have heard estimates of its size. One day while browsing in the piles of papyrus, he read about a very deep well in the city of Cyene, 5000 stadia almost due south up the Nile, where exactly at noon on the day of the summer solstice, the sun was reflected in the water below. One can imagine the usually dark walls of the well suddenly lighting up for a few seconds and people crowding

around, squinting down and shading their eyes to see the sun's brilliant reflection in the midst of a dark circle of heads. Probably this
phenomenon had been noticed for many years before an unknown
Egyptian historian recorded it.

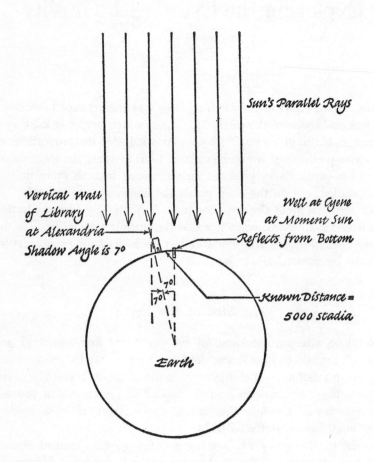

Fig. V-1 The Size of the Earth

A Opposite interior angles formed by a line crossing two parallel lines are
equal.

B $\dfrac{7°}{360°} = \dfrac{1}{50}$ of earth circumference

C 5000 stadia from Alexandria to Cyene

D 50 × 5000 = 250,000 stadia = Circumference of the Earth

QED Eratosthenes (300 B.C.)

It seemed a remarkable fact that somehow could be put to use. Eratosthenes thought it over. The next year, at noon on the day of the solstice (when the sun was furthest north of the equator) he carefully measured the angle the sun's shadow made with one of the vertical walls of his library. It was slightly over 7°. From simple geometry, as shown in Figure V-1, he knew this to be equal to the angle formed at the center of the earth by lines through Cyene and Alexandria. Seven degrees out of a total of 360° is 1/50 of the earth, and knowing the distance from Alexandria to Cyene to be 5000 stadia, he quickly calculated the circumference of the earth to be 50×5000 or 250,000 stadia. Since an Egyptian stadia is approximately one-tenth of a mile, Eratosthenes' estimate of 25,000 miles is within a few hundred miles of the figure used today.

In 320 B.C. Aristotle wrote a book called *About the Heavens* in which he set forth the opinion that the earth was a sphere and that the World Ocean covered the other side of it and might connect the Pillars of Hercules with India—an idea that waited 1800 years before being tested by Columbus. The idea, however, was not Aristotle's; it was much older and he was merely summarizing, in logical fashion, the knowledge that had been handed down. He cited the disappearance of ships over the horizon as evidence of the earth's roundness and pointed out that the shadow of the earth on the moon during an eclipse is round. He noted how stars seen in southern lands could not be seen in northern ones and vice versa. This proved that the earth was a sphere —and not a very large one—otherwise the difference in the sky's appearance at the two places would not be so great. Later, one of his students calculated the size of the earth by measuring the heights of stars above the horizon at two places and achieved fairly accurate results even though the phenomenon of light refraction by the atmosphere was unknown.

One difficulty in getting people to believe these ideas was that gravity was not understood. Anyone could see objects had a "natural tendency" to fall, so it was hard to understand why things on the other side of a spherical earth would not fall off into space. This still troubled sailors as late as the fifteenth century, making it difficult to recruit crews for deep-sea voyages until after Magellan sailed around the world.

The approximate size and shape of the earth has been known for a long time but the use of gravity to make refined measurements of it dates from the observations of Galileo in the early 1600's.

Galileo and Newton

Today the earth's shape and size are determined by instruments that measure the force of gravity by employing the principles Galileo discovered through his two most famous experiments. He noticed that a suspended lamp which swung like a pendulum in the cathedral at Pisa took exactly the same length of time to make a wide swing as a small one. From this he concluded that the period of the pendulum—the time to swing from one high point to the other and back again—depended only on the length of the supporting chain. Lamps with long chains had longer periods than the short ones, but the period of each lamp always stayed the same.

The modern pendulum gravity-measuring instrument is a remote descendant of those cathedral lamps. A carefully built pendulum will always have the same period if kept in one place. If, however, it is moved to a place having a different gravitational attraction, then its period will also be different. Thus, a precise measurement of a pendulum's period is a measure of the force of gravity.

Galileo's other famous experiment was to drop two stones of different weights from the top of the Leaning Tower at Pisa. He discovered that both stones fell at the same velocity, or, as it is usually stated, acceleration due to gravity is a constant. In Galileo's honor, this constant has been named the *gal*. It has been standardized by careful measurements at the Helmert Tower in Potsdam, Germany. Thus, a gal is the force of gravity acting at Potsdam where, if you were to drop a stone, the distance it would fall in any second would be exactly 981.274 centimeters further than the distance it had fallen in the previous second. Of course, the stone or other object need not be falling; the force of gravity acts on it just the same. In either case the acceleration due to gravity, which is usually noted by a small g, is 981.274 gals—a gal being 1 cm/sec/sec.

Some time after Galileo's death it was discovered that the force of gravity is not quite a constant although it is always the same at any one location. If a measuring instrument is moved about on the earth, the acceleration due to gravity is found to vary considerably.

Galileo was a fine experimentalist but it remained for Sir Isaac Newton to produce a satisfactory theoretical explanation of the operation of gravity. About 1685 Newton formulated the theory of gravitational attraction which states: Every particle in the universe attracts every other particle with a force that is equal to the product of their masses divided by the square of the distance between them.

Even today, no one knows what gravity is or why it exists. However, after Newton gave an explanation of the rules under which gravity operates and after precise measuring instruments were developed, a new science grew up around it: geodesy. Its practitioners, geodesists, use the variations in gravity to determine the size and shape of the earth.

The layman, who believes the earth to be a sphere, is correct by any ordinary standard since it is rounder than a billiard ball or a ball bearing. If there were an exact model of the earth a foot in diameter it would be quite impossible to see the flattening at the poles or the pear-shapedness. The highest Himalayas and the deepest ocean trenches would vary from the smoothness by only a thousandth of an inch. The continental edges could not be distinguished by their relief alone and the oceans would be a thin film of dampness. On a table-sized globe, the blue paper which represents the ocean is about the correct scale thickness.

Most people, therefore, would be satisfied to say the earth is a smooth round sphere, but not the geodesist. For him, it is an ellipsoid of rotation—a sphere slightly flattened at the poles—whose mean equatorial radius is 6378.388 kilometers and whose polar radius is 6356.912 kilometers. The difference between the two is 21.476 kilometers or about 13.7 miles.

The equatorial bulge, originally predicted by Newton, is caused by the centrifugal force of the earth's rotation. Fortunately this force is small compared to that of gravity and the spinning earth does not fling us off into space. At the poles the combined effect of being 21 kilometers closer to the earth's center and of being at its axis, where the centrifugal force is zero, makes the value of gravity about half a per cent more than it is at the equator. If a polar bear weighing 1000 pounds at home was quickly transported to an equatorial zoo, he would weigh in at only 995 pounds.

Geodesists needed an ideal earth, a reference figure, in order to determine how and to what extent the real earth varied from it. They devised several. One of these, a mathematical figure developed by rotating an earth-shaped ellipse on its axis, is called the reference ellipsoid. From it a formula has been developed which gives the theoretical force of gravity at every latitude. It serves as a standard for judging the variations of gravity from place to place.

Since the earth is pulled out of shape by variations in its own mass, it is not an exactly regular figure and another standard has come into use —the geoid or sea-level earth. The shape of this figure coincides with the ocean surface and with the water surface in imaginary narrow sea-level canals intersecting the continents. The geoid can also be described as a surface which is always perpendicular to a plumb line—as a water surface is.

A third shape called the spheroid, which is in general use today, is a combination of the previous two. A world-average form of the geoid, it is a little easier to work with mathematically.

Equipped with Galileo's concepts, Newton's theory of gravitation, and a theoretical shape, the geodesist's next step was to make many field observations. Precise instruments were needed to define the shape of the earth's crust.

The Measurement of Gravity

The determination of the gravitational constant furnished a unit— the gal. But the variations in gravity are very small—the largest being the five-gals difference in attraction between the poles and the equator. So the milligal has become the standard unit of geophysics—one thousandth part of a gal.

There are two general methods of measuring gravity. One is the pendulum device in which the swinging of a pendulum is accurately timed. Think of this type of instrument as a pendulum clock bought in Potsdam, Germany, from a reliable company who guarantees that it keeps perfect time. The buyer takes it to his new home in Peru, high in the Andes, and sets it by means of a precise radio time signal from station WWV in Washington, D.C. At the end of a few days he checks the clock against the radio time signal and finds that his clock is slow. The owner, being a thoughtful fellow, says to himself, "My clock must have a longer period here than in Potsdam; that means it makes fewer swings per day. Since everything else remains the same, the force of gravity acting on the pendulum must be smaller here. If I very accurately measure the amount of time the clock loses, I can calculate just how much difference there is in gravity between Potsdam and here." That is approximately what the scientists do. With modern pendulum instruments they measure the absolute value of gravity to about a tenth of a milligal.

The other kind of instrument makes an even more precise measure-

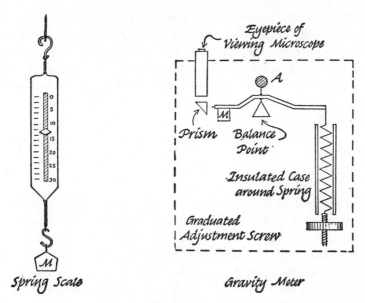

Spring Scale   *Gravity Meter*

Fig. V-2 The gravity meter is a highly refined version of an ordinary spring scale which always weighs the same object. Small differences in the weight of M from place to place are exaggerated as auxiliary weight A moves out of a position of perfect balance. The displacement of the end of the beam is viewed through a microscope and returned to precise center by means of the adjustment screw which can then be read.

ment of gravitational differences by weighing a standard object. This is the gravity meter shown in Figure V-2. In it a standard mass is permanently attached to a spring scale. As the meter is moved from place to place, changes in the weight of the standard mass are caused by differences in the gravitational attraction. These instruments, which can be contained in a case as small as six inches in diameter and a foot high, are capable of determining the force of gravity to a hundredth of a milligal.

In measuring gravity a very careful correction must be made for the height of the instrument above sea level—ten feet of altitude being equivalent to a milligal. For according to Newton's law, the change in gravity is proportional to the square of the distance between the center of the earth and the center of the instrument. However, even after the altitude correction has been made, the instrument reading may still show a variation from the theoretical spheroid. This anomaly is what the geodesist is searching for. It furnishes a means of determining the missing piece of information in Newton's law—the mass. For although the total mass of the earth is known, the proportion contributed by the local rocks must be determined by gravity measurements. When gravity was first measured accurately, large variations were discovered which can only be accounted for by differences in the density of the adjacent rocks. This was the first clue to the existence of a crust on the earth and of the shape of the boundary which was later called the Moho.

Isostasy

The first man to stumble upon the importance of density variations was the French mathematician-surveyor Pierre Bouguer. While on an expedition to the Andes in 1740, Bouguer was astonished to discover that the value of gravity in the mountains, even after he had accounted for the altitude, was less than in plains areas not far away. This was exactly the opposite of what he had expected since it seemed reasonable to think that the huge mass of rock would exert considerable additional attraction on his pendulums. After studying the information, he correctly concluded that the Andes are composed of light rock which extend far down and separate the gravity-measuring instruments from the denser rock of the earth's interior. This was a great discovery and in his honor, differences between the observed values of gravity and theoretical ones for the spheroid are called Bouguer anomalies. In calculating them the influence of the mass of rock between the instrument and sea level must be subtracted. Another method of calculating anomalies makes the assumption that only "free air" occupies the space between the instrument and sea level.

If the gravity anomalies across the Alps are plotted as shown in Figure V-3, the value of gravity is observed to be lowest where the mountains are highest and vice versa. Similar measurements extending into ocean areas show the value of gravity there to be even greater. Why should this be so?

This is explained by the theory of isostasy. According to that theory, a level of compensation exists at some depth below the earth's surface—a sort of imaginary surface on which the crust of the earth floats. Whatever projects above that surface must be compensated for in proportion to its height and density by an appropriate amount of material extending downward into the denser mantle rock beneath. High mountains are supported by a mass of similar relatively light

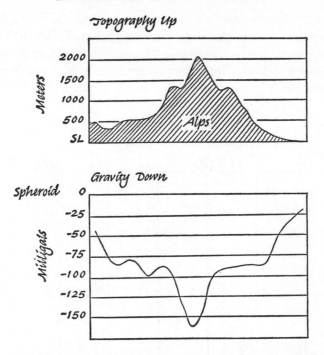

Fig. V-3 Bouguer gravity anomalies across the Alps from Passau, Germany, to Venice, Italy, show minimum values where mountains are highest.

material that extends far down into the denser material below; valleys and plains need correspondingly less material below for their support. As a result the bottom of the crust has an undulating shape something like a smoothed-out mirror image of the surface above. Beneath mountains the crust and the Moho bulge down; beneath valleys and under the oceans the crust is thin and the Moho is relatively shallow.

It had long been suspected that major variations in the force of gravity occurred in the ocean basins but no instrument existed for measuring gravity at sea until the 1920's. Then a Dutch geodesist, F. A. Viening-Meinesz, devised a method that would work on shipboard. He swung pairs of pendulums in opposite directions. This compensated for the horizontal motions of the ship which had prevented earlier scientists from making accurate measurements. He mounted his instrument on a submerged submarine—the most stable ship available—and set out to survey the changes in gravity.

Measuring the force of gravity might seem to be a rather dull way to make a living but one of the early submarine cruises to measure gravity anomalies in the Caribbean produced some of the most hair-raising experiences in the history of geophysics. Professor Viening-Meinesz, the inventor of the seagoing pendulum instrument, was the senior scientist; Harry Hess, then a graduate student at Princeton, went along to help.

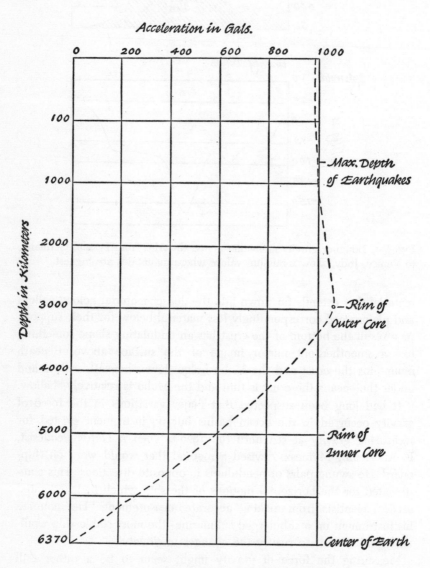

Fig. V-4 Change in Gravity with Depth

The year was 1932. The boat was the old S-48, which according to rumor, had been sunk, salvaged, and sent to sea again, the oldest submarine in the U. S. Navy. The captain's name has been forgotten but the executive officer was Lieutenant Hyman Rickover—only a few years out of Annapolis.

The scientific objective of the cruise was to measure the changes in gravity along a line extending from the deep Atlantic Ocean across the West Indies to the Caribbean Sea. However, it is remembered by those aboard for the four near-disasters encountered within a month.

The first occurred during a routine dive when some air vents jammed open and a modest downward angle suddenly became dangerously steep. Even with the diving planes fully inclined surfaceward, the curving path along which the ship was moving threatened to take it deep enough to collapse the hull, so the skipper gave emergency orders: "Full astern on both engines and blow all tanks." Before the downward trend was reversed the ship reached 450 feet—virtually a record for the old S boats—and when it came up, it came fast. The sub did not leap clear out of the water as some later claimed but dishes and instruments were smashed, the galley was made a shambles, and a half-dozen crewmen were slightly injured. As a result of this incident, ship-operating procedures were tightened considerably and future dives were cautiously made.

In a week nerves had steadied and confidence in the ship returned. Then one day the S-48 was surfacing in mid-Caribbean, where the chances of even seeing another ship were not particularly good. The chance of being on a course that would come within a mile of another ship was very small and the chance that the only submarine in the area would surface directly in front of a large ship was astronomically minute. As is the custom on surfacing, when periscope-depth was reached, the skipper took a routine look around. On this occasion he was horrified to find himself looking directly at the bow of a large cruise ship bearing down on the submarine at around 25 knots. Needless to say, any bump, much less a full ramming, would very likely have resulted in the sinking of the sub with all hands.

The captain ordered an emergency dive and he and the men of the S-48 had a few very bad minutes as the two vessels missed by a few feet—or maybe it was inches.

The third incident happened two weeks later. Submarine practice, at least before the executive officer of the S-48 finally put a nuclear reactor in one, was to run on the surface at night using diesel engines to recharge the batteries that power them underwater. The sub was slowly approaching the Bahama Islands on the surface one calm, moonless night. Two officers took independent star sights to determine the ship's position and, on plotting these on the chart, decided that they were safely distant from land. Suddenly the lookout on the conning-tower heard breakers ahead and caught the glint of foam on a reef. The watch officer rang full astern and the sub slowly churned to a stop, not quite nuzzling a coral reef before it backed away to a safe distance. A new navigational check was made and, puzzlingly, it showed that according to the chart the sub was exactly where it was supposed to be, far from land. On returning home it was discovered that the chart they were using showed the Bahamas eight miles out of position.

By this time some fifty gravity measurements had been made. Even when the sub was behaving well, Harry Hess recalls that starting the pendulums on the gravity meter was a trying procedure. The pendulums had to swing in opposite directions simultaneously and they had to be started by hand exactly at the same instant. Often this required ten or more exasperating tries. Considering the circumstances, the results of the cruise were very satisfactory and everyone was ready for a little time ashore in some good safe place.

The place they picked for shore leave was Santiago, Cuba, and Hess and a Lieutenant Brown sought out the best available room of the Venus Hotel. It happened to be on the top floor overlooking the main thoroughfare. They checked in at midnight and were soon asleep—but not for long. Accustomed to sleeping on naval vessels which make rumbling sounds and conduct target practice at odd hours, their reaction to the great Santiago earthquake which began at 2:00 A.M. may have been a little slow. Hess's sleepy impression was that the sea was rougher and the gunfire heavier than usual. When he finally sat upright in bed, it was just in time to see the hotel wall fold back, giving him a panoramic view of the city directly down its main street. He got under the bed. Brown, an earthquake-experienced Californian, found a doorway. When the shocks ceased, the two men dressed and climbed down nine floors of rubble to the street. Then they repaired to a nearby park to spend the rest of the night.

Despite all the trouble, the measurements of gravity made on that fabulous cruise are still standards of comparison in the area.

In recent years Dr. J. Lamar Worzel of the Lamont Geological Observatory has been the most enthusiastic oceanic gravity surveyor.

Worzel also uses submarines for platforms but sometimes it is difficult to persuade the Navy to take their subs to remote parts of the ocean for the sole purpose of making geophysical measurements. So one of his pet projects has been the development of a surface-ship gravity meter that can be used on Lamont's ship, *Vema*, while the ship is under way.

The gravity meter on the *Vema* rides in gimbals next to the gyrocompass at the center of the ship, thereby keeping accelerations due to waves at a minimum. In other words, it's where a man subject to seasickness would want to be, since it holds relatively still and the rest of the ship tends to rotate around it. As an additional means of keeping the meter level, a mechanism, sensing the motion of the ship, automatically levels the platform on which the instrument rests.

The meter itself is a spring-mass device, something like the land gravimeters but magnetically "damped." That means that the standard mass—an aluminum bar—floats between the poles of a magnet. Any tendency for the bar to move rapidly is resisted by the generation of eddy currents. Thus the magnetic field tends to prevent the aluminum bar from responding to the short jerky accelerations caused by the waves but does not restrain its slow response to the change in gravity.

By properly locating and damping the gravimeter much, but not all, of the undesirable motion of the mass can be eliminated. Even so, the record of this ultrasensitive instrument is often unusable. It is least disturbed by the waves in a following sea—that is, when the waves and the ship are going in the same direction—or by a flat calm, which is rarely encountered. Its measurements are poorest when the ship is bucking into the sea or directly opposing the waves. Then the instrument is so busy measuring the accelerations of the ship as it pounds along that the acceleration due to gravity is lost in the background.

The recording mechanism on the *Vema* is located in the scientific control center, where, on a more or less standard strip-chart recorder, a pen traces a red-ink line from which the value of gravity can be read directly. However, even on a calm day corrections must be made that take into account the special characteristics of a moving instrument. For example, the direction in which the ship is headed makes a substantial difference in the measured value of gravity. At the same spot gravity pulls harder on the standard mass if the ship is moving west than if the ship is moving east. This is the Eötvös effect—a result of the earth's centrifugal force. Any object moving eastward adds its velocity to that of the turning earth and has an increased tendency to be thrown off; thus the force of gravity appears to be lower. A ship moving westward has a slightly decreased speed so gravity appears stronger than it actually is. Although this is not a major error, a change in course of the ship from west to east can make a difference in the gravity measurement of as much as 25 milligals.

The information obtained from gravity meters at sea can be used to work out the relative thickness of the oceanic crust and the general configuration of the mantle surface but it cannot obtain the actual depths to the Moho. For these, seismic surveys are required.

Before going into the manner in which suboceanic seismic exploration is done, we will consider another aspect of crustal motion.

Continental Drift

If continents, or at least large blocks of them, can move up and down in response to isostatic forces, perhaps they can also move about sidewise in response to other forces. No principle is more certain in geology than that of continual change and probably no piece of real estate on earth is now the same shape and size—or in exactly the same place—as it was, say, fifty million years ago. Although that is not a long time geologically speaking—perhaps only 5 per cent of the time since the original continents formed—it is plenty of time for small forces, acting steadily, to produce remarkably large changes. So it is reasonable to believe that there have been substantial shifts in continental shapes and positions. Unfortunately, it is not possible to give very satisfactory answers to such fundamental questions as: How much change? How fast has it taken place? and especially, What causes the motions?

Ever since the first crude maps of the Atlantic Ocean were drawn, people have noticed the parallelism of the opposite shores. Francis Bacon is said to have remarked on it in the early 1600's and the serious scientific suggestion was made in 1858 that North and South America had, as a unit, broken off and drifted away from Europe and Africa. In recent years it has been noted that the mid-Atlantic ridge parallels the shores as though it were a remnant of an original juncture between the continents.

The name most associated with the modern theory of continental drift is Alfred Wegener, a German geologist who spent several decades in the early part of this century developing an elaborate theory and seeking support for it. Wegener believed that the continents were once a single large land mass which broke up and drifted apart—huge rafts of rock that slid sidewise over the earth's mantle from the positions shown in Figure V-5a to the present ones in Figure V-5b.

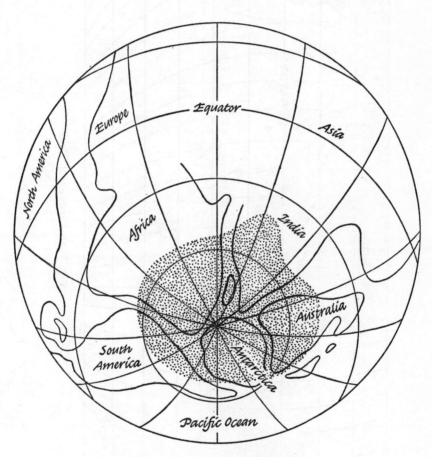

Fig. V-5a Continental Drift—Before

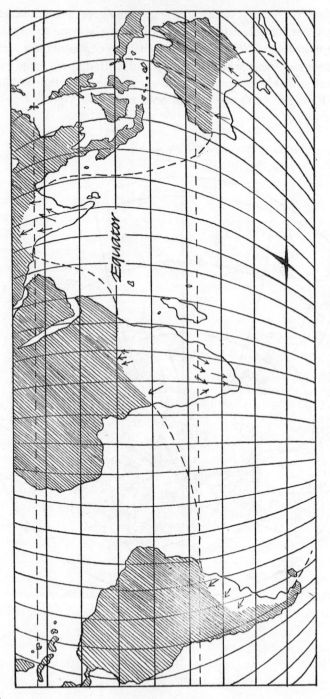

Fig. V-5b Continental Drift–After

To prove his theories Wegener argued that if one huge continent had cracked into slabs which separated, the pieces would be expected to contain evidence of their previous attachments. Earthquake zones and mountain ranges on each side should match up, showing where the two continents had once been connected. Animal species on each raft should have begun divergent evolutionary trends at the time of separation. Evidence of previous connections should be revealed by the study of ancient climates. If two blocks in different latitudes, now having quite different climates, were found to have been on the equator or had been glaciated at the same time in some previous geological period, this might indicate that one or both blocks had moved. He searched for and found evidence which he believed supported each of these ideas.

Wegener used the changes in the distance between Greenland and Europe to support his hypothesis. Measurements purported to show that the two had separated at a rate of nine meters a year between 1870 and 1907. This apparent shift of one to three kilometers per century would be comparable to the circumnavigation of the earth by a continent in two million years—a completely unreasonable figure. When the surveys were repeated with greater accuracy in later years, no evidence was found of movement and since Wegener had made such a point of this, great doubt was cast on the entire theory of continental drift. In recent years, however, new support has been found for the basic idea that sidewise continental motion takes place and the once discredited theory is the subject of renewed discussion.

The sliding of the continents also implies the "wandering" of the magnetic poles. There is no real evidence that the axis of the earth has changed with respect to the mantle or that the earth has "rolled over" as some have claimed. However, the thin crust may have shifted so that the magnetic pole emerges through it in a new place. As a molten rock cools, tiny magnetic particles in it align themselves with the earth's magnetic field. If these directions can be ascertained and the time of the cooling dated, the direction of the pole at the time the rock hardened can be obtained. From such investigations—described in the chapter on magnetism—the Wegener theory has received a great deal of renewed support in the last decade. The magnetic record in the rocks appear to prove that the poles were once in areas far from the present poles.

A remarkable amount of evidence has been discovered which seems to support the theory of continental drift. In addition to the magnetic evidence, glacial deposits apparently were formed in areas which are now tropical and at the same time coal deposits formed in areas which are now near the Arctic circle. The position of the equator seems to have shifted and the ancient mountain ranges, which must have supplied the sediments that eventually became the Appalachian mountains, appear to have been located in what is now deep ocean. Figure V-5b suggests that India slid into Asia and in so doing caused the buckling that forced up the Himalayas. The last evidence of a connection between India and South Africa is in Cretaceous time—70 million years ago. If India did indeed separate 5500 kilometers from South Africa over a period of 70 million years, the average rate of motion is only nine centimeters (four inches) a year. This is a more reliable way of reckoning drift rate than that used for Greenland. However with such a low rate of movement—only six meters in a man's lifetime—it is difficult to make direct measurements that can confirm or deny the concept of drift.

Recent evidence suggests that Africa and Asia are in an early stage of splitting apart and that the Red Sea may be the beginning of the rift. This is supported by the recent finding that on the islands in its midst rocks are exposed which could be chips of mantle squeezed up between a separating crust.

There are difficult problems with which Wegener and his successors never really made much progress: Why should a great land mass break up into smaller continents? What forces could cause this to happen? How is it that some areas apparently stayed near their original location while others moved large distances? Why should the pieces move in opposite directions?

One possibility which has been suggested is that slow convection currents within the earth's mantle rose beneath the original block and spread out sideways, their frictional drag carrying the continents apart—something like a slow fountain of water rising under a wide thin ice floe. The floe would crack up and the pieces would drift apart. This is the most promising explanation of continental drift and it is discussed in detail in Chapter VIII.

Many geologists agree that continents move somewhat. In the words of Dr. Arthur Holmes, "The motions are too obvious to be denied." Answers to the questions of how much and how fast they move may be found in rock and sediment samples from beneath the ocean floor. It is readily apparent that if a crack opened to form the Atlantic Ocean in the last hundred million years, there can be no sedimentary record beneath the Atlantic older than that. The sliding continents would have bulldozed away any sediments that previously existed in the ocean basin over which they advanced—perhaps piling these into mountains or pushing them downward into the mantle, where they would be remelted. Behind the drifting continent there would be successively older sediments. The oldest would mark the original place of separation and permit it to be dated.

Thus a moving continent could be expected to leave a "wake" in the rock crust like a ship does in the ocean. Where no continent has passed, there could be uninterrupted sediments as old as the ocean. In the theory of continental drift may lie an explanation for what seems to be the remarkable thinness of the soft sediments of most of the ocean floor. Certainly a series of holes to explore the age and depth of the sediments would be very helpful in deciding whether or not such drifting has occurred.

VI

Probing with Earthquakes
and Explosions

Much of man's knowledge of the rocks far beneath the earth's surface comes from the study of the seismic waves produced by earthquakes. The use of these waves to explore the earth dates back about seventy-five years although there has been speculation on the nature of the deep rocks and the meaning of earthquakes since ancient times. Pliny the Elder studied the earthquake that destroyed the city of Pompeii in A.D. 63, and the nearby volcanic mountain Vesuvius, until he lost his life in the first eruption of Vesuvius within historic times. But most of the early interest in earthquakes was in correlating their occurrence with other phenomena.

In the great encyclopedia *Natural History* assembled by Count Buffon and published in 1750 the "facts" as they were then known were set forth. "One kind of earthquake is occasioned by the action of subterranean fires and explosions of volcanoes; these are felt to small distances. The other kind is different both in effects and causes. It is felt to vast distances and its horizontal tremblings shake a long stretch of ground without the intermediation of any new volcano. These may be of short duration, not more than a few seconds, or they may extend over many days or months. A hollow thundering noise precedes or accompanies the shock. Earthquakes occur at all seasons, by night and by day, and under all varieties of constellations and phases of the moon, indifferently. They travel without hindrance across plains, under mountains and below deep valleys. In some earthquakes, rivers flow from the ground and lakes are formed; in others, lakes and rivers vanish. The surface of the earth may be raised or lowered." As far as they went, these ideas were correct, but mixed in with them were others which confused thinking.

Among the latter were tales that earthquakes were accompanied

by strong winds, fireballs, and meteors, that they occurred more generally in large towns or along rivers, that they are most likely to happen
when a rain follows a great drought, in which case they were supposed
to be succeeded by a pestilence.

Buffon suggested that earthquakes were caused by "the fermen-
tation of pyrites or other sulphurous matter at a depth of about 200
fathoms. These matters taking flame will produce a great quantity of
air which is compressed in a cavern and will attempt all ways of
escaping. The passages which it uses are those of subterranean rivers
and into these the rarefied air will be precipitated with violence into
a furious wind, the noise whereof is heard at the surface accompanied
by shocks and tremors."

John Milne and the Seismograph

Man's ideas about earthquakes were based largely on such un-
founded speculations until an English mining engineer named John
Milne founded modern seismology.

In 1875 Milne, having already worked in the mines of Cornwall
and Central Europe as well as having served as a geologist on two
scientific expeditions, was appointed professor of geology and mining
at the Imperial College of Engineering at Tokyo. Characteristically,
he started for the new post overland and alone, making geological
observations as he went. The trip took eleven months and when he
finally did arrive in Tokyo, he was greeted on the first night by an
earthquake. It proved to be symbolic of his association with Japan.

Milne at once became interested in studying earthquake phenomena
and before long he founded the Seismological Society of Japan. The
society had several important functions, not the least of which was
educating the Japanese public to observe earthquakes so that data on
time and direction of shocks would be available. There was one fool-
proof earthquake-measuring instrument that Milne relied upon for
the direction of earth motion. Virtually every Japanese house had
a small garden with a stone lantern on a pedestal in its midst. As
the quake waves passed, the lanterns toppled toward the source. These
permitted the epicenter to be located and this, in turn, could be correlated with building damage. These eyewitness reports were helpful
but it was clear that an instrument was needed to obtain more precise
and reliable data, an instrument that would automatically and graphi-
cally record a seismic disturbance—a seismograph.

Milne did not actually invent the seismograph; Sir Alfred Ewing and Thomas Gray contributed the principal ideas. But to Milne must go the credit for developing a practical instrument and for thoroughly testing it in earthquake country.

Milne's instrument was a combination of both horizontal- and vertical-motion seismographs, all recording on a continuously moving strip of paper. The principle it used, a heavy mass suspended on a gate, was old, having repeatedly been rediscovered from 1830 on, but when Milne showed the first records to the Seismological Society in 1885 they created tremendous excitement, and a new science—that of interpreting the records of shock waves in the earth—was launched.

Earthquakes were an unreliable source for testing the instrument. They came at odd times without warning and from unexpected directions. In order to create simpler and more satsifactory shock waves, Milne made the first seismic experiments by dropping a weight of nearly a ton from heights up to thirty-five feet. This method of creating seismic shock waves has recently been reinvented and is now being used by oil exploration crews in West Texas, where it is known as "the thumper." Milne also was the first to use dynamite as a shock-wave source and in tests with it he was able to separate compression waves from shear waves, noting the characteristic difference in velocity between the two.

He compiled a historic catalog of 366 great Japanese earthquakes between 295 B.C. and 1872 and then set up an organization for keeping it up to date. To get a better idea of earthquake distribution, he circulated bundles of postcards among the government offices in all important towns within a hundred miles of Tokyo. Every week a postcard was mailed to him with notes of any quakes observed. In two years this simple method was demonstrated to be successful and he persuaded the Imperial Meteorological Department to extend the area covered and to do the paper work involved. Then, with only one assistant, Milne actually mapped the areas of Japan that had been disturbed by 8331 earthquakes over a period of eight years—about three a day—using the postcard data. When the earthquake centers were plotted he found that 84 per cent had originated along the east coast or beneath the ocean and, somewhat surprisingly, that central Japan, in which active volcanoes are numerous, is singularly free of earthquakes.

In 1883 he returned to England and wrote "it is not unlikely that every large earthquake might, with proper instrumental appliances, be recorded at any point on the land surface of our globe." This was a revolutionary idea; to prove it he built an observatory on the Isle of Wight and measured distant earthquakes himself. Milne then conceived the idea of encouraging the creation of a world-wide network of seismograph stations and by the turn of the century thirty-four were in operation. With these stations he was soon able to make a world-wide map of the zones of earthquake origins—a map which is substantially unchanged to this day.

Milne furnished the tools and established the methods of the new science. After him discoveries came thick and fast as men used the new tools to survey the earth's interior. By 1907 the velocities of seismic waves in the earth's mantle were accurately known and the existence of a core had been discovered. In 1909 Andrija Mohorovičić discovered the discontinuity that forms the lower boundary of the crust and by 1913 Beno Gutenberg had determined that the radius of the core was 3500 kilometers.

Only in this century has man really looked beneath the surface to any great depth and used instruments to help him determine the nature of the interior of the earth.

Seismic Waves

An earthquake is literally a "shaking of the earth." The ground surface moves back and forth, side to side, and up and down. According to Newton's first law of motion, a body at rest will remain at rest until acted upon by an external force. Thus, if a weight is suspended in such a way that the movement of the earth cannot readily exert a force on it, when an earthquake occurs the weight will hold still and the earth will move beneath it. If a pen is attached to the weight and a clock mechanism continuously moves a paper-covered cylinder—which is firmly attached to the earth—beneath the pen, the shaking of the earth will be recorded as a jagged line on the paper. The instrument just described is the Milne seismograph.

Modern versions of these instruments have weights as large as twenty tons and pen motions that are amplified many times by optical and electrical devices, but the basic principle is the same. The seismograph weight swings on the end of a hinged bar like a child upon a gate, so it can only swing back and forth along one path. Therefore at seismograph stations it is customary to have three instruments; two paths at right angles to each other (usually north-south and east-west)

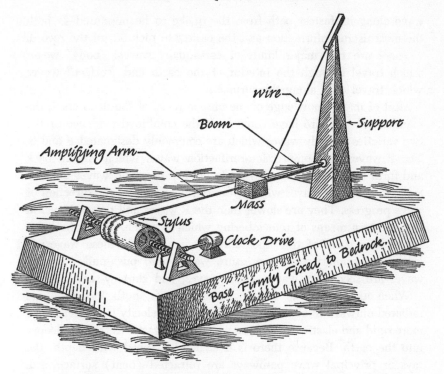

Fig. VI-1 Milne Seismograph. Early seismographs recorded by scratching a line on a carbon-coated disc moved by clockwork.

and one up and down, on a vertical spring. These give the three components of direction.

From the study of the records written by seismographs a great deal has been learned about the nature of earthquakes—their depths, locations, and magnitudes. And from the study of earthquakes a great deal has been learned about the interior of the earth. This is possible because a quake sends out several kinds of shock waves, each traveling in its own way at its own characteristic velocity. To the uninitiated the seismograph record appears to be a meaningless "hash" of jagged marks, but after a little study each wave variety can be identified and timed and its route determined. When records from several stations of a single quake are examined by an expert in the light of what is known about the earth's structure, the meaning of the seismograph writing becomes clear. Fortunately the first large jiggle—which marks the first arrival of each wave and permits the time of travel of the wave along its fastest path from the quake to be measured—is both the most useful information and the easiest to pick out of the record.

There are two major kinds of earthquake waves: "body" waves which travel through the interior of the earth and "surface" waves which travel only along the surface.

Most of man's knowledge of the unseen rocks of the deep crust, the mantle, and the core have come from the combined evidence of the two varieties of body waves which are commonly designated P and S. The P waves are compression-rarifaction waves which vibrate back and forth in the direction of wave travel just as sound waves do. The S waves are shear waves which vibrate transversely to the direction of wave progress. They are slower than the P waves and do not travel in liquids. As a means of remembering which is which, it may be helpful to hear some of the other alliterative names of these waves: P waves are primary waves, pressure waves, and push-pull waves; S waves are secondary waves, shear waves, and shimmy-shake waves.

When an earthquake occurs, seismic waves, both P and S, are radiated outward in all directions. Since their velocity is greater in the more rigid and elastic rocks, these waves travel faster as they go deeper into the earth. Because there is a change of speed with depth, the rays or principal wave pathways are refracted (bent) surfaceward. This bending is caused by the varying rigidity of the deep rocks and has two interesting consequences. First, it causes the waves to echo in curved paths along the underside of the earth's surface; second, it causes a curious ring-shaped zone of seismic blackout on the opposite side of the earth.

As the waves from an earthquake speed downward and outward—P waves first, S waves following more slowly by the same paths—they are bent toward the surface. When the P waves strike the surface or an interface such as the Moho, they are reflected back, so that they bounce along under the surface. With every bounce, new waves are propagated. P becomes PP on the first bounce, PPP on the second, and so on. The original P also sets up a new S wave—PS—and this, when it reflects, is PSS. By the time the original burst of elastic energy radiated by an earthquake reaches a seismograph, it is spread into a series of waves each of which has come at its own proper speed and by its own path.

Figure VI-2 indicates the wave pathways from an earthquake to a series of seismographs and shows the kind of a record each would write. Thus the shock of an earthquake echoes about inside our earth

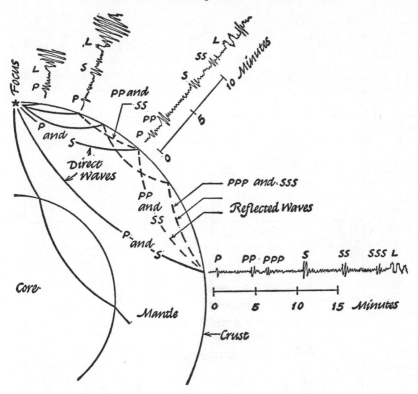

Fig. VI-2 Section through a part of the earth, showing the paths of a few of the many earthquake waves and the records they leave on the seismograms of four stations.

and is recorded over and over by seismographs. The records are complex but by carefully studying the jiggles the structure of the deep interior can be worked out.

At 103° away from a large quake the P record suddenly becomes indistinct. (In working with long distances, seismologists use degrees as a measure of distance. One hundred and eighty degrees would be at the antipodes or exactly opposite point on the earth; 103° would be a little over halfway around.) For some distance there is no P wave and then suddenly at 145°, it comes in again. This is called the shadow zone for P. When the P wave finally reappears, it is found to have traveled some part of its journey much more slowly than one might have expected. Instead of traversing the earth in 16 minutes, it took 20. Why was it slow?

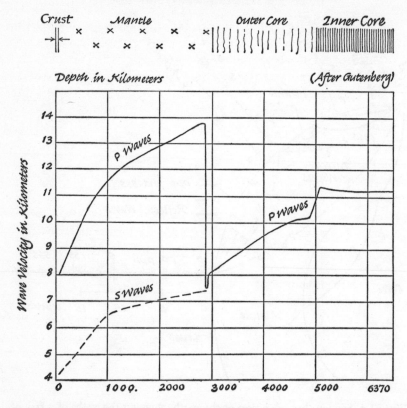

Fig. VI-3 Seismic Wave Velocities. The major divisions of the earth's interior are identified by the velocities of the seismic waves. The liquid outer core does not conduct S (shear) waves at all. The core's low rigidity and high density slow the P (pressure) waves down.

The answer is given in Figure VI-3 which shows the speed of seismic waves at all depths. Notice that the P wave suddenly slows when it enters the core of the earth and that the S wave no longer exists. This emphasizes the point that the velocity of seismic waves decreases as the density becomes greater. The earth's core is almost certainly a nickel-iron mixture which, although much denser than the mantle material, is much less rigid. In fact, the best evidence of its liquid state is that the shear waves do not pass through it. The explanation for waves increasing their speed with depth in the mantle is that although the density is increasing, which should slow the waves down, the rigidity is increasing more rapidly. Both effects presumably are due to the weight of the rock above. Because the relation between the velocities of S and P is known, the lag of S behind P can be employed to determine the distance of a quake from the recording station.

This technique was in use by Ocotber 8, 1909, when an earthquake in the Kulpa Valley in Croatia sent out seismic shock waves that were recorded at many seismograph stations throughout Europe. Most of the scientists who examined the records regarded them as routine. Each noticed the double sets of waves and regarded this as evidence of a double tremor, in which one shock was larger than the other. One scientist examining the records of several stations noticed that on records made close to the epicenter the larger of the two waves came first but on those made beyond 150 kilometers, the smaller ones arrived first. This seemed odd; moreover, he observed that the greater the distance of the seismograph station from the epicenter, the more separation between the two waves. This indicated that only a single shock had occurred but it had moved outward by two pathways, one of which was faster than the other. Close to the disturbance, the large direct wave had reached the recorder first but as the distance increased, the smaller wave traveling by the faster route had pulled away from the other. Since the travel time of the slower waves coincided with what was expected in the surface rocks, he concluded that a higher velocity layer existed beneath. He calculated the depth to the layer, at which the seismic waves abruptly increased in velocity, as 55 kilometers and published his findings in a paper entitled "The Great Earthquake of 1909."

The author was Professor Andrija Mohorovičić of the University of Zagreb in Yugoslavia. Thus was the layered nature of the earth established and the crust of the earth scientifically defined.

The word *crust*, however, was not new. It had long been in use but the meaning had been different. Originally, when it was supposed that the earth had cooled from a liquid ball, the analogy of molten metal in a smelter pot was used. When it cooled, a slaglike crust formed, covering the liquid material. However, when the work of Sir Isaac Newton and Lord Kelvin showed that the earth was not molten, the idea of a crust was abandoned. But after Professor Mohorovičić established the existence of a surface layer on the earth, separated from the material beneath by a seismic discontinuity, the use of the word *crust* returned. Its lower boundary, whose nature the AMSOC Committee hopes to discover, is the Mohorovičić discontinuity —the Moho.

Two forms of surface waves have, in recent years, been effectively

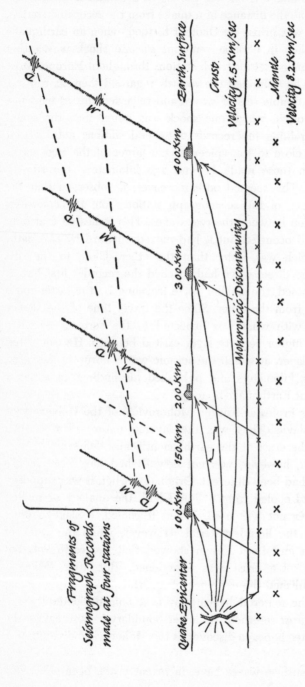

Fig. VI-4 Professor Mohorovičić's discovery, greatly simplified. D = direct waves in crust. M = waves traveling through the mantle. The professor observed that seismograph records at increasing distance from the Croatian quake of 1909 showed pairs of P waves tending to separate. He theorized that the smaller ones (marked M) which overtook and passed the direct waves must have traveled to the stations by a deeper, faster route beneath the crust. This seismic discontinuity is now commonly known as the Moho.

used for crustal studies. Rayleigh waves run along the earth's surface like waves that travel down a carpet when you shake one end up and down; Love waves are like waves that travel down a garden hose as you shake it from side to side. These two kinds of waves are named after the men who discovered them mathematically long before they were identified on seismograms. Each has its own characteristic velocity, the Love wave being slower than the S waves and the Rayleigh wave being slower still. Traveling only on the surface, they are started when the P wave strikes the surface. Once started, the travel time of these waves is directly proportional to the distance from the epicenter and is not complicated by an uncertain pathway as are the body waves.

All kinds of seismic waves are created by the sudden breaking of rock under pressure—a fascinating natural phenomena.

Earthquakes

Over long periods of time, stresses build up within the rocks of the earth—both in the crust and in the upper mantle. If the pressure increases very slowly, confined rocks will bend or flow like plastic. This is evidenced by the warped and folded rocks sometimes seen in road cuts or on mountain sides. The folds, formed by unequal pressures deep underground, have been exposed by erosion of the rock which formerly surrounded them. If the same amount of pressure were applied rapidly, the rock would break or "fault" instead of bending. This ability of the same rock to either deform or break depending on how rapidly the pressure is applied can be demonstrated with a plastic substance sold under the trade name of Silly Putty. If you strike Silly Putty with a hammer it will shatter, but if you rest the hammer head on it for a few moments, the putty will flow to conform to the stress imposed by the hammer.

When a fault occurs in the earth and the accumulated pressure is suddenly released, the energy is instantly transformed into seismic waves. The result is an earthquake.

The question of how the pressure originates has never been satisfactorily answered. Presumably it is connected in some way with the expansion and contraction of rocks due to differential heating. At one time it was customary to account for most faults—and mountains—by saying that the earth was cooling and shrinking; this of course would put the whole crust in compression. Now it is realized that earth features are not so easily explained; moreover, it is no longer certain that the earth is cooling.

In order to describe the size of earthquakes, two kinds of scales have been developed. These are the intensity scale—which is descriptive of the effects of the earthquake on man—and the magnitude scale—which is used to compare the amounts of energy released by the faulting. Both scales are needed because, although an earthquake only has one magnitude, its shock intensity changes, decreasing rapidly with distance. Consequently, if an earthquake of large magnitude occurs far from a populated area, it will have a small intensity.

Some of the main points on the intensity scale, always written in Roman numerals, are:

I, only perceptible to a few people
III, noticeable indoors, especially on upper floors—rattles dishes (in Australia this is given as "like a horse rubbing itself against a veranda post")
V, felt by all, heavy furniture moves, plaster falls
VII, chimneys fall; everybody runs outside
IX, ground cracks, landslides, most masonry buildings destroyed
XI, (the highest grade) objects thrown into air, total damage.

The magnitude scale, named after Professor C. F. Richter of the California Institute of Technology who devised it, makes it possible to compare the amounts of energy released by an earthquake at its source by assigning an absolute value to each quake. The scale ranges from 2, equivalent at the epicenter to II on the intensity scale, to 8.5, the maximum possible value. These numbers are determined by measuring the maximum amplitude recorded on a "standard" seismograph 100 kilometers from the epicenter. Of course, there would almost never be a station exactly at that distance but it is possible to interpolate between records and determine what the amplitude would have been. The logarithm of the measured amplitude is the scale value and thus it is analogous to the astronomical brightness scale.

Although inaccuracies are introduced by the differences between seismographs and by the fact that large quakes radiate more of their energy in long-period waves than do small ones, the magnitude scale is useful for comparing earthquake energies. For example, the San Francisco quake of 1906 was 8.2; several of the Chilean quakes of 1960 were equally large.

Earthquakes also are classified by the depth of their focus beneath the surface. Shallow quakes are those above 60 kilometers; the deep ones go down to 720 kilometers. However, most earthquakes are shallow and have their focus above the Moho at depths of 15 to 30 kilometers. Occasionally the faulting breaks the surface and leaves a long scar to mark its place. California's San Andreas fault, for example, extends for hundreds of miles and is clearly visible from the air as a long line of lakes, offsets, and low scarps.

About 80 per cent of large earthquakes and at least as large a proportion of small ones occur in a wide belt surrounding the Pacific, with branches extending into the East and West Indies. Most of the remainder are included in another belt extending across Asia and through the Mediterranean region of Europe. Beneath the oceans, the mid-Atlantic ridge and the Tonga trench are often active with deep quakes.

On the average, about two quakes a year have magnitudes of over 8; a thousand, magnitudes of 5 or more; and more than a million, magnitudes of 2. Although earthquakes are very common, fortunately for the seismologist only a few send waves any great distance. If his instruments recorded all the quakes, his records would be so confused it would be impossible to interpret them.

Seismic Surveying

Earthquakes are not a dependable source of shock waves. Although they release great amounts of energy detectable at great distances, they can hardly be relied upon to occur at the right place and the right time. A geophysicist who wants to use seismic waves to examine the strata in a particular area usually makes them himself with explosives. This technique, called explosion seismology, has been widely used in geophysical prospecting for oil.

It takes two forms—reflection shooting and refraction shooting. With the reflection technique the sound waves (P waves) from the explosion are reflected *from* interfaces in the strata below and received by geophones. In the refraction method the receivers are placed a considerable distance from the explosion, enabling the sound to travel from source to receiver *in* the various rock layers at velocities dependent on the rigidity of those rocks. The two techniques are used at sea as well as on land. Figure VI-5 shows ray patterns for reflection shooting in sedimentary rocks on land. Figure VI-6 illustrates the principal paths

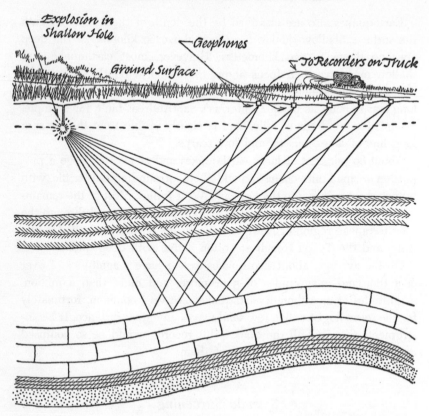

Fig. VI-5 Seismic-Reflection Surveying on Land. Depths and slopes of subsurface formations can be determined by measuring the time it takes seismic waves to reflect back to a series of geophones.

of the waves between two ships doing seismic refraction work at sea.

On land, explosive charges of two to two hundred pounds are placed in holes drilled through the loosely consolidated overburden to solid bedrock. At a short distance an array of geophones are spaced out in a line of shallow holes. Wires from the geophones are strung to a recording truck; the recording instruments are started; and the shot is fired. The electrical impulse that fires the shots makes a little mark on the record at the instant of explosion. Then the subsequent jiggles on the record are echoes from successively deeper layers. The time expended as sound waves travel from the shot to the principal layers and back again can then be read directly. After this process has been repeated many times in the area being surveyed, the depths to the reflecting surfaces can be plotted to show the rock structure below.

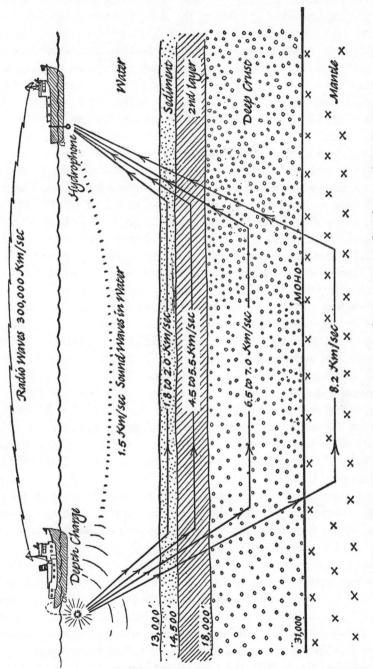

Fig. VI-6 Seismic-Refraction Surveying at Sea, Showing Principal Pathways of Seismic Waves

Much the same procedure is followed in reflection shooting at sea except that, instead of geophones, the ship lowers a string of hydrophones over the side. Small charges of TNT are fired from a small boat a short distance away. Although reflections sometimes can be obtained from various layers within the sea bottom, no one has yet obtained an echo from the Moho surface. This suggests that either the top of the mantle is a very irregular surface which scatters and absorbs the sound, or the Moho is a gradational change without a distinct surface.

For surveys of the layers beneath the sea, the refraction surveying method is preferred. This is the best means of determining what the Mohole drill will encounter as it probes beneath the ocean. Two or more ships are required for refraction studies, one of which fires the explosions while the other listens. Depth charges left over from the submarine hunts of World War II, containing about three hundred pounds of TNT, are used for more distant shots. As the firing ship approaches the listening ship, smaller explosions are used until, when the two are close together, a two-pound charge is sufficient.

Refraction surveys are made as follows: The listening ship lies quiet in the water. Not only are its main engines and propellers stopped but so are virtually all other auxiliary engines and motors aboard. This reduces background noise. A generator to power the lights and instruments is the only machine left operating. The array of hydrophones is streamed over the side—usually they are carefully weighted to float about fifteen feet under the surface, just below the effect of the small wind waves. The listening ship is ready. Its position is accurately known, its chronometers precisely in accord with the radio time signals from WWV at the Bureau of Standards in Washington, D.C.

The shooting ship—perhaps 80 miles away—approaches it at 10 knots or more, firing explosives at regular intervals. Each of the two ships, in constant radio contact, always knows what the other is doing and its state of readiness.

When everyone is ready the fuse is lighted, the recorders on the listening ship are started, and the depth charge is pushed overboard. In about twenty seconds it will explode at a depth of several hundred feet. The explosion, detected by a hydrophone on the firing ship, is transmitted by radio to the listening ship, where it is automatically marked on the seismic record. Marking the instant of explosion in this manner gives the geophysicist a zero point from which the travel times of the sound waves through the rocks can be measured. The sound waves travel outward from the charge in all directions but, as with the earthquake waves, we are concerned only with their fastest path in each layer.

The shortest route for sound to travel between the two ships is via the water, but this route is not as simple as one would imagine. In the ocean there is a zone known as the "deep sound channel" lying generally about 300 meters below the surface in northern latitudes and about twice that depth near the equator. The combined effects of temperature, salinity, and pressure cause sound waves traveling long distances to be bent into this channel. In the deep sound channel, sound velocity is at a minimum but sound energy is conserved so effectively that the explosion of a single pound of TNT can be detected by hydrophones 3000 miles away. Thus, in seismic surveying, the sound waves moving from shot to hydrophone follow this natural but slow pathway where the speed of sound averages only 1.5 kilometers per second (4920 feet per second).

In the soft sediments of the sea floor—the unconsolidated red clays, blue muds, calcareous and siliceous oozes—the sound velocity is not much greater: 1.8 kilometers per second. At least it is possible to sample the upper few feet of these sediments with oceanographic corers and correlate actual specimens with measured sound velocity. But below the reach of the coring tools, the ocean-going geophysicist has to rely entirely on the velocity of sound for his knowledge of the composition of the rocks.

Based on the evidence of sound, the next layer, generally known as the second layer, is believed to be a hard rock with an average thickness of about two kilometers. Depending on where the velocity measurements are made, they vary from 4.5 to 5.5 kilometers per second. Experimental evidence indicates that three rocks which might reasonably make up the sea floor have such velocities. These are: (1) well-consolidated sedimentary rocks such as sandstones or quartzites, (2) limestones (calcium carbonates) or dolomites (calcium magnesium carbonates), (3) basalt. Dr. Russell Raitt of the Scripps Institution of Oceanography conducted some seismic tests in the shallow waters of the Marquesas Islands where the sea bottom is known to be basalt and found that the sound velocities there were precisely the same as those in the second layer under deep water. Furthermore, the Pacific floor has so many basaltic volcanoes and sea mounts that one would expect basalt to underlie much of that

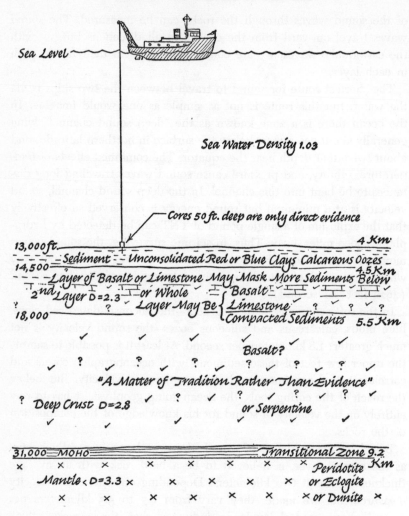

Fig. VI-7 The Oceanic Crust

ocean. This is an important but by no means conclusive piece of evidence as we shall see presently.

A fourth possibility is that the two-kilometer-thick second layer is composed of two parts: a thin upper zone of one of the previously mentioned hard rocks—compacted sediment, limestone, or basalt—with thick lower section of more soft sediments like those of the present sea floor. If this were the case, the high-velocity rock of the upper zone would screen the soft sediments beneath from detection by seismic waves.

One trouble with theories about the second layer is that in the areas where seismic surveying has so far been done, including much of the Atlantic and Pacific Oceans, there is an apparent uniformity of bedding thickness. Therefore, a hypothesis which holds that the second layer is limestone must explain how a thick layer of limestone formed beneath all the oceans. There does not seem to be sufficient calcium in the world to make that much lime. If there were, the lime would have had to come from the disintegration of igneous rocks on land and this raises an even more difficult question. If the lime went into the ocean and covered the floor solidly, where did the other components of the original rock go? The basalt hypothesis has a similar difficulty. Although there is an ample supply of basalt, how could it have been evenly distributed over the entire ocean floor? One would expect it to be very thick in some places and absent in others.

Geologists will be delighted if the second layer turns out to be composed of sediments consolidated into rock, for this would solve the most vexing mystery of the ocean: Where is all the sediment that should be on the ocean floor? If one takes the measured rate of sedimentation in the deep ocean today and multiplies it by the length of time that sedimentation must have been going on, there should be a layer of sediment about five kilometers thick. Instead there is a layer of soft sediment about half a kilometer thick and a second layer of unknown composition averaging less than two kilometers thick. It would be nice to find the second layer composed of highly compacted sediments or at least some more soft sediment. If not, over 90 per cent of the sedimentary record is missing.

Unfortunately, no physical or chemical mechanism is known that could have transformed the sediments now found on the ocean bottom into rocks with sufficiently high sound velocities to match those of the second layer. Therefore, the most promising hypothesis is that beneath some hard high-velocity layer there are other layers of soft material. Perhaps hard and soft layers alternate and the missing sediments are interlayered with thin basalts and limestones. It seems unlikely that this mystery will be solved until the Moho drill brings up actual samples of each of the layers.

Sound waves from the depth charge traveling through the third layer, or "deep crust," move at about seven kilometers per second. Geologists have even fewer ideas about the composition of this rock and although it traditionally has been called basalt—more from force of habit than from evidence—the seismic evidence suggests that it is not. More likely it is a serpentinized peridotite, but no one will know until cores are obtained. The penetration of this thick, hard, deep layer will consume most of the time and create most of the problems of drilling to the mantle.

Below the deep crust is the mantle and in transferring from one to the other the seismic waves abruptly increase their velocity from 7.0 to 8.2 kilometers per second. This jump in seismic-wave velocity—actually not as great as the jumps between the layers above—is the Mohorovičić discontinuity. An ocean-going seismologist is satisfied if his explosion-generated waves travel in the outer mantle at "Moho velocities" of over 8.0 kilometers a second. There is not enough energy in the depth charges to probe deeper.

When the seismic surveying ships are widely separated, the first wave to arrive and be recorded at the receiving ship is the one that traveled via the mantle; next comes the deep-crust wave, then the ones through the second layer, the sediment, and finally those in the water, all in upside-down order.

As the firing ship closes the range, exploding a charge every few miles, a large number of records are made. When the ship returns home, the tedious work of analysis begins. The time of arrival of the first wave in each layer must be meticulously measured on the record, corrected for various small errors, and plotted on a travel-time graph. Then a certain amount of judgment must be used in selecting the most significant points. A conscientious seismologist may study the data a long time before deciding to commit himself on the seemingly insignificant point of whether a layer has a velocity of 6.8 or 7.0 kilometers per second. By applying the velocities obtained for each layer to a geological concept of the suboceanic structure, the geophysicist can determine its depth. Finally, he determines the depth to the Moho and discovers that there are places where it approaches within 9.5 kilometers of the sea surface. This depth, AMSOC believes, can be reached with a drill.

The Sea-Land Boundary

Thus the geophysicist has two valuable tools for probing the unseen rocks. He can use the measurement of gravity to determine the relative thickness of the crust—the undulations of its underside—and he can use the methods of seismology to determine the actual thickness of the various layers and the depth to the Moho. If he combines the two kinds of measurements in the catalytic presence of a geological theory, he may begin to understand crustal structure.

In the first chapter of this book the statement was made that ocean

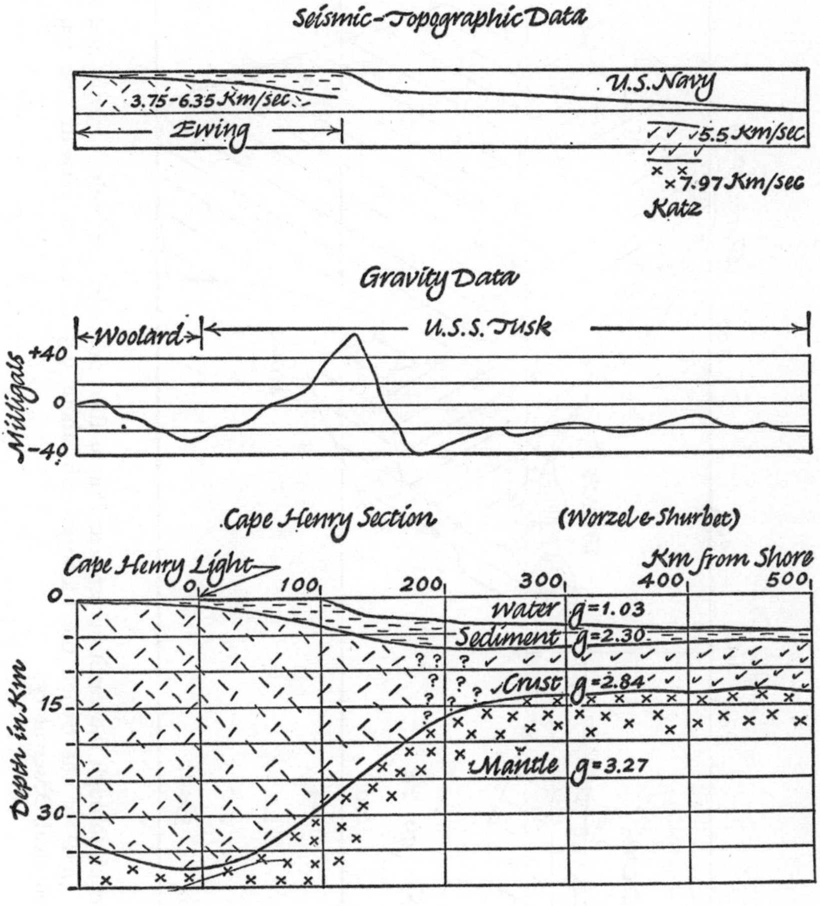

Seismic-Topographic Data

Gravity Data

Cape Henry Section   (Worzel & Shurbet)

Fig. VI-8 Seismic-Gravity Work Combined. This section through the boundary between continental and oceanic crust at Cape Henry, Virginia, was assembled by Worzel and Shurbet, who combined their data with those of other scientists.

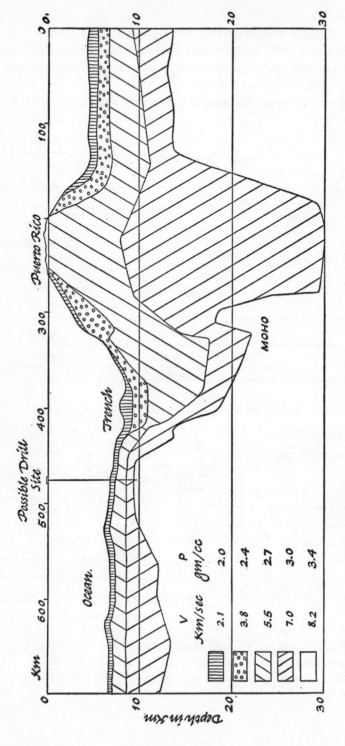

Fig. VI-9 Section through the earth's crust near Puerto Rico made by combining gravity and seismic data. Just to the north (left) of the trench the Moho is only about 9.5 kilometers beneath the sea surface. (Source: Lamont Geophysical Observatory)

basins and continents have their own special characteristics. The continents are a relatively thick light rock; the ocean basins are made of thinner, heavier rock. Both apparently float on a viscous mantle. The reasons why this structure is believed to exist have been outlined and the methods of surveying described. One final piece of evidence should corroborate this theory: a combined seismic-gravity profile across an actual boundary between a continent and an ocean. In this transitional zone—because of the slopes of the layers, the changes in rock type, and the complex nature of the interfaces—neither seismology nor gravity measurements alone give a satisfactory picture of the crust.

In 1955 Professor J. L. Worzel and his associates at the Lamont Geological Observatory published a series of profiles of the eastern continental edge of North America which assembled all the known seismic and gravity data. Figure VI-8, a section through Cape Henry, Virginia, is a good example of the way in which the work of many scientific groups is combined in the formulation and proof of a geological idea. The topography of land and the sea bottom was worked out by the Navy and the Coast and Geodetic Survey; ashore the gravity survey was made by Dr. George Woollard and the seismic survey by Dr. Maurice Ewing. At sea the gravity surveys were made on the submarine *Tusk* by Drs. Worzel and Shurbet; the seismic surveys were made on the Woods Hole Oceanographic Institution research ship *Atlantis* by Dr. Katz and others.

This one profile took many man-years of time and still it is not a complete or final answer. Although it is the best that can be done today, notice that the critical point of contact between the deep igneous rocks of the oceanic and continental crust is marked by that familiar geological symbol: the question mark. Plainly, in order to understand the evidence that gravity and seismic explorations have produced about the undersea rocks, one must understand the ocean.

VII

The Examination of the Oceans

The Mohole project is an adventure which will test man's most advanced geological ideas and engineering abilities in an oceanic laboratory. It is a bold attempt to release the secret history of the earth, forcing the lock by the combined application of reasoning and massive drilling equipment. Virtually every aspect of the project depends to some extent on the way the ocean has behaved in the past and how it will behave while the drilling is in progress. Thus the understanding of the Mohole's objectives and requirements and operating problems requires a fundamental understanding of the ocean. The best way to think about the ocean is to take the point of view of the oceanographer, the man who studies it constantly.

The earth is sometimes called the water planet. Mars, though famous for "canals," has not enough water to cover it a millimeter deep all over; the thin frost caps at the poles account for the entire supply. The moon and the other planets with the possible exception of Venus are dry as dust. Only the earth has oceans—and oceanographers.

Oceanographers are drawn from many scientific disciplines and bonded together by a curiosity about the sea. But oceanography is not a science; rather it is an arena of effort where contestants from the basic sciences test their skill. Using titles thinly disguised by the prefix "marine," biologists, chemists, physicists, geologists and, engineers have set about applying the fundamentals of science to the study of the ocean.

Although it may seem glamorous to those on the shore, scientific work at sea is not easy. Many lose their enthusiasm after one voyage, sharing the opinion of the wag who said, "No man need go to sea that hath the wit to get himself in jail." Even if jails and ships have retained their respective positions, a hard core of oceanographers prefers the latter and in recent years they have made remarkable progress toward understanding the oceans. The more optimistic of them believe that 1 per cent of the total knowledge which the oceans may eventually yield already has been discovered.

How does a curious scientist examine the ocean? Standing on the shore he sees a great gray surface stretching away to what he knows is a hundred horizons. More often than not it is cold, windy, and rough. A formidable antagonist.

There are two general styles of attack. One is to begin by formulating a hypothesis about some process in the sea—what drives ocean currents, for example. Then it is necessary to devise means for testing the idea by making specific measurements at sea that will prove or disprove it. The other kind of attack is to go to sea equipped to make measurements of everything that is changing. Having measured temperatures, salinities, water motions, winds, depths of various layers, etc., the scientist returns to his laboratory, analyzes the data, and tries to find consistent patterns. He ends up with a hypothesis.

Both methods are valid means of working and usually they are combined so that the exploration of the sea is carried on as a series of expeditions in which theoretical concepts are tested by direct measurements. It is a system with "feedback," in which each hypothesis is constantly modified by newly-developed data. Then subsequent work is planned that will develop the idea further. Dr. Roger Revelle, director of the Scripps Institution of Oceanography, likes to say, "You must go to the sea with a question." Let us examine some of the questions that oceanographers ask and for which partial answers have been obtained.

The Age and Origin of the Ocean

One major question is: Where did the ocean come from? In order to answer it, a great deal of complicated and intertwined evidence must be unraveled and tested. The implications of the answer are of great importance to a dozen sciences for with it is bound up the question of the origins of the solar system and of life.

There are two major hypotheses about the origin of the oceans. The first, more often enunciated and therefore generally believed by the public, has the great advantage of simplicity. It holds that the earth was once molten throughout and that its primitive atmosphere was a great cloud of steam. When the earth cooled, the water vapor condensed and formed the oceans. Known as the "residual" theory, it is probably incorrect.

The alternative hypothesis does not require the earth to have been very hot. It holds that gases and liquids have been rising to the surface from the earth's interior throughout most of geologic time. Most geologists now believe that the present crust, including the continents, the ocean basins, the oceans, and the atmosphere, have continuously evolved. Over billions of years of time there has been a slow but unceasing segregation of earth components—the denser ones migrating toward the center of the earth, the lighter ones moving outward. The lightest, of course, are the air and water which are now at the surface. If the rate at which lavas, steam, and gases are spewed out on the surface today has been continuous throughout geological time, this is sufficient to have provided for the crust and oceans and atmosphere.

Dr. William Rubey of the U. S. Geological Survey, one of the foremost scientists to think about the origin of the oceans, first examined the quantities and constituents of rocks weathered and deposited during geologic time. This left little doubt that the major rock-forming elements (silicon, aluminum, iron, calcium, magnesium, sodium, potassium) in sedimentary rocks have been derived from the weathering of earlier igneous rocks. However, he found that the decomposition of the original rocks could not have produced sufficient water or carbon dioxide to account for the ocean and the atmosphere. Thus the balance of these, which he has called "excess volatiles," must have escaped to the surface from the earth's interior.

The early ocean and atmosphere, which may have had characteristics quite different from their present ones, had a great influence on the origin of life. There are fundamental questions about them, still unanswered, of whether the conditions under which life first formed were oxydizing or reducing and whether the early ocean was acidic or basic.

Biologists are particularly eager to know whether free oxygen, uncombined with other elements, was available to the first living organisms. Most of the oxygen in today's atmosphere has been formed by its release from carbon dioxide and water during photosynthetic fixation of carbon by green plants. However, certain primitive forms of bacteria can fix carbon in the presence of hydrogen sulphide or other compounds. This suggests that living organisms may have come into existence long before free oxygen was available. In fact, the major hypotheses of the origin of life require a reducing environment, main-

139

taining that even small amounts of free oxygen would prevent the development of primitive life.

Dr. Aleksander Ivanovich Oparin of Russia, a leader in the study of the origin of life, believes that life began in an atmosphere of methane and ammonia in which simple compounds were built up by sunlight into amino acids, and that these in turn, after uncounted millions of opportunities and failures, became proteins which could reproduce themselves.

There is some evidence that the earth's early atmosphere was composed of methane (CH_4) and ammonia (NH_3). If so, these gases satisfy the requirement that primitive life have a reducing atmosphere in which self-duplicating molecules can be formed by photochemical processes. At the University of Chicago in 1955 two physicists, Dr. Harold Urey and Dr. Stanley Miller, actually succeeded in synthesizing amino acids by passing a lightning-like discharge through a mixture of water vapor, methane, ammonia, and hydrogen. This direct experiment does not prove the Oparin hypothesis but it strengthens it considerably.

There is no doubt that oxygen has been produced since the earth's beginning by a photo dissociation of water vapor on the outer edge of the atmosphere and that it has been constantly carried down to the earth's surface by air turbulence while the hydrogen escapes into space. As Dr. Rubey points out, we are led to a paradox: Life could not have originated in the presence of oxygen and yet free oxygen has been forming in the upper atmosphere since the beginning of the earth's history.

Probably the answer is that most of the early oxygen went into oxydizing carbon monoxide and ferrous iron. Life then could have appeared in localized reducing environments. This suggests that the ancestors of the first unicellular organisms were anerobic (requiring no free oxygen) but that over a period of many millions of years they learned to photosynthesize and also to make use of the oxygen in the atmosphere.

Clearly the origin of life on earth is bound up in the origin and development of the ocean, which is but one aspect of the development of the crust. It is quite possible that new information about the geological and chemical history of the earth will be found by the Mohole project drillings which will shed light on primordial conditions.

Dr. Rubey's major thesis—that the earth's air and ocean have slowly accumulated by escape from the interior—is not affected by the question of which gases were dominant in the early atmosphere. As

Roger Revelle says, "The ocean waters seem to have been gradually squeezed out of the interior of the earth." Most of their colleagues now agree, but the question that remains is: at what rate? There are several answers.

The quantity of water now flowing from volcanic springs is more than sufficient to account for all the water in the ocean (1) if it is really reaching the surface for the first time and is not merely recirculated rain water, and (2) if it has been flowing constantly throughout geologic time. This means that the increase of the amount of water on the surface has been steady and there has been a gradual rise of sea level as the oceans grew. If so, one should be able to find some indication of the position of sea level in previous geologic periods.

One of the few pieces of evidence is found in the Pacific basin, where there are many flat-topped undersea volcanic mountains whose upper surfaces are, on the average, about four thousand feet below the sea surface. It is believed that wave erosion at some former stand of sea level sliced off the tops of the mountain peaks. Oceanographers, dredging for samples on the tops of these sea mounts, have brought up fossils of various animals that lived in shallow water in Cretaceous time, about 100 million years ago. Since each mountain is surrounded by deep water, this suggests that these animals lived and grew to maturity at a time when the oceans barely covered the truncated mountaintop. This must mean that since Cretaceous time either the sea level has risen 4000 feet because additional water has entered the ocean or the sea mounts have subsided by that amount or a combination of the two. If the explanation lies solely in the increase of water, then one-fourth of all the ocean's water appeared on the surface since the Cretaceous—only about one-fortieth of geologic time. This seems improbable and a better explanation is still being sought.

Waves and Currents

Having theorized about the origin of the sea, the oceanographer sets forth to examine his quarry. Almost immediately he observes that his ship is influenced by waves and currents, both of which are driven by the wind.

Waves are born when the frictional drag of a breeze on a calm sea surface creates ripples. As the wind continues to blow, the steep sides of the ripples present a surface against which the moving air can press directly so that the wind becomes increasingly efficient at transferring energy to the water. Because winds are by nature turbulent and gusty, wavelets of all sizes are created. As these grow, the small steep ones break, forming whitecaps, but the larger lower ones continue on. Thus, even though new waves of all sizes continue to be formed, the trend is always toward larger waves which can store the energy better.

In the "generating area" where waves originate, the wind moves faster than the waves; in a large storm this area may extend over thousands of square miles. If the wind is so strong that it applies more force than a wave can accept, the crest is blown off, forming a breaking wave at sea. This happens when the height of a wave (the vertical distance between trough and crest) is greater than one-seventh of the wave length (distance between successive crests). This means that a long wave can accept more energy from the wind and become much higher than a short wave passing under the same wind. The result is that short waves tend to be destroyed while the longer ones continue to grow.

The effectiveness of the wind in creating waves is due to three factors: the velocity of the wind, the length of time that it blows, and the distance of open water, known as the "fetch," across which it blows.

Within the generating area the waves are confused and irregular with rough diamond-shaped hillocks and crooked valleys. They are random mounds of water so infinitely variable that they must be described statistically. But as these waves move out from under the winds that formed them, they become lower and more rounded, their form becomes more symmetrical, and they move in trains of similar period and height. Now they are called "swell" and they are more like the ripples caused by tossing a pebble into a pond. They are identified by their period—that is, the time in seconds for successive crests to pass a point. The usual period of ocean swell is between seven and fifteen seconds; however, the total range of the wave-period spectrum extends from fractional seconds to several hours. Period and wave length bear a simple relationship to each other that is easily remembered and is useful for estimating the effects of waves on a ship. The wave length in feet is about equal to five times the period (in seconds) squared. Thus a wave with a period of ten seconds is about 500 feet long.

The height of waves at sea is not related to the period and it is somewhat complicated by the fact that there are usually several

PLATE I   *Andrija Mohorovičić* was born January 23, 1857, in Volsko, Istria, Croatia. As a boy of 15 he spoke Italian, French, and English as well as his native Croatian; later he added German, Czech, Latin, and Old Greek. He studied physics at the University of Prague under some famous professors including E. Mach and did his graduate work at the University of Zagreb, from which he obtained a Ph.D. in 1894. Dr. Mohorovičić became Director of the Institute for Meteorology and Geodynamics and Professor at the University of Zagreb in 1897, where he remained until his retirement in 1921. His special interest was the precise measurement of time for both astronomical and seismological events, but his reputation mainly rests on his classic paper in the field of seismology, "The Earthquake of October 8, 1909," which contains the news of his discovery of a major seismic discontinuity at a depth of 55 kilometers. This discontinuity, now generally known as the Moho in his honor, defines the crust of the earth. Professor Mohorovičić died in 1936 in circumstances approaching poverty.

PLATE II *Submersible mobile platform of the Penrod Drilling Company being towed to a drilling site in the Gulf of Mexico. There the flotation tanks will be flooded so that they sink to the bottom and the fixed legs will support the drilling platform well above the water surface. Submersibles can be used in water as much as 40 feet deep.*

PLATE III *Jack-up mobile platform* built by Le Tourneau floats on the triangular "hull" while it is being moved. When the site is reached, the legs are lowered to the bottom, where they embed themselves. Then the platform climbs up the legs until it is a safe height above the waves. Similar platforms have been built to operate in 100 feet of water.

PLATE IV *The Humble SM-1* is one of several similar small vessels built to do exploratory drilling off the California coast. These ships have drilled holes over 5000 feet deep in water 250 feet deep.

sets of waves from different directions passing over each other. The result is a diamond-shaped sea surface in which crests that coincide add their heights, occasionally producing a very large wave.

The largest waves have been encountered on the downwind side of a large generating area during a prolonged storm. Waves larger than forty-five feet from trough to crest are not uncommon in great storms and there are several well-documented observations of waves over seventy feet high. But waves only a few feet high are much more likely. In order to understand how they act on ships and structures it is necessary to understand the mechanism of wave motion.

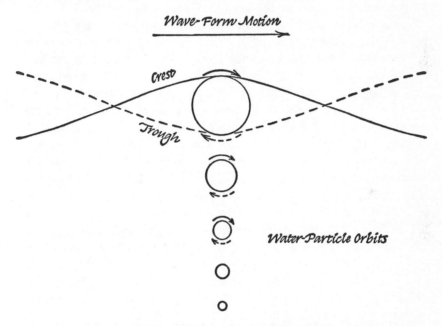

Fig. VII-1 When a wave passes, the water particles describe circular orbits. The orbits at the surface are equal to the height of the wave. The size of the orbits diminishes with depth but at all levels the water moves in the wave direction as a crest passes and against it as a trough passes.

The easiest way is to look through the glass sides of an experimental wave channel. If tiny markers are used having the exact density of water, their motion, which will be the same as the water particles, can be studied. The markers at the surface stay on the surface and as a wave train passes they describe circular orbits the size of the height of the waves. As a wave passes, each water particle traces out an orbit and returns to its original position so that in the end only the wave form has moved and the water remains in the same place. As the depth below the surface increases, the orbits become smaller but they still exist. This means that objects in the water well below the surface move in circular orbits just like those on the surface, a condition that requires submarines to submerge deeply to avoid the effect of large waves.

The velocity of the wave form, in miles per hour, is roughly 3.5 times the period in seconds. Thus, a ten-second wave moves approximately thirty-five miles per hour.

Ocean currents are, for the most part, driven by the wind. A wind constantly blowing on the sea surface exerts frictional drag, especially after it has raised ripples and waves, and this sets the surface layer of water in motion. If the winds blow intermittently or in random directions, temporary localized currents are set up. But constant and strong winds can establish an endlessly circulating motion of water on a huge scale. Once these large circular current patterns or gyres are established, a relatively small amount of wind energy is required to maintain the motion. The great currents in the ocean today appear to have been operating much as they are now for thousands of years. For example, the Gulf Stream system or Atlantic gyre starts in the trade-wind belt along the Windward Islands of the West Indies and the Bahamas, moves north along the United States East Coast to Cape Hatteras, where it turns out to sea, passing the Grand Banks and moving nearly due east toward Norway. When it encounters the coast, it divides, throwing off one eddy into the Norwegian Sea and sending another south toward the equator, where it once more comes under the influence of the trade winds and is driven back across the Atlantic.

The comparable Pacific current or Kuroshio begins in the low latitudes where it is started westward by the trade winds. Then it moves north along the Japanese coast, shoots out across the Pacific, striking the eastern shore near Vancouver, Canada. It sends a loop northward into the Gulf of Alaska but most of the water turns south, becoming the California current until it reaches the trade-wind belts, where it is propelled to the westward to complete the loop.

The trades are two belts of west-moving air which flow around the earth a little north and south of the equator. Between these belts is the doldrums, where winds are light and variable and the current actually flows in the opposite direction.

The depths to which these currents extend and the change in velocity with depth is uncertain, but since so few measurements of currents below the surface have been made, they are regarded as surface currents in the absence of evidence to the contrary. Surface currents are assumed to extend down to the thermocline—an abrupt change in the temperature of the water which is found from 100 to 900 feet below the surface. This seems to be about the maximum depth to which the wind affects the ocean and it is probably related to the depth at which the orbits of passing waves are sufficient to cause mixing. At any rate, water in this uppermost or "mixed" layer moves turbulently so that its temperature is warm and uniform throughout. Beneath the mixed layer the water is relatively cold and still all the way to the bottom. The boundary between these two major layers of water is the thermocline—shown in Figure VII-2.

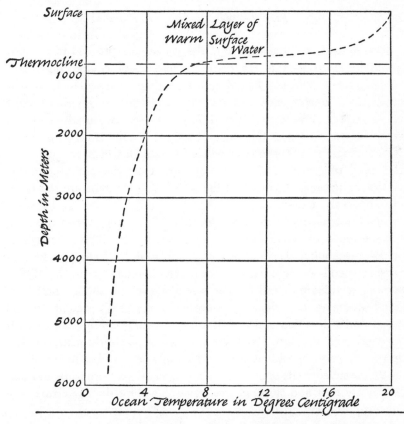

Fig. VII-2 Decrease of Ocean Water Temperature with Depth

The question of how fast the deep water below the thermocline moves is much more difficult to answer because measurements are hard to make. Work in the Atlantic by Dr. John Swallow, a British oceanographer, with neutrally buoyant sound sources which can be set to float at any depth and tracked by means of the pings they send out, has revealed currents of a knot or more. Similar deep current measurements in the Pacific by Dr. John Knauss of the Scripps Institution of Oceanography have rarely obtained velocities of over a tenth of a knot. The difference between the two oceans is not a fundamental one, rather it indicates a need for many more measurements to better define the deep currents. The amount of current, both shallow and deep, at a drilling site is obviously of great importance to the Mohole project as we shall see later on.

The Depth of the Ocean

Having examined the surface of the sea we can proceed to the next question: How deep is the ocean? There is, of course, no simple answer, for the ocean basins are exceedingly irregular in shape, crossed with deep trenches, ridged with mountain ranges that project above the sea surface, and dotted with sea mounts. But the eventual complete description of the shape of the sea bottom is an objective of the oceanographer. His answer will be a chart in which every point is composed of two discrete bits of information: the position on the earth's surface and the depth of the water. Both of these are routinely, but not easily, measured.

First, he must know the exact location of the ship. When traveling between ports the navigator ordinarily uses either celestial navigation or dead-reckoning. If conditions are favorable, celestial navigation, which depends on sighting the sun or certain stars with a hand-held sextant, can obtain a position that is accurate within about a half-mile. Dead-reckoning, however, is a projection of the ship's present position based on its direction and speed after correcting for the "set" caused by winds and currents. For short distances and steady runs between accurately known positions dead-reckoning works well as long as there are no strong currents or storms. As the distance increases or if the ship alternately runs and stops, as oceanographic ships do, the errors continuously become greater.

In recent years a number of electronic navigational systems have been devised but most of these have been either experimental or used for special local purposes. Of these, LORAN, abbreviation for long-range navigation, is the most widely used. LORAN can determine the location of a ship by measuring the arrival times of pulses of radio waves that are simultaneously transmitted by two or more shore stations. Position can be found with an accuracy of about a quarter of a mile at a distance from the transmitters of a thousand miles. Other radio methods are briefly mentioned in Chapter XII.

Because of these navigational errors the positions of deep-water soundings as shown on the charts are reliable only to about one mile.

Determining the depth has its problems too. It is said that Magellan, the first circumnavigator of the earth, used up some of the crew's energy when his ship was becalmed in the South Atlantic by having them splice together all the excess rope on board. He tied a weight to the end and hung it overside. Not finding bottom with 600 fathoms of line out, he concluded they were in the deepest part of the ocean. He was far wrong, for we know now that the average depth of the ocean is over 2000 fathoms. Until the 1920's, sounding lines, usually weighted music wire, were used to measure ocean depths. Since the wire was rarely vertical and it was not always easy to tell when the weight touched bottom, measurements made by this method were not accurate.

The echo sounder, which sends a "ping" of sound downward and measures the time for the echo to return, is now the standard means of mapping the shape of the sea floor. Many of the deep-water instruments send a 12,000-cycle ping every second or two in a cone-shaped beam. This means that if the ship is moving at 10 knots (nautical miles per hour), the soundings are about sixteen feet apart. The first returning echo is from the nearest reflecting surface within that beam. On flat bottom, this is a point directly beneath the ship and the record is simple. If the ping interval of the echo sounder is carefully regulated and the Precision Depth Recorder is used to record the time of sound travel, water depth can be read directly with an accuracy of about one foot in three thousand.

The result of plotting the various positions of the ship and the depth of water beneath it is a "track" along which the profile of the sea floor is known. By combining a large number of crisscrossed tracks a chart of the sea floor can be made.

When the ship is over hilly topography, echoes are received from nearby hilltops as well as the bottom directly beneath the ship and a complicated record of overlapping echoes is received which must be carefully studied before the depth can be specified. In order to map details of rough bottom topography which cannot be determined by the usual echo sounder, Dr. J. B. Hersey of the Woods Hole Oceanographic Institution has adapted the sonar "pinger" developed by Dr. Harold Edgerton of the Massachusetts Institute of Technology for positioning bottom cameras. The pinger sends out sound pulses (pings) at regular intervals. It is lowered on a cable from the surveying ship until it is only 20 meters or so above the bottom. The men on the ship, listening with hydrophones, hear two pings, one which traveled directly through the water, followed shortly thereafter by the echo of the same signal which bounced off the bottom. The ship maneuvers to keep the wire vertical while surveying at a rate of about one mile an hour. The winch operator, who watches a scope that visually shows the time between the pairs of pings, is instructed to pull in or let out the cable supporting the pinger so that the time between the pings is constant. The cable moves in and out, raising and lowering the pinger to follow the humps and valleys in the sea floor along the path of the ship. Then a record of the length of cable over the side plus the distance from the pinger to the bottom is easily plotted to make a bottom profile. There is some uncertainty about the depth because the cable does not hang exactly vertical but a correction can be made by measuring the travel time of sound from the ship to the pinger.

With increasing knowledge of the sea floor, man's ideas about it are changing. Not many years ago it was generally believed to be mainly composed of broad expanses of lifeless muddy plains with only an occasional mountain range and trench to break up the monotony. Now it is known that there is complex life at all depths and that there are many rugged geological features. Sea mounts, faults, trenches, canyons, and many kinds of geophysical anomalies are liberally scattered across the ocean floor. When more is known about it, ocean geology will prove to be as complex as that on land.

Not all the scientific work at sea has been accomplished by oceanographic ships on survey missions. For example, Harry Hess managed to use a naval vessel to map part of the western Pacific during the war. In so doing he discovered that there are many isolated volcanic sea mounts rising from the ocean floor and that some of them, which he named "guyots," have had their tops planed off by wave action.

In 1943 Lieutenant Hess was ordered to report to a Los Angeles pipe company which had just received a contract to convert a bare hull into an amphibious transport ship. Never having remodeled a ship before, the company was happy to have a naval officer coming who could give them a little guidance. When they found out that he was only a geologist, their enthusiasm cooled. Fortunately the next reserve officer to show up was suitably experienced and this left Hess free to concentrate on the only aspect of construction that interested him—the installation of an echo sounder. Ordinarily a ship of this sort carries an instrument capable of measuring depths in the shallow waters of bays and harbors, but by adamantly insisting that some fine print in the specifications be followed, Hess managed to get a deep-sea echo sounder installed.

From its launching, the *Cape Johnson,* as the ship was named, served as a private survey ship, although this was disguised by the fact that it spent eleven unbroken months delivering men to the beach in five major amphibious operations. In geologically interesting areas, it followed mysterious zigzag courses which were attributed by the captains of nearby ships to fear of submarines. The men in the chartroom kept busy plotting soundings. Two Navy regulations covered the subject of echo sounders. One said, "Don't turn it on, it may attract submarines"; the other said, "Keep it going, we need the soundings." When other ships picked up the pings on their antisubmarine sonar and asked what the "funny noise" was, they were referred to the latter.

Just after the end of the war the *Cape Johnson* was one of a fleet of twenty ships that was going from the Philippines to Japan. The Commodore of this fleet believed that intership communication was best carried on by means of semaphore flags and he wanted his signalmen to practice. Commander Hess solved the problem of what messages should be sent for practice. "Why not," he proposed, "have every ship take continuous depth recordings and report in every hour by semaphore on what they have observed." The scheme was ideal from the Commodore's point of view because it kept the signalmen busy and the messages checked each other—after the twenty men in the control center plotted the depths on Hess's charts. This fleet took a swath of soundings ten miles wide and two thousand long, and like the amphibious troops before him, the Commodore remained unaware of his contribution to marine geology. Hess, now Captain, USNR, takes his annual two weeks of active duty in the Navy Hydrographic Office still trying to improve the charts of the Pacific Ocean.

Charts which show the topography of the ocean floor make it

possible to plan systematic geological and geophysical studies, for knowledge of the existence and locations of suboceanic mountain ranges, trenches, and plains is a necessary prelude to laying out a program of exploration. It is, therefore, no coincidence that Prof. Hess, the dedicated oceanic mapper, is chairman of AMSOC's Panel on Site Selection.

Winches, Cables, Cores, and Dredges

Much of what the oceanographer knows about the depths and the bottom has been learned by dangling instruments and sampling devices on the end of a long wire rope. That wire, and the winch that supports and reels it in, are among the oceanographers' most important tools. Ocean research vessels often have several winches, but the one of most interest to us here is the big "dredging" winch. Many of these big winches carry wire enough to reach to the bottom of the deepest trenches in the ocean—canyons whose bottoms are 35,000 feet or more below the surface. Because the weight of 35,000 feet of any diameter of wire rope is about equal to its breaking strength, these long wires are tapered in several steps so that each section can support the weight of the wire beneath in addition to the instruments or tools that are to be used. For example, the lowest step might be 10,000 feet of ⅜-inch wire rope; above it would be a series of increasingly stronger wires, up to ¾-inch at the upper end. The total weight of such a wire is about fifteen tons and with a 100-horsepower winch the maximum in-haul speed of the winch is about 200 feet a minute. Even though the best wire rope available is used, the safe working load at the bottom is only about two tons. Later when the engineering of deep drilling is discussed, we will see that the Mohole requires a bottom lifting-capability twenty times this great.

The capabilities of the winch and its wire, more than any other piece of equipment except the ship itself, tends to limit the oceanographer's work. Its strength governs the sizes of corers and dredges he can use; its length, the depths of water that he can sample and photograph; its speed, the amount of time he must remain on station.

On an exploratory cruise, the oceanographer programs a series of stations—points of particular interest where the ship will stop to take samples and make measurements. It is customary to schedule the work so that the ship runs at night and arrives on station at dawn, allowing the scientists to work in the daylight hours; if this is not feasible the work goes on anyway, day or night. Work on station may begin by lowering an instrument, a corer perhaps, on the wire. Even at maximum speed it will take almost an hour to reach bottom and nearly twice that long to return.

There are several kinds of corers generally used by oceanographers today. The simplest is the gravity corer. One version of it is a pipe about an inch and a half in diameter and six feet long weighted at the top with some thirty pounds of lead. It is tipped on the lower end by a sharp cutting edge and lined with a plastic tubing. When the pipe is lowered to the bottom, the weight pushes the pipe into the soft sediments and a cylindrical sample, neatly packaged, is obtained. In order to keep the core from slipping out when the pipe is withdrawn from the bottom, a ring of springy metal fingers point upward and inward, forming a little crown just inside the lower opening. This is the "core catcher"; it permits the cored material to enter but not to leave.

The gravity corer can take satisfactory short cores in soft oozes and muds but oceanographers usually want to penetrate deeper and to reach further back in time. For this they use the piston corer devised by Professor Börje Kullenberg of Sweden. With the piston or Kullenberg corer, cores twenty feet long are often obtained; if conditions are perfect and the oceanographer is lucky, he may be able to get one sixty feet long.

Like the small gravity corers, the Kullenberg is a weighted piece of pipe with a cutting edge at the bottom. Its pipe, or core barrel, is three inches in diameter and thirty feet long—for longer cores a second piece of pipe is added. The problem is to plunge this pipe into the bottom and fill it with sediment. Although the bottom materials are soft and the corer is heavy, merely lowering the corer rapidly will not get much of a core. Kullenberg's innovation is to have the weighted core barrel falling free when it touches the bottom and to have a piston suck the sediment into the core barrel. The sequence of events is illustrated in Figure VII-3.

The corer is rigged-out on deck and lowered away on the big winch. A triggering device, consisting of a lever arm held down by the weight of a small auxiliary corer, feels ahead for the bottom. When it touches, the trigger arm is raised; this releases the corer, which then falls freely for the last thirty feet, gathering momentum as it goes. A loop of wire

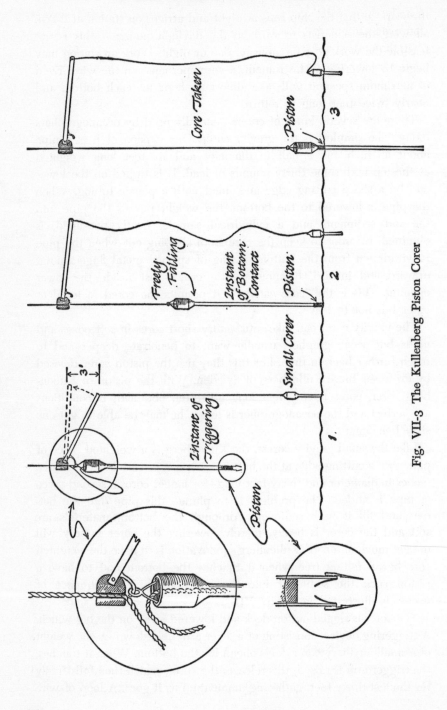

Fig. VII-3 The Kullenberg Piston Corer

exactly thirty feet long is held in reserve so that the corer can be retrieved after its plunge into the bottom.

If the end of the wire is attached to a piston seated at the bottom of the core barrel, the wire comes taut on the piston precisely at the moment the tip of the core barrel touches bottom. The piston jerks to a stop and the core barrel slides downward around it, penetrating as far as the friction of the bottom material will permit. Relative to the core barrel, the piston has moved upward to suck material into the barrel.

The triggering and coring takes place in about a second. The winch operator on the ship a mile or so above can tell when the load is suddenly removed and immediately he starts hauling in the wire. The piston is, of course, prevented by stops from coming free of the core barrel.

Once the core barrel is back on deck, the cored material is extruded by pushing the piston back down the barrel with a stiff rod. The result is that a vertical section of the ocean floor is laid out on deck in half-round core trays—thirty feet of core equaling one to ten million years of oceanic history.

The senior scientist will inspect it carefully, looking for major changes in composition and for fossils that will reveal the geologic age of the layers. Then the core will be carefully wrapped and sealed to prevent contamination and the escape of moisture, which would invalidate the careful chemical analysis to which it may be subjected when it reaches the home laboratory. Eventually it will become part of the library of records of the sea floor.

Not all the deep-sea floor is composed of materials so soft that they can be easily cored. Hard rocks, principally basalt, outcrop on the slopes of sea mounts, in the walls of oceanic trenches, and on the deep sea ridges.

Hard materials are sampled with the deep-sea dredge, a very simple and rugged device which is dragged along the bottom with the hope that it will break off a corner of a solid rock or that it will encounter loose rocky fragments. Dredges have parallel cutting edges of heavy steel plate forming a rectangular opening about one foot by three feet. Behind the rigid steel mouth is a loose net of chain which collects the larger pieces that are broken off or dredged up; the fine materials and muds pass on through the mesh.

Dredging is not an entirely satisfactory method of sampling because the specimens that are brought up may not be oceanic rocks. They

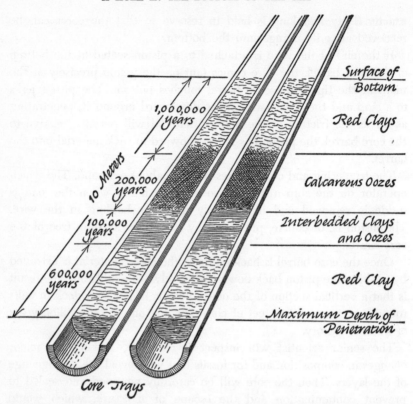

Fig. VII-4 A soft-sediment core from beneath the ocean, sliced down the center for inspection.

may, for example, be continental rocks that were carried to sea in icebergs and dropped when the ice melted. Therefore two British geophysicists, Dr. Maurice Hill and Sir Edward Bullard, are working on what the latter calls the Hill Hole—Britain's answer to the Mohole. They are developing a drilling machine which is to be lowered to the bottom on a cable. There they hope it will drill a hole about three feet deep into the hard rock and take a picture of the place it is drilling. Their first goal is a true sample of the mid-Atlantic ridge which can be used for radioactive dating.

The Deep Sea Sediments

The soft material that oceanographers are so eager to sample with their corers is the accumulated oceanic dust of millions of years. Tiny particles of insoluble materials—dust carried from land by the winds, chemical precipitates, the skeletons of small animals—have gradually settled, one grain at a time, to the deep-sea floor until now they form deposits hundreds or thousands of feet thick. One very important question is: At what rate have they accumulated? As we saw in the last chapter, there appears to be a considerable discrepancy between the thicknesses of sediment that oceanographers expect and seismologists find. A better knowledge of the deposition rate would help resolve this point.

The deep-sea sediments are classified as either pelagic or terrigenous. The pelagic deposits are very fine-grained and they are found in the central part of the ocean basin. The terrigenous sediments, which accumulate with comparative rapidity form borders along the continents that supplied the materials.

The material eroded from land is carried downward by streams and rivers until it is eventually deposited on the great dumping ground of the continents, the continental shelf. The large particles settle to the bottom on the shelf near the shore and the finer ones move just beyond the edge of the shelf to the nearby ocean where the water is relatively quiet before they deposit. The very fine ones, which may stay in suspension for months or years, are carried far out from shore by the ocean currents and become part of the pelagic sediments.

Terrigenous deposits may be blue or brown in color and often contain a substantial percentage of organic material, including the shells of small marine animals. It is even possible that they contain petroleum deposits but there is little evidence to support or disprove this opinion.

Some of the sediments found at a considerable distance from a continent apparently accumulated originally on the continental shelf and were transported to the deep sea by turbidity currents. Turbidity currents are masses of liquid mud which flow at high velocities down gentle slopes. They start when a deltalike deposit of silt poised on the edge of the continental slope is set in motion by an earthquake or a violent storm. As the mass of sediment moves down the slope gathering speed, water mixes with the silt, making a dense liquid mud. This fluid moves with a rolling motion in such a way that bottom friction is negligible. Considerable momentum is attained and the turbid material may spread out for a considerable distance across the flat sea floor beyond the bottom of the slope. Just how far out to sea these currents flow is the subject of geological debate but some scientists believe it may be hundreds of miles.

After the material in the turbidity current stops its forward motion,

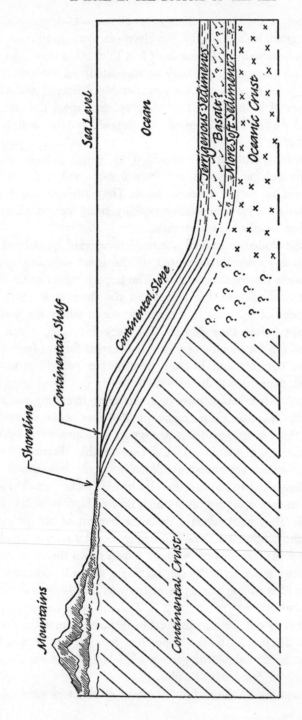

Fig. VII-5 The continental shelf is a great dumping ground for the material eroded from land.

it settles to the bottom to form layers that are graded according to particle size—the layers of larger grains are at the bottom—which can often be recognized in cores.

It is not yet known how important these currents are in furnishing sediment to the deep-sea floor. However, when selecting a site for the sampling of pelagic sediments, areas should be avoided where the sediment could have been largely contributed by turbidity currents. Such a site would be well out away from the continents, either on a rise in the sea floor or beyond a ridge or depression that would have screened it from these currents.

The best record of the history of the oceans will probably be obtained by sampling the pelagic deposits, the true deep-sea sediments.

The pelagic sediments are classified as inorganic, usually meaning red clay, or organic, meaning calcareous or siliceous oozes. As indicated by Table VII-1, much of the Atlantic is paved with calcareous ooze; much of the Pacific has a red-clay floor.

TABLE VII-1

The Composition of the Soft Sediments

	Indian Ocean	Pacific Oceans	Atlantic Oceans	Total
Calcareous oozes Globigerina Pteropods	54.3%	36.2%	67.5%	47.7%
Red Clay	25.3	49.1	25.8	38.1
Siliceous oozes Diatoms Radiolarians	20.4	14.7	6.7	14.2
	100.0%	100.0%	100.0%	100.0%

Relative amounts of pelagic materials

First, the origin of the clays. As already indicated, these are made up primarily of very fine particles that originated on the continents and have been carried long distances by ocean currents. Because these particles stay in suspension for such a long time and move so far before they settle out, these sediments have a universal quality. Their component grains may have originated almost anywhere.

Another major source of pelagic red clay is the oceanic volcano. The large pieces of ejected material fall into the sea close to the source; the smaller ones fall farther way. By measuring the sizes of the particles in a pattern of cores it is possible to determine the approximate positions of ancient volcanoes. However, the fine dust from an eruption is spread by the winds so that it eventually falls over great areas of land and sea. The ocean currents further distribute it so that the result may be a thin layer covering many thousands of square miles. Such a layer was found by scientists on the Lamont Observatory's oceanographic ship *Vema*, which was cruising off the west coast of South America in 1958. The echo sounder picked it up first as a double reflection—a second echo from a bottom below the bottom—and the ship followed it for hundreds of miles. When the layers above thinned so that this "second bottom" was within reach, the long piston corer obtained samples. It turned out to be a layer of white volcanic material which Maurice Ewing promptly named the Worzel Ash after Dr. J. Lamar Worzel, the expedition leader.

Erosional and volcanic contributions to the deep-sea sediment are very important, but over 60 per cent of the sea floor is covered with soft organic oozes. The calcareous oozes on the deep-sea floor are composed primarily of the skeletons of planktonic organisms. *Plankton*, a Greek word meaning wanderer, is used to describe all the floating and drifting life of the deep sea. These organisms, either plant or animal, are usually very small, and although some swim feebly, they are at the mercy of the currents. Most of the calcareous strata of the deep sea are composed of the shells of foraminifera, more specifically a globular-shaped genus called Globigerina, one of the most prolific animals that has ever lived. There are over 18,000 known species of Foraminifera including fossil forms and 128 million square kilometers of ocean floor are covered by their shells.

Plankton generally are near-surface dwellers, creatures of the mixed layer. They are usually found in the uppermost 200 meters of ocean where there is light and warmth and food. Occasionally they will exhibit some curious and puzzling characteristic. For example, in studying the distribution of Globigerina pachyderma, David Ericson, an oceanographic paleontologist, discovered that when the climate is cold their shells spiral to the left; when warm, they coil to the right. The dividing line is a surface water temperature of 7.2° C. The reason for this is a mystery; as Ericson says, "To conceive of any mechanism by which temperature could act upon coiling is difficult, to say the least." Perhaps this discovery can be developed into a method for determining ocean temperatures in the geologic past.

Two principal kinds of sea life create beautiful and intricate shells of translucent silica. These are diatoms—unicellular microscopic plants that live in the colder waters—and radiolarians—small animals, of which there are 4400 species, that prefer the equatorial Pacific. Both kinds exist in fantastic quantities. A single liter of water from the open North Pacific contained 200,000 diatoms.

These siliceous skeletons are rather easily dissolved on the ocean floor. As a result, deposits with significant amounts of these fossils are found only in zones where the "productivity" of life is high, such as beneath the track of the Equatorial current, the Kuroshio, and the Antarctic Circumpolar Current. This suggests that currents cause an upwelling of deep nutrient-filled water in which sea life can grow profusely. Thus, when these tiny creatures die and their skeletons settle to the bottom, the surface current leaves a permanent record of its position of the ocean floor. Dr. Gustaf Arrhenius, who began to study this matter in 1947 during the world cruise of the Swedish research ship *Albatross*, found that below the zone of upwelling which is associated with the equatorial current, the rate of deposition of planktonic shells—and therefore the thickness of the sedimentary strata —is three to five times greater than a few degrees to the north and south. From other studies it is known that in the nutrient-rich equatorial zone of upwelling the plankton productivity is about twenty-five times as great as it is ten degrees to the north or south. This suggests that a remarkably thick and well-defined fossil pathway marks the track of a current which in turn marks the equator. If the earth's equator has shifted through geologic time, a line of north-south bore holes could reveal the corresponding shift of the concentration of calcareous material in the sediment and thus establish how much the equator has moved and when.

Now, with the origin and composition of the deep-sea sediments in mind, we can return to the problem of their rate of accumulation. Certainly it is very slow.

The surface water of the deep ocean hundreds of miles from land has a characteristic deep electric-blue color. There the underwater visibility is several hundred feet, and only when a lens-like wave focuses a sun ray into a fleeting searchlight can one see the occasional glint of a tiny particle. It is difficult to imagine that these rare specks could form sediments at all, but they do in time.

We had already noted the discrepancy between the apparent thickness of soft sediment measured by seismic methods and the calculated thickness obtained by multiplying the sedimentation rate by the age of the ocean. In most places the measured value seems to be far too low. Assuming that most of the ocean has been present on the earth since Cambrian time, about 520 million years, we have a minimum age to multiply by. But how does one measure deep-sea sedimentation rates which are so small that a layer not much thicker than a sheet of paper may be deposited in a man's lifetime?

Several ingenious methods have been proposed.

One of these methods uses the length of the last glacial period, since it is accurately known from the radioactive dating of land sediments, and from the counting of yearly laminations in sediments near the receding ice. A series of cores, taken across the narrows between South America and Africa by the German research ship *Meteor* in 1926, revealed a stratum of red clay overlain by a layer of globigerina ooze. The bottom and top of the red clay could be identified as the beginning and end of the last glacial period. Since the duration of glaciation and the time since it ceased was known, it was a simple matter to divide the thicknesses of the red clay and of the ooze by the number of years and determine their deposition rates. At this location the average rate of red-clay deposition was calculated to be 0.9 centimeters per 1000 years and that for globigerina ooze, 1.2 centimeters per 1000 years.

It also is possible to date sediment layers directly with radioactivity. For example, the ratio of radium to ionium radioactivity in the strata, as described in Chapter IV, can be used to obtain sedimentation rate. However, in recent years several new methods, including that of measuring the carbon 14 in fossil shells made of calcium carbonate, have been developed which are more satisfactory.

In general the results indicate that on the average, one meter of deep-sea sediment is formed each 100,000 years, a kilometer each 100,000,000 years, and 5.2 kilometers since the beginning of the Cambrian. If this is correct, there should be about ten times as much sediment on the sea floor as the evidence of geophysics suggests. What happened to the sediments, or how did the measurements go wrong?

Only the red clays of the central ocean areas are deposited at a sufficiently low sedimentation rate to agree with the seismic probings. In the incredibly clear water where red clays accumulate, the rate is one millimeter per thousand years.

There are a number of mysteries associated with deep-sea sedimentation. For example, the sedimentary record obtained by coring is not always continuous. It is hard to conceive of a situation in which there would not have been deposition somewhere on the ocean bottom. Thus, if adjacent strata are widely separated in time, this must mean that oceanic currents either prevented deposition or eroded the missing layer after it was deposited. Where did the material go? It must have been redeposited elsewhere, making the sedimentary section there thicker. But everywhere that surveys have been made the section seems to be too thin.

There are areas of the Atlantic floor where fossil evidence indicates that the surface strata were formed at least 60 million years ago in Cretaceous time. Why have these sediments not been covered by more recent ones? At the one-centimeter-per-thousand-year average rate of sedimentation, 600 meters of sediment are missing. Where could it be?

Another puzzling aspect of the sea floor is the absence of sediment in many of the deep trenches. There are a number of these trenches in the ocean basins, the deepest parts of which are about 35,000 feet below sea level—20,000 feet below the average depth of the ocean. Several are a thousand miles long and nearly all are V-shaped in section with wall slopes of 15 to 30 per cent. One would expect such features to be excellent sediment traps but surprisingly enough they seem to contain very little sediment. Why not? Do deep currents keep them cleaned out? And, if so, where do these currents deposit their load?

The existence of vast quantities of manganese nodules on the surface of the sea floor poses another problem in sedimentation. Apart from the undecided origin of the nodules, which may have been chemically precipitated or biologically concentrated, why should they lie on the bottom as though recently scattered there? An average-sized nodule the size of a golf ball would be buried in five thousand years and radioactive dating indicates that their growth rate is very slow. Why then are the nodules still on the surface?

It is plain that we do not clearly understand the chemical and sedimentary history of the ocean. A great deal of thought and many measurements will be required before the questions raised can be answered. The study of the ocean is just beginning and, as in any new area, scientists must organize their thoughts by setting down on charts all that is known.

Charts that provide details of the topography, composition, and geology of the sea floor in small areas are just beginning to appear and are causing substantial re-evaluations of the character of the ocean basin. Not much over two decades ago geological experts believed that the ocean floors were great flat muddy plains, a very dull topography with only an occasional mountain range or trench. Now we know that the ocean basins have a topography and history which is at least as complex as that of the continents. There are thousands of sea mounts and volcanoes; small faults and trenches dissect the sea floor; sediments move about and apparently disappear; there are fault scarps a thousand meters high and horizontal fault displacements of 200 miles; magnetic and gravity anomalies indicate other complications in the rocks beneath the sea floor.

All of these factors influence, to some extent, the selection of drilling sites for the Mohole and for the series of sedimentary holes that will lead up to it. It is evident that a site representative of a substantial part of the ocean basin will not be easy to find. On the other hand, so much remains to be learned that cores from nearly any place would yield valuable information. The best way to answer the old questions and to develop hypotheses which may raise new and more difficult ones is to drill boldly into the sea floor where the evidence is stored.

VIII

Magnetism, Heat, and Pressure

Man's experience with magnetism goes back at least 2500 years to the ancient Greeks, who were familiar with the ability of magnetic rocks called loadstones to attract and repel iron. In 1269 a French crusader, Petrus de Maricourt, made a small sphere out of the mineral magnetite (loadstone), explored its surface with bits of iron, and applied the word *pole* to places where the magnetic force seemed concentrated. In his account of these experiments De Maricourt described in detail methods already in common use for navigating ships by means of a floating compass. He reported the general belief that the strange forces which moved the compass came from the sky.

It remained for Dr. William Gilbert, an English physician, to discover in 1600 that the earth as a whole acts like a magnet. Gilbert recognized that the magnetic field which surrounds and permeates the earth is much like the one that would exist if there were a huge bar magnet inside the earth connecting the north and south magnetic poles. He first thought that some kind of permanent magnet was the correct explanation for the earth's field but then he performed some experiments that changed his mind. He heated an iron bar magnet to a red heat and discovered that it lost its magnetic properties. Although the bar regained its magnetism when it cooled, the hypothesis of a permanent interior magnet had to be abandoned, for it was known that the temperatures inside the earth were higher than those of red-hot iron.

The earth's magnetic field is probably the least understood of all geophysical phenomena, for it is the most remote from direct investigation. Clearly its source is deep within the earth, and since little evidence about the interior was available to the early theorists, for many years no acceptable hypothesis was offered. Only recently has the dynamo theory of Professor Walter Elsasser of the Scripps Institution of Oceanography been recognized as a possible explanation of why the earth has a magnetic field.

The Elsasser hypothesis starts by summarizing the observations of the magnetic field on the surface: The lines of magnetic force at the surface of the earth are aligned almost north and south; the magnetic field is irregular and shifting; the shift is constantly to the westward. He then marshals evidence about the interior from the other branches of geophysics: The earth has a large spherical core; the outer part of the core reacts to seismic waves as though it were molten; the earth's density and the inference made from meteorites suggest the core is nickel-iron.

The existence of liquid ferromagnetic material capable of motion and the observed changes in the earth's field hint at a connection between the two. But how is the field created and what supplies the energy? Professor Elsasser believes that motions in the core act like a huge natural dynamo to generate electric currents and produce a magnetic field.

The dynamo converts mechanical rotation to electricity. A primitive version is a water wheel which rapidly turns a copper disc in the field created by a permanent magnet. As the spinning disc cuts the magnetic lines of force, an electrical current is generated. If some electricity so generated is sent through a coil of wire, an electromagnet is created. And if the electromagnet is then used to replace the original permanent magnet, the machine becomes a self-contained generator. Driven by the power of the water, it produces electricity which creates a magnetic field so that more electricity can be generated. Many commercial power generators operate on this principle.

The above-mentioned small disc generator, invented by Michael Faraday in 1820, cannot be rotated fast enough to sustain a current. However, if it had a diameter equivalent to that of the earth's core, it could generate large currents even if it moved very slowly.

Thus a possible mechanism exists for generating a continuous magnetic field with a machine the size of the earth's core. The driving force of the dynamo and the origin of the first currents which started this mighty generator producing current remain to be explained. The driving force undoubtedly is heat, which causes convection currents in the molten metal of the core something like those observed in a pan of boiling water. The original electrical currents may have resulted from the electrolytic interaction of dissimilar metals within the core early in the earth's history. Once started, the motion of the molten dynamo amplified these original weak currents, building them up until equilibrium was reached. Thereafter the earth had a self-perpetuating magnetic field.

The Earth's Magnetic Field

The illustration of the earth's main magnetic field or axial field in Figure VIII-1 shows the general configuration of the lines of magnetic force. A compass needle, free to move in any direction, will tend to align itself with these lines. Thus the magnetic poles are defined as the places where the magnetic lines of force are vertical, where a compass needle mounted on a horizontal axis points straight down. At the magnetic equator, which is at right angles to the magnetic axis and so is not over the geographic equator, the lines of the magnetic force are horizontal.

The earth's actual lines of force are not so symmetrical and in attempting to follow these lines with an ordinary compass, magnetic surveyors find notable irregularities. The local deviations of the compass from this major pattern are caused by the fact that rocks containing magnetite superimpose their own magnetic field on that of the earth. This ability of a rock to modify a magnetic field is called susceptibility. When this local effect is subtracted from the main axial field, the result is the residual field—the one commonly used by navigators.

The earth's magnetic field is not only irregular but is constantly changing, shifting in strength and position. As S. K. Runcorn, a leading British geomagnetic expert, puts it, "The residual field may be likened to a formation of moving clouds; it is continually changing in form and also drifting as a whole." Centuries of observation have shown that the entire residual field is moving westward at a rate which will move it completely around the earth in 1600 years. This suggests that the core is turning eastward a little slower than the mantle and lags behind a full turn in 1600 years.

The other changes in the field indicate that there are turbulent eddies in the molten core. For example, the north magnetic pole, now located on the Boothia Peninsula in northern Canada, is believed to have shifted its position as much as 200 miles in the last sixty years.

The combined result of the susceptibility of the local rocks and of

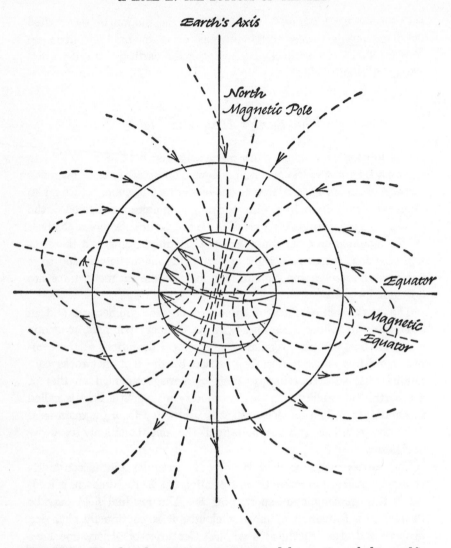

Fig. VIII-1 Circular electric currents generated by motion of the earth's liquid nickel-iron core produce the magnetic field that is observed at the surface.

the shifting of the north magnetic pole is that in order to navigate accurately with a compass it is necessary to know the declination—the angle between true north and the direction the compass points—for each point for each year.

The magnetic field of the earth at any point is defined by its direction and intensity, in units called gammas, by means of three kinds of compasses, each used in a different way. An ordinary compass is used to measure the direction of the field. The horizontal intensity of the magnetic field is obtained by measuring the period of the compass as it swings back and forth on its pivot. This is the magnetic equivalent of the pendulum that is used for measuring the force of gravity. By using the period of the compass and the angle which the needle deflects when an auxiliary magnet is held at a standard distance, the horizontal intensity of the earth's magnetic field can be computed. The third compass has an elongated needle hanging on a vertical axis. The needle's angle of dip is a measure of the vertical intensity of the magnetic field.

Although compasses can be used to obtain forces and directions with precision, mapping the field by moving them from point to point was a slow and tedious task, for they had to be mounted firmly and carefully leveled at each new point to get an accurate reading. Clearly a device was needed which could be carried by a ship or aircraft and used to make rapid continuous measurements of the variations in magnetic intensity. The magnetometer was the result.

The proton precession magnetometer, invented by Dr. Russell Varian, is one of several varieties. It uses the influence of the earth's magnetic field on the motion of nuclear particles.

The proton, like most other nuclear particles, constantly spins on its axis and, since it carries an electric charge, the spin generates a magnetic field. The proton can be regarded as a tiny gyroscope. If an ordinary gyroscope is tilted, it does not fall; instead its upper end precesses, that is, it makes slow circles about the vertical. The gravitational pull of the earth acts to swing the axis around more rapidly rather than to increase the tilt. Where the force of gravity is greater, the precession is faster. Thus, the rate of precession of an ordinary gyroscope is a measure of the force of gravity. However, if the gyroscope is a proton and the force disturbing it is a magnetic field, the precession rate is a measure of the strength of the magnetic field.

The Varian instrument has beautiful simplicity, at least in theory. The sensing element is a small cylinder of a liquid hydrogen compound—a glass of water could be used—with a coil of wire around it. When an electric current passes through the wire, a magnetic field is created which aligns the protons in a new direction. When the current is suddenly stopped, it releases the spinning nuclear magnets (the protons) which are now out of position. In order to realign them—

selves they begin to precess about their axes at a rate dependent upon the strength of the earth's field. By using the same coil of wire to measure the rate of the proton precession, the earth's magnetic field can be measured.

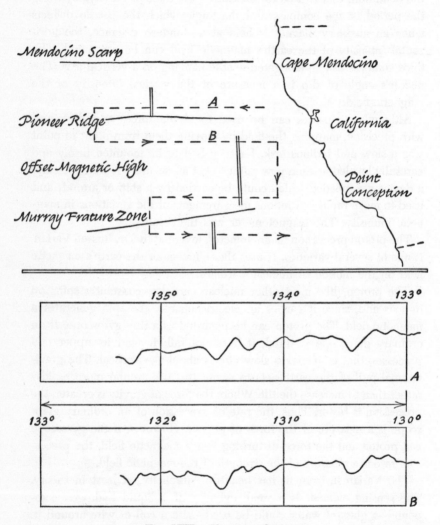

Fig. VIII-2 Vacquier Survey

Above: Track of magnetic survey ship that discovered the movement on the Pioneer Ridge fault.

Below: The two magnetic profiles made along A and B match up perfectly when B is offset 138 miles to the east.

Magnetometers towed behind ships and aircraft are now standard geophysical survey tools used to outline ore deposits, oil structures and to broadly survey the crust of the earth beneath the ocean.

In 1958 a remarkable and unexpected discovery was made by Dr. Victor Vacquier on a ship of the Scripps Institution of Oceanography which was towing a magnetometer in the Pacific. A series of great escarpments extend out across the deep-sea floor from the west coast of North America; two of the major ones are called the Murray fracture zone and Pioneer Ridge. Long believed to be the traces of faults, they continue for hundreds of miles in straight lines and rise abruptly higher on one side than on the other. Vacquier's survey proved this conclusively. The ship ran west along the Murray scarp on its north side and then returned east following a parallel path on the south side. The two courses were about 70 miles apart.

On comparing the record of the magnetic anomalies for both sides of the fault, it was observed that the two records were almost exactly alike *if* they were displaced the proper distance. In order to make the record pairs of the Murray fracture zone match up, they had to be displaced 84 miles, as shown in Figure VIII-2. The Pioneer ridge records matched when the records were offset 138 miles. The unmistakable similarity of the magnetic records make it clear that a huge area of crust had broken and the pieces on opposite sides of the fault had moved the distances indicated. The original announcement says rather modestly, "This reveals an unsuspected mobility of small blocks of the oceanic crust."

The cause of the magnetic structure within the crust is uncertain; the humps in the record may represent north-south lines of mineralization either in the deep sedimentary strata or in the igneous rocks. However, these variations in magnetism cannot come from any great depth because of the high temperature of the deeper rocks.

Obviously, the magnetic structure of the sea floor is a matter to be considered in the selection of deep-sea drilling sites. In the first hole it will be desirable to choose a location which has been magnetically mapped and is not anomalous. Then subsequent holes can be located on magnetic highs and lows in an attempt to determine what causes the variations. Finally, after each hole is drilled, a magnetometer will be lowered to measure the intensity of the magnetic field in the rock at depth.

One of the interesting aspects of geomagnetism, that of the relation between heat and magnetic properties, was investigated by Gilbert himself. As we noted earlier, he discovered that the temperature of the earth's interior was much too high to allow any material to retain permanent magnetism. But Gilbert's experiments failed to establish another equally important point. Just before the turn of the twentieth century Dr. Pierre Curie of France made measurements of magnetic materials at high temperatures and discovered that above a critical temperature they not only become temporarily nonmagnetic but that upon cooling they acquire a new magnetization having the direction of the magnetic field in which they are cooled. In iron this critical temperature is about 800° C; in nickel, 350° C; and in magnetite, 575° C. The temperature at which the magnetic particles reorient themselves is now known as the Curie point.

In the years since that discovery it has been found that certain rocks, principally basaltic lavas, contain evidence about the direction of the earth's magnetic field at the time they were formed.

As lava cools below the Curie point, its magnetic particles become permanently aligned with the magnetic lines of force existing at that time. This means that the magnetic direction of a sample of lava is indicative of the direction of the magnetic poles at the time that rock cooled. In order to determine this direction, carefully oriented samples of rock are required. The samples are sliced into small cubes and placed in a device which measures the direction of the rock's original magnetism. In this manner the original magnetic directions of a great many igneous and sedimentary rocks of all ages from various parts of the world have been determined. The sedimentary rocks which possess the strongest permanent magnetization are the red sandstones. These sandstones, as well as certain shales, apparently obtained their original orientation when tiny elongated particles of magnetic minerals settled to the sea bottom as sediment accumulated and aligned themselves with the earth's field that then existed.

The measurements indicate that the positions of the magnetic poles have been constantly changing for hundreds of millions of years. If these measurements are meaningful, they indicate that the poles have wandered or that the continents bearing the rocks which contain the magnetic pointers have shifted, or both.

This polar wandering must be distinguished from the rapid short-term motions of the pole previously mentioned. The long-term position of the magnetic pole is assumed to coincide approximately with the geographic poles. Considerable data on polar positions relative to rocks of various geologic ages in North America and Europe have been

Fig. VIII-3 Polar wandering according to S. K. Runcorn. Solid line is position of pole inferred from European rocks. Broken line is position of pole inferred from American rocks.

1 = positions of pole in Silurian time
2 = positions of pole in Triassic time

plotted as polar wandering curves such as those in Figure VIII-3. From the study of these curves, Professor S. K. Runcorn, the leader in this field, has found certain noteworthy features. First, the polar positions of successive geologic periods lie on a smooth curve, indicating a long and steady shift, the later positions being increasingly close to the present pole. Second, the curves drawn through these pole positions are similar for Europe and America. Third, the systematic displacement between the curves for Europe and America indicate that a relative motion between the two continents of about 24° took place after Triassic time, a situation for which continental drift may be responsible.

Many geophysicists are not in complete agreement with Runcorn about whether or not the measurements of rock magnetism are significant and can be used in such sweeping interpretations. They point out that high rock pressures over long periods of time may change the magnetic orientation of the particles, that the earth's field may have reversed its polarity, that lightning bolts may strike a rock, destroying the original evidence, or that magnetic minerals may have been formed in the rock long after its origin, giving an erroneous orientation. These objections are valid and certainly they make the determination of polar orientation difficult; however, scientists must work with whatever evidence they can find. In the majority of cases a single geological formation over a wide area gives a well-grouped set of directions of magnetization from which the average direction can be determined. This average direction can be used with some confidence.

Studies of rock magnetism lead inevitably to the conclusion that the poles and the continents have changed their relative positions. Moreover, the principal part of the motion appears to have taken place since the late Mesozoic, relatively late in the history of the earth. Thus, the new geomagnetic evidence gives strong support to the theory of continental drift.

If both the poles and the continents have moved, scientists must find a more stable object to use for a reference. One possibility is the oceanic crust. We have noted that there are local faults and displacements in crust beneath the sea; however, the Pacific basin is so large—it accounts for nearly one-third of the earth's surface—one would expect it to hold its position relatively well. Therefore, if oriented cores of the igneous rocks beneath the sea can be obtained, dated, and geomagnetically oriented, the measurements on land can be compared with a new reference.

If the oceanic directions of ancient north are regarded as absolute, a series of samples from the Mohole at different depths, representing different geologic ages, may help determine if the north pole has moved and where it was in various geologic periods. If the pole has not actually moved, its apparent motion must be attributed to the drifting of the continents. By comparing the direction of continental north with that of oceanic north in various geologic periods, it will be possible to learn which continents have moved and how much. Thus the cores obtained by the Mohole project can contribute greatly to the understanding of polar shift and continental drift.

In the earlier discussion of that drift it was noted that Wegener's original theory was deficient because he failed to propose a mechanism which could move the continents.

One possible explanation is the presence of thermal convection currents within the mantle that move crustal blocks similar to those within the core which create the magnetic field. Since these currents are driven by the earth's heat, we should begin by looking at the source of that heat and its mechanisms of transfer.

Temperature and Heat Flow

There is a version of the second law of thermodynamics which is easy to remember and helpful in keeping heat-transfer processes straight: Heat always flows downhill! Of course, this is not to be taken literally. It means that heat can only move from a warmer body to a cooler one. In the case of the earth, if we measure the heat being conducted outward through the crustal rocks, we conclude that the deep interior is much warmer than the exterior and that the earth is losing heat into space. Near the surface of the earth, the increase in temperature with depth can be measured; in fact, the very existence of this temperature gradient is evidence that heat is flowing outward. However, the amount of heat lost into space is very small and since new heat is constantly being generated in the interior by radioactivity, it is not certain whether the earth is heating up or cooling down. Either way it will make little difference to man who depends on the sun for warmth. If the internal heat supply were eliminated, the surface temperature would fall only about a hundredth of a degree.

The interior heat of the earth comes from two sources. One is the primordial heat that has remained since the earth's formation; the other is the heat generated by radioactivity since that time. On that there is agreement; however, the proportion of the total that each contributes is the subject of active scientific debate because the evidence is scanty and inconclusive.

There are two major theories about the origin of primordial heat, the classical one being that the earth was originally a molten body, perhaps a fragment of the sun, which has been cooling ever since it first was flung into orbit to travel on its own. The other theory, now more generally accepted, is that the protoplanet earth began with the condensation of a cloud of cool dust and gases. Its size increased as it encountered and attracted other space travelers. The pieces assembled violently; as they did they contributed the heat generated by friction and collision. As the earth grew larger its central zone was compressed by its own gravity and by the weight of the new materials constantly being added to the outside. This caused adiabatic heating, meaning the temperature rose because the pressure increased.

In either case the temperature in the interior of the newly formed earth was great enough so that the materials could segregate themselves by density. The heaviest ones went to the center and eventually became surrounded by concentric spheres of lighter and lighter materials. The earth need not have been molten for this segregation to take place. Over a long period of time "solids" can flow like liquids in response to a steady force like gravity.

The other source of the earth's heat is the constant disintegration of radioactive isotopes of thorium, radium, and potassium, which are contained in most rocks in minute amounts. In the course of their normal decay, the ejected nuclear particles give up energy by ionizing neighboring atoms and exciting their electrons. This loss of energy is manifest as heat and although the amount of heat is very small, most of the rocks of the earth's crust contain enough of these radioactive components so that over long periods of time a substantial amount of heat is produced. The radioactivity of the various rocks of the crust has been measured, and it has been determined that continental granites contain enough radioactive material to produce approximately three times as much heat as oceanic basalts. Moreover, the granite is, on the average, about five times as thick. Therefore, it would be reasonable to expect that the heat flow from the continents would be considerably greater than that through the ocean floor.

Men set about measuring it to see. It was found that the flow of heat from the interior of the earth could be determined if one knew the amount of temperature change with depth and the ability of the rock to conduct heat. This means that if the temperature is measured at two different depths within a drill hole and the thermal conductivity of a sample of the rock removed from the hole is measured in the laboratory, the amount of heat flowing through that part of the crust can be calculated. Many measurements of heat flow on land using this method showed that on the average about a millionth of a calorie per square centimeter per second reaches the surface of the earth.

The measurement of heat flow through the 70 per cent of the earth's surface covered by ocean was much more difficult. Only in the last decade Sir Edward Bullard, Dr. Roger Revelle, and Dr. Arthur Maxwell developed a technique for determining the thermal gradient in the soft sediments of the sea floor. The method used by Bullard and his friends is to lower a "temperature probe" on a cable from an oceanographic ship. As shown in Figure VIII-4, the probe is a steel needle about two inches in diameter and ten feet long which contains temperature-measuring elements. It penetrates the soft sea bottom and measures the temperature at two points about two meters

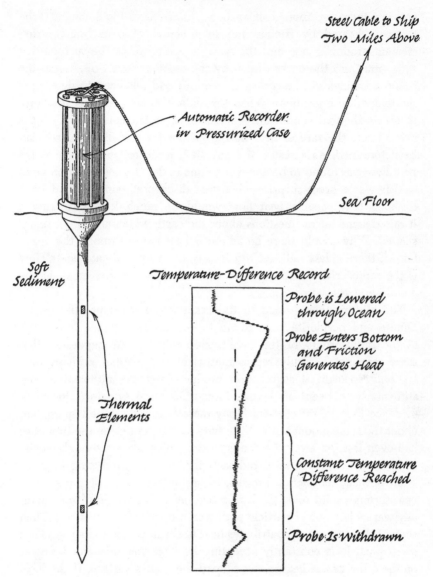

Steel Cable to Ship
Two Miles Above

Automatic Recorder
in Pressurized Case

Sea Floor

Soft
Sediment

Temperature-Difference Record

Probe is Lowered
through Ocean

Probe Enters Bottom
and Friction
Generates Heat

Thermal
Elements

Constant Temperature
Difference Reached

Probe Is Withdrawn

Fig. VIII-4 The Temperature Probe

apart. Mounted atop the needle is a heavy pressureproof case housing an automatic recorder that traces a record of the difference in temperature between the two elements.

The probe is dangled just above the bottom until it becomes the temperature of the water; then it is quickly plunged into the bottom

175

and left there for about half an hour. As it enters the sediments, the probe is heated by friction but in a short while each measuring element gradually becomes the same temperature as the surrounding sediments, and the curve drawn by the recorder levels off. When the probe is recovered, the record is removed and analyzed to determine the temperature gradient. When this data is combined with measurements of thermal conductivity made on sediment cores taken at the same place, the rate of heat flow from the interior of the earth can be determined. As a result of many such measurements, the average heat flow was found to be about the same under the oceans as on land.

This was a great surprise when first discovered, since it had been assumed that oceanic heat flow would be much less. Futhermore, it raised some major questions about the earth which are as yet unanswered. Why should there be as much heat rising through the ocean floor if there is less radioactivity in oceanic crust to create heat? How is the radioactivity distributed in the rocks beneath the crust—in the mantle and the core?

The inquiry then turned to the examination of mantle-like rocks. Dunite and peridotite were found to contain less than a hundredth of the radioactivity of the basalt. Hopefully it was suggested that these may not be truly representative of the mantle; perhaps they are only specialized segregation products and the radioactive constituents have been left below. Meteorites were examined for what evidence they might contain. Stony meteorites were found to contain about the same amount of radioactivity as the peridotite; the iron ones had even less. As a result there is still considerable mystery about the amount and distribution of radioactivity which is producing heat.

In the heat-conduction process, the principal means of transferring heat through solid rock, the heat moves as each particle of rock actually warms any cooler particle with which it is in direct contact. Then each of those particles contributes heat to the next one and so on. Thus every particle is constantly accepting heat on one side and losing it on the other as the heat moves toward the earth's surface. If the local differences in temperature are very small, as they are in the earth, this process is incredibly slow. Professor Louis Slichter of the Institute of Geophysics at UCLA has calculated that radioactive heat, generated below a depth of 200 miles since the earth first formed, has not yet reached the surface in appreciable amounts by conduction alone even though it has been moving for several billion years.

One would expect heat transferred by conduction to be evenly distributed, but measurements with the temperature probe show that beneath the oceans there are substantial variations from the average. A chart of the pattern of heat flow through the eastern Pacific floor shows a long narrow hot zone flanked by zones cooler than average. This could hardly have been produced by particle-to-particle conduction. It must mean that some other mechanism is transporting heat from the depths to produce the patterns observed on the surface.

We have seen that there is evidence supporting the opinion that the earth's outer core is a liquid material moving in turbulent eddies and that the mantle is a solid material. Now, without exactly changing that opinion, we must modify it a little since deep in the earth where pressures are great, distances large, and time almost unlimited, these words have a slightly different meaning. Actually the solid rocky mantle of the earth has many characteristics of a very viscous liquid when subjected to large forces for a long period of time. The vertical motion of crustal segments into isostatic equilibrium requires motion in the mantle; so does, or did, the segregation of core and mantle materials into their present positions. This means that although the outer mantle is solid enough to break and send out earthquake waves, it may also flow plastically right up to the bottom of the crust. Having conceded that these rocks can flow, the next step is to postulate temperature differences in the earth's interior that can cause convection currents.

As heat is applied to the bottom of a liquid, its particles tend to expand, become lighter, and rise. At the surface the particles give up some heat and are pushed to one side by warmer material rising from beneath. They become cooler and denser; they sink again. Convective circulation is established. Convection currents are favored by low viscosity and low conductivity. In the mantle, although the conductivity is suitably low, the viscosity is very high. Even so, the size of the earth and the apparently large temperature differences at great depth make convection possible. These currents may be started when heat is applied to the bottom of the mantle, probably by direct contact with the hot, moving, liquid material along the rim of the core.

There are various estimates of how fast material moves in an active convection current, but ten centimeters (about four inches) a year seems to be a reasonable figure. This means that approximately 30 million years would be required for a slug of hot material to travel from the rim of the core to the bottom of the crust—not a very long time geologically speaking.

The rising convection current may play like a slow fountain against the bottom of the crust, transferring heat which is then conducted through the crustal rocks to the surface, where it can be measured. Then the moving rock spreads out horizontally and eventually sinks downward again. As it moves, the viscous drag of the flowing rock can be expected to exert a considerable force against the bottom of the crust. The diameter of such a convection cell may be 7000 to 10,000 kilometers and it has been suggested that ocean basins exist because they have been swept clean of continental debris by such currents. It seems possible that such a mechanism is responsible for

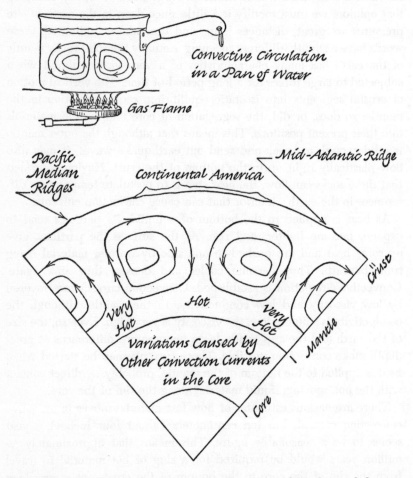

Fig. VIII-5 Convection currents in the earth and one hypothesis of the way in which they move continents.

continental drift and that one or more large "fountains" rising beneath a large continent could have broken it up and rafted the pieces off in different directions. This may be the explanation that Wegener was seeking. On the other hand, continents may represent a rocky scum at a zone of convergence between two great rising convection currents as shown in Figure VIII-5.

Convection, as well as continental drift, is still regarded by many geologists as a speculative hypothesis; however, two interesting pieces of information lend support to the idea. One is the actual measurements of heat flow through the eastern Pacific floor, which is consistent with those that one would expect convection currents to produce. A long ridge of high heat flow centers on an upwarped area

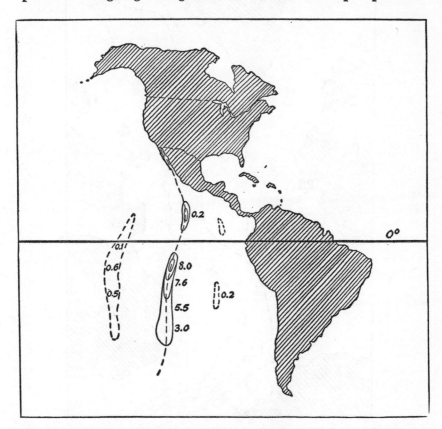

Fig. VIII-6 Pattern of heat flow through the floor of the Pacific Ocean showing median line of high heat flow with flanking lines of low heat flow. Numbers are in micro-calories per square centimeter per second. Average for Pacific—and for earth—is about 1.2.

of ocean bottom known as the Albatross Plateau. Expansion of normal oceanic crustal rocks by an unusual amount of heat could have caused this uplift and the consequent shallowness of water which makes the "plateau." Low heat-flow measurements on its flanks suggest that these may represent lines of downward motion.

Not enough measurements have been made to really define the pattern of heat flow throughout the Pacific basin, but other zones of high and low heat flow will undoubtedly be discovered which will give a much better basis for interpretation. In the Atlantic, high heat

Fig. VIII-7 The mid-Atlantic ridge is equidistant from the shores of Europe and America. It is a zone of high heat flow and may indicate an upward-rising convection current in the earth's mantle. The sidewise motion of the mantle could be responsible for the continents drifting apart.

flow has been observed along the mid-Atlantic ridge. This suggests that the ridge marks the top of a long linear fountain of convection. Perhaps an outflow of moving mantle material in both directions contributed to the separation of the Americas from Europe-Africa, if, indeed, that has actually occurred.

A fascinating group of model experiments vividly demonstrating convection currents was made by Dr. David Griggs, now of the Institute of Geophysics at UCLA. He used a viscous liquid, glycerine, to represent the mantle and covered it with a layer of sawdust and oil which represented the crust. On a small scale, these materials accurately model the properties of mantle and crust. Then, as shown in Figure VIII-8, drums were rotated within the glycerine to simulate convection in the mantle, one minute in the model being equal to a

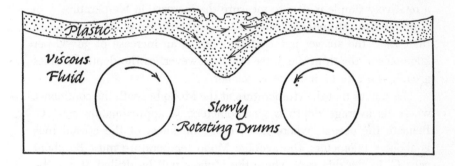

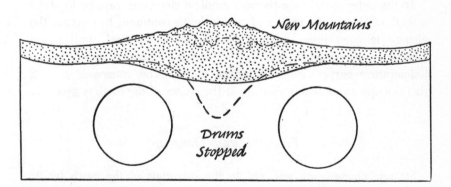

Fig. VIII-8 Section through model made by Dr. David Griggs to simulate the drag of convection currents in the mantle on the earth's crust. If convection ceases (drums in the model are stopped) the thickened section of crust will rise to regain isostatic balance and form mountains.

million years of actual time. When the drums are turned, the plastic crust is thickened and pulled into a downfold. If they are stopped, the thickened mass rises in isostatic equilibrium so that its final surface is considerably above the original level. Whether or not this kind of a model is a realistic representation of the forces in the earth is debatable; however, it does demonstrate that convection is one likely mechanism for moving the crust and forming mountains.

Finally, we come to the question of the actual temperatures at various depths and at the center of the earth. Because heat travels slowly and the great depths will always be inaccessible, it is possible that man will never have a very accurate answer. The temperature at the center of the earth has been estimated by various scientists at from 2000° C to 10,000° C.

In the crust, where heat transfer is entirely by conduction, it is a relatively simple matter to measure the increase in temperature with depth and to extrapolate it downward. Either in continents or beneath the oceans the answer is the same; there is an increase of 30° C per kilometer of depth in the outer crust. However, as the depth becomes greater the rate of increase is smaller.

This means that the temperature at the Moho beneath the continents, where its average depth is 33 kilometers, is approximately 700° C. Beneath the oceans, where the average thickness of the crustal rock is about 7 kilometers, the average Moho temperature must be about 200° C. In the thin spot where the Mohole will be drilled, it may be as little as 150° C.

In the outer mantle the thermal gradient decreases rapidly to about a tenth of that in the crust and as the depth continues to increase the change is even more gradual. Combining theoretical studies and laboratory experiments with the geophysical evidence results in the temperature curve shown in Figure VIII-9. The concensus now is that the approximate temperature at the center of the earth is 3500° C.

Pressure and Density

Strange changes are wrought in the materials of the earth by its great internal pressures. These pressures are caused by the force of gravity and they are measured in bars—a bar being roughly equivalent to an atmosphere or 14.5 psi. As the depth increases the pressure increases, for each layer must support the weight of all the material

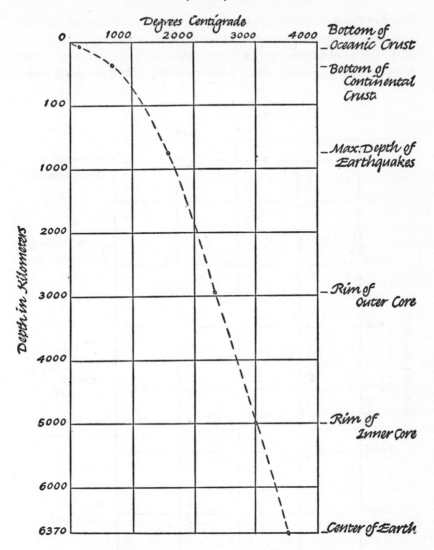

Fig. VIII-9 Temperatures in the Earth's Interior

above. In the crust the pressure increases about one atmosphere every four meters. At greater depths the increase is more rapid and at the center of the earth the pressure is estimated to be about 3.92 million bars or 57 million psi.

Each of the earth's major layers—core, mantle, and crust—seems to be made of reasonably homogeneous materials, but within each layer there is an increase in density toward the bottom, the direct

183

result of the materials being compressed into a smaller volume. These increases in pressure and density have been estimated by Professor K. E. Bullen of Cambridge University with the result shown in Figure VIII-10. This was a difficult trial-and-error calculation since the densi-

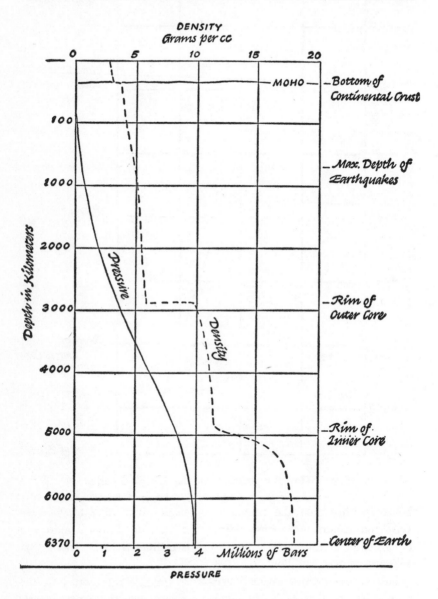

Fig. VIII-10 Pressure and Density

ties and thicknesses assigned to each layer must add up to agree with the known total mass and moment of inertia of the earth.

The study of the changes in rock characteristics and composition caused by extreme pressure leads to some interesting conclusions. For example, the increase in pressure has a marked effect on the depth at which earthquakes can occur and on the speed of the seismic waves which the quakes send out.

Rocks confined under high pressures deep in the earth become stronger and more ductile. That is, the pressure of the surrounding material makes it possible for a rock to resist more stress than it could near the surface; when the rock does yield, it tends to be distorted rather than to break abruptly. Since even the deepest earthquakes have their foci above a depth of 700 kilometers, where the pressure is 250,000 atmospheres, rocks apparently cannot fracture under the higher pressures that exist beneath that depth.

The capability of the rock to conduct seismic waves is simultaneously helped and hindered by increasing pressure. The high pressure makes the rocks more dense and this tends to slow the waves down, but it also makes them more rigid and this tends to speed the waves up. Since the rigidity increases faster than the density, the net effect is an increase in the velocity of seismic waves as they move deeper in the mantle. At the edge of the core where liquid metal of much greater density is encountered, their velocity abruptly slows again.

At the depth of the core the pressure is sufficient to actually alter the materials. One hypothesis holds that the core of the earth is not nickel-iron but compressed silicate rock; another proposes that it is compressed hydrogen. These ideas have not been generally accepted; however, scientists reviewing them took into account new measurements of the compressibility of iron and discovered that the earth's core is less dense than iron would be at the pressures that must exist in the core. This suggests that the core contains alloying elements lighter than iron. Another opinion is that the inner core is made of the same material as the outer core except that the pressure has caused the molecular structure to collapse. We probably will never know for certain, but an increasing effort is going into the search for more evidence about the properties of materials under intense heats and pressures.

The temperatures and pressures of the outer mantle can be duplicated on a small scale in the laboratory and can be imposed on real and synthetic rock fragments to determine what changes take place in the rocks at depth. In experiments on minerals at Harvard University, pressures of 30,000 atmospheres and temperatures of 1500° C have been used to simulate the environment of rocks 120 kilometers below the surface. After a few hours in the apparatus, the material is removed and examined under a microscope with an X-ray diffractometer to see if any new minerals have been formed. For example, Dr. Francis Birch of Harvard has used high temperatures and pressures to transform a mineral called albite into jade. Both minerals are composed of the same elements (aluminum, sodium, silicon, and oxygen) but they differ in crystal structure. When he applied high pressure to the albite he squeezed some of the silicon and oxygen out. This excess material crystallized into quartz and the remainder became jade.

These changes occur at the molecular level, the atoms of one substance apparently entering into the space lattices of another to form what is known as a solid solution. Changing the temperature and pressure greatly effects the proportions of the two materials that can exist together in this manner. As the pressure varies, the elements in a rock reorganize into a new family of minerals. When the rock freezes, the structure and minerals created by the pressure is preserved. This result is known as a phase change. A number of scientists believe that the Moho seismic discontinuity and several minor discontinuities deep within the mantle are the result of such phase changes. It is possible that complex silicate rocks, unknown at the surface, have been created by the special conditions of temperature and pressure at depth. Thus the rocks of the crust may be material that has been squeezed out of the mantle.

One way to find out about this crust-mantle relationship is to bring up samples of the materials above and below the Moho for detailed analysis. Fortunately phase changes are irreversible reactions, and if these deep rocks are brought to the surface they will not revert to ordinary surface rocks.

IX

Evidence in the Skies

The geological maxim "The present is a key to the past" is equally valid in the science of astronomy. If we carefully observe our heavenly neighbors and the processes going on in the skies today, we can learn a great deal about the origin of our universe, our galaxy, our solar system, and our earth. For it is abundantly clear that the history of the earth is inextricable from the history of the rest of the cosmos. Thus the evidence in the skies serves as an independent check on the hypotheses of composition and origin derived from earthly studies, for the concepts of astronomy and geophysics must be compatible if either is to be believed.

Earth's Place in the Cosmos

Our sun is one of 100 billion stars in a lens-shaped spiral nebula or galaxy called the Milky Way. Since many of the stars in a galaxy have groups of satellites or solar systems—estimates range from a few dozen to millions—and our galaxy is one in a billion, the earth is a very undistinguished speck in space. However, the great number and variety of cosmic events going on all about us gives us an excellent opportunity to see stars in all stages of development.

Geophysicists eagerly quiz astronomers on two heavenly points which bear directly on earthly problems: How old is the solar system, and how was the solar system formed?

The age of the solar system is obviously less than that of the universe, and the age of the universe can be determined by measuring the speed of flight of the stars as the universe expands. All stars appear to be moving outward from a common point as though propelled by tremendous explosion at the beginning of time. By measuring the shift of the red calcium band from its normal position in its light spectrum, a star's velocity can be determined. By measuring the brightness of a star, its distance can be obtained.

When distance and brightness are compared it is found that the stars farthest away are moving the fastest. Astronomers, calculating backward from these data, estimate that the great expansion began between 8 and 14 billion years ago. During the expansion the galaxies took shape, the heavier elements were created, and our sun and its solar system was formed. It may have happened as follows:

Within the arms of the spinning galaxies, which are composed of uncountable millions of stars, there are dark patches of cold dust and clouds of hydrogen. Such opaque globules of dust and gas, whose original dimensions would be reckoned in light years, could be pushed together by the pressure of starlight. When they are sufficiently compressed, their mutual gravity will cause them to collapse into a smaller and smaller sphere. The increase in temperature and pressure in the interior caused by the compression is then sufficient to start a thermonuclear reaction. Hydrogen fusion begins and a star like our sun is born.

If this concept is correct, it seems likely that enough material would be left over to make a solar system. Dr. Harold Urey feels that the older hypotheses of the solar system are unsatisfactory because they try to account for the origin of the planets without accounting for the origin of the sun. However if we begin with the formation of the sun, it is possible to think of reasons why the material that comprises the planets remained outside it.

Turbulent effects started the sun spinning; out away from it the remaining gases and dusts formed into a thin disc and were held neatly balanced between centrifugal force and the sun's gravity. Eventually the disc was subdivided into turbulent preplanetary rings which must have looked something like the present rings of Saturn; in these rings the fine particles coalesced and became larger ones. In time planetesimals of considerable size developed—some as big as the moon. These moved at different velocities, the larger ones sweeping the space within the ring with their gravitational pull and capturing the smaller ones. Finally a single mass became dominant and easily gathered the remaining debris unto itself. The collisions which resulted generated heat and fused the mass together, eventually resulting in a segregation of materials in the interior. These protoplanets grew larger and larger as they accumulated the sun's leftover materials. The largest ones—the giant planets—were massive enough to have sufficient gravitational attraction to retain some of the lighter elements. Consequently their composition, which seems to be largely methane and ammonia, is more representative of the materials of the original rings. The smaller planets kept only the heavier elements— iron, magnesium, silicon, nickel, sulphur, aluminum—and gases such as oxygen which formed solid compounds. The remainder of their gases, including the two principal constituents, hydrogen and helium, and whatever neon, nitrogen, and water vapor existed, evaporated into space.

These original gases would not have disappeared from a completely formed Earth with its strong gravitational field, therefore they must have escaped at an earlier stage. This reconfirms the geological opinion that the materials of the present atmosphere and oceans must have been safely locked within the interiors of the plane- tesimals and only emerged after these had joined together to form the Earth. Whether or not the primordial Earth was cool or hot, the water was not at the surface in the beginning.

Since the other planets of the solar system were formed at the same time as the earth and of approximately the same materials, any information that can be obtained about their composition and internal structure has an important bearing on the study of the earth's interior.

The planets fall into two classes. The terrestrial or inner planets are similar to the Earth in size and density. They include Mercury, Venus, Earth, and Mars, plus the asteroids and the Earth's moon. The giant planets, including Jupiter, Saturn, Uranus, and Neptune, are much larger, less dense, and farther from the sun. Table IX-1 sets forth the dimensions and properties of these bodies which are of greatest interest to the geophysicist.

First, he wants to know the mass of each one. Mars and Earth have satellite moons and this permits their mass and the mass of their moons to be determined precisely. The masses of Mercury and Venus, however, must be deduced from the slight disturbance that their gravitation produces on the other members of the solar system— a more difficult set of observations and computations.

When the mass of a planet is known, its escape velocity can be determined—that is, the velocity at which matter, including molecules of gases and water vapor, must be traveling outward in order to

TABLE IX-1

The Planets and the Moon

		Distance from sun in terms of Earth's distance	Diameter miles & km.	Atmosphere	Density	Density relative to Earth	Escape Velocity	Number of Moons
Terrestrial Planets	Mercury	.38	3,100 mi. 4,960 km.	none	4.1	0.76	2.4 mi/sec 3.8 km/sec	0
	Venus	.72	7,700 12,320	CO$_2$ and water vapor	4.9	0.89	6.3 10.1	0
	Earth	1.00	7,927 12,683	nitrogen, oxygen, & water vapor	5.53	1.00	7.0 11.2	1
	Mars	1.52	4,220 6,752	like earth, but a very small amount	3.85	0.70	3.1 .5.0	2
	Asteroids	2.7	over 2,000 pieces	none	about 5.5	about 1.0	—	—
Giant Planets	Jupiter	5.2	88,770 142,032	ammonia, methane	1.33	0.24	37 59	11
	Saturn	9.5	74,200 118,720	ammonia, methane	0.72	0.13	22 35	9
	Uranus	19.2	32,400 51,840	methane, ammonia	1.26	0.23	13 21	4
	Neptune	30.0	30,900 49,440	methane	1.60	0.29	14 22	1
	Pluto	40.0	7,900 12,640	not known	5±	1?	7? 11?	0
	Earth's Moon	240,000 miles from earth	2,160 3,456	none	3.33	.60	1.4 2.4	0

escape the pull of that planet's gravity. From such data it is possible to predict the presence or absence of an atmosphere.

The combination of mass and size gives average density and when the density is known it is possible to make a reasoned estimate about the materials of which the other planets are composed. Iron-magnesium silicate rocks such as peridotite, which is most likely to be the material of the earth's mantle, have a density of 3.3. If 85 per cent of the earth is made of peridotite and if the terrestrial planets had a common origin, we can expect to find that the others are also largely made of peridotite-like rock. The density of the moon is 3.3, which suggests that it is made entirely of material like that of the earth's mantle. Venus, which is only a little smaller and has a slightly lower density than Earth, probably has an internal structure and composition very much like our own, with crust, mantle, and a somewhat smaller nickel-iron core. Mercury and Mars, which have considerably lower average densities than Earth, probably have relatively small metallic cores and are composed mainly of rocky material. Their crusts are similar in composition to our own but are thinner and have not been subjected to erosive effects of an atmosphere.

All of these ideas about the composition of our fellow planets are based on excellent but indirect evidence. There is one "planet," however, from which we have actual samples that can be brought into the laboratory, analyzed, and compared with samples of the earth.

Meteorites

Geophysicists do not have to depend entirely on devious astronomical computations for evidence of the composition and age of the solar system. They have the direct evidence of meteorites. Meteorites are believed to be fragments of the asteroids which have been drawn to us by the Earth's gravitational pull. If one makes the "meteorite analogy," which is simply that the asteroids were once a planet similar to the other terrestrial planets, then it is apparent that one might get an equivalent sample of the interior of the earth by analyzing meteorites.

Long ago it was noticed that the distance of the planets from the sun increased in an orderly ratio with one exception—a vacancy seemed to exist between Mars and Jupiter. On closer examination it was found that this slot is not entirely empty but is occupied by over

2000 small objects or asteroids. The larger of these are several hundred miles in diameter and the smallest that are visible have been described as "mountains broken loose." Although there are a great many asteroids, the total mass of the swarm is less than 2 per cent of the mass of the earth.

Why is there a great mass of small particles instead of one large planet? No one is sure, but the most plausible answer is that a planet which at one time traveled in this orbit disintegrated and that some of the fragments still travel in the old pathway. A collision with some heavenly wanderer or an explosion could have caused the breakup. In any event a shower of particles of all sizes seems to have been flung off into space and our earth occasionally encounters the fragments. Those which enter the atmosphere and collide with the earth we call meteorites. If, as seems likely, these pieces represent a random sample of a one-time planet, then we have only to collect a large number of these fragments together and analyze them to get an idea of that planet's composition and proportion.

For many years while other aspects of astronomy were making rapid progress, astronomers refused to believe that stones actually fell from the sky. Stories about finding meteorites were ridiculed as old wives' tales and medieval superstitions. Not until 1803 when several thousand small meteorites fell on the town of L'Aigle, France, did scientists believe that the stones came from outside the earth.

Meteorites which have fallen in the past and are later recognized are called "finds." Since it is not easy to distinguish stony meteorites from terrestrial rocks, a more reliable sample comes from the analysis of the "falls," that is, those meteorites which were actually observed to fall and were immediately picked up. They arrive at the earth's outer atmosphere traveling at many miles per second and, even though they are slowed by the friction of the air, reach the ground in a few seconds. In this short final flight, they push a luminous ball of compressed air ahead which is much larger than the meteorite itself. This, in addition to the surface particles which melt off and leave a glowing trail, makes even small meteorites visible to watchers on the ground. Their terminal speed is no greater than that of a similar-sized stone falling from a high building and even in soft earth a small meteorite will not bury itself more than a few feet. Immediately after they have alighted, their outer surface may be too hot to touch, but because the heat conductivity of stony meteorites is low the interior remains at the temperature of outer space. Consequently, as soon as the superficial heat is conducted away a coating of frost often forms on the outside.

An astonishing number of meteors enter the atmosphere. They appear to be traveling in the same orbital direction as the Earth. More strike the Earth in the afternoon than in the morning and more are sighted between April and July than in the other months. According to a recent census made with Baker-super-Schmidt telescopic cameras operating in New Mexico, ninety million meteors bright enough to be seen under good viewing conditions enter the earth's atmosphere each day. Professor Hans Pettersson, the Swedish oceanographer, estimates that five million tons a year is now reaching the earth but he points out that the rate has varied considerably in the last 10–15 million years, based on his analysis of the tiny cosmic spherules in deep-sea sediments. And Professor Harrison Brown, a geochemist who has studied meteorite falls extensively, believes that 160 meteorites large enough to be identified and picked up reach the earth each year.

Meteorites come in all sizes from that of dust particles to ones weighing thousands of tons but those weighing between 8 and 32 kilograms predominate. In the passage through the atmosphere the intense frictional heat erodes flow lines and pockmarks on the surface of the large ones. It may even give them a rough conical shape. Internal temperature differences may cause them to break up in the air and the very large ones, such as that which fell in prehistoric time near Winslow, Arizona, explode on contact with the ground, leaving huge craters.

Meteorites are classified according to composition. They range from essentially pure nickel-iron to pure silicates and include all mixtures of the two.

Aerolites, or stony meteorites, are largely composed of the silicates olivine and pyroxene. They are by far the most common of the "falls," the ratio being about thirty-five stony to one iron. However, if the stony ones land unnoticed, they look like earthly rocks and are rarely found. Siderites, as the nickel-iron meteorites are called, are much more rare but an untrained person easily recognizes that they are unusual. Consequently the proportion of "finds" greatly favors the iron meteorites.

Analysis of a great number of specimens of both iron and stony meteorites in the proportions in which they are seen to fall gives the composition shown in Table IX-2. Since the ratio is thirty-five stony

TABLE IX-2

Composition of Meteorites

Analysis Based on the Proportion of "Falls"

Siderites	nickel-iron 13%	
Aerolites	peridotite 87%	olivine 35%
		pyroxene 42
		anorthite 4
		troilite 5
Tektites	glassy material (very rare)	

to one iron, it is evident that the general average does not vary much from that of the average for stony meteorites alone.

Tektites are rare glassy objects the size and shape of pebbles which are scattered over a few restricted parts of the earth. Their extraterrestrial origin is not absolutely certain but many scientists believe that they are meteorites formed from the outer crust of a one-time planet.

To complete the meteorite analogy, we liken the siderites, aerolites, and tektites to the core, mantle, and crust of the ex-planet and of the Earth. They are in the same proportions and their composition suggests that they originated in a spherical body which increased in density toward the center and cooled from a semiliquid state before it was disrupted. Furthermore, the body cannot have been much smaller than the earth because otherwise there would not have been sufficient gravity to have caused the segregation. Radioactive age determinations of a number of meteoritic samples give an average value of about 4.5 billion years. This is the most reliable figure we have for the age of the solar system but it is about twice as old as any rock yet dated on earth. When a sample of the earth's mantle taken in the Mohole is dated, it is expected to be about the same age as that of stony meteorites.

The case for the meteorite analogy with the interior of the earth is a strong one because it supports, and is supported by, the scientific opinions about the materials and age of the earth which were reached by completely independent evidence and reasoning. Clearly the understanding of the earth's interior requires the geophysicist to know something about the earth's fellow travelers in space. Conversely, the more we learn about the earth the better we will understand the rest of the universe. For the earth is unique only because we are on it.

In these times when there is great popular interest in traveling to the moon and the nearby planets partly to see what they are made of, it is well to remember that much remains to be known about the earth. Since it is likely that the moon, Mars, and Venus are composed of materials much like those only a few miles below our feet, it seems a little impractical, though perhaps more glamorous, to go hundreds of thousands of miles out into space to get a sample of material.

X

Objectives and Sites

The previous chapters have presented a panoramic picture of the sciences of geology and geophysics. We have seen the stratigraphers examine the layered crustal rocks, the oceanographers plumb the depths of the sea, the seismologists probe the deep interior, and the astronomers reach out into the cold infinity of space. Other earth scientists follow the internal workings of the earth by studying earthquakes and volcanoes, by taking the earth's temperature, and by recording the shifts of the magnetic field.

Together they are like a group of consultant medical specialists hovering over a giant patient, trying to find out as much as possible about its interior before having to resort to a difficult exploratory operation. In the case of the Earth, each specialist has contributed important, though indirect, evidence about the age, composition, and structure of the unseen rocks below. The geophysical generalist must now assemble these in an orderly fashion and devise a unified theory so that we will know how to proceed with the direct exploration.

The generalist's fundamental question is: What is the history of the earth? In order to answer it, an intricate four-dimensional jigsaw puzzle of scientific knowledge with many missing pieces must be assembled. He starts by recalling a few of the major facts about the Earth.

It is a sphere whose dimensions are known rather precisely. As it spins on its ancient orbit about the sun, it influences and is influenced by the other members of the solar system in such a way that it is possible to determine its mass and average density. Meteorites provide excellent specimens of a similar planet's interior. Spectroscopic analysis of light from the most distant parts of the universe tells something of the time and place of the beginning of the elements. When assembled, this evidence forms a pattern which is indicative of the Earth's cosmological history.

But the more immediate and in many ways more interesting history of the earth is buried in the earth itself. Careful examination of surface rocks has revealed a logical and orderly pattern in the deposition of the sediments and the development of life. For 500 million years we can look backward into the history of life in shallow seas perched atop the continental masses. But *only* for 500 million years—not much more than 10 per cent of the time since the birth of the earth. What happened outside the continents or before that time when the record of life began is a great mystery.

The circumstances surrounding the origin of life and its early evolution for what may have been a billion years or more are unknown. It is generally believed that life started in the ocean. But when did the ocean originate and what was it like in its earliest days?

Perhaps we first should ask if there were continents in the beginning and what they were like. Probably great lumps of light granitic materials segregated in the early years and floated like icebergs on the primordial surface; these protocontinents were undoubtedly much smaller and of very different shapes and positions than the present ones. The dark surface around them may be the one we now call the Moho. Above them the sky was dark, for there was little atmosphere to scatter the sun's rays; temperatures were extreme.

The appearance must have been something like that of the moon today with steep ragged mountain ranges and desolate lava seas. It would have stayed that way except that the Earth had one great advantage. Its greater mass created sufficient gravitational attraction to prevent the water and the gases which rose to the surface, along with the lighter rocks, from escaping into space. In time an atmosphere began to develop; then came the first winds and rains.

During the day surface temperatures were high on the naked rocks; at night they were low. Water alternately froze and thawed, splitting the mineral grains apart and rounding the sharp edges of the rocks. Chemicals were released which had a corrosive effect. Weathering and erosion began to soften the harsh landscape. After a rain the water would collect into rivulets and run down the barren slopes, carrying a few grains of sand. These joined to form streams and thence torrents that raced down the steep side of this raw new continent to the dark basaltic plains a mile or so below. At first the waters collected into disconnected puddles and lakes but as more water arrived at the surface and the sand filled in the lowest spots, these became a single sea—salty with chemicals. An ocean. By now the evaporation-rainfall-stream cycle was firmly established and it worked like a great conveyor belt to erode and transport fragments of the highest rocks to the lowest basins. Systematic sedimentation was under way.

New volcanoes erupted and built cones that towered miles above this vast shallow sea; as they grew each new eruption brought forth more water and new gases. The lavas spread out to form, or at least thicken, the crust. The oceans deepened and the atmosphere became more dense; the geological machine began to turn more rapidly. The year was three billion B.C. plus or minus a billion years.

The gases of this primitive atmosphere were constantly bombarded by cosmic rays and crossed by lightning flashes. New compounds, pre-life compounds, assembled and disintegrated again and uncounted opportunities for life to begin were lost. Perhaps the spark actually caught on and died out again thousands of times as the unknowing search for the secret of life went on. But finally a perfect set of circumstances existed and one more flash of lightning furnished some necessary ingredient to this primitive compound. Suddenly a living thing existed, exceedingly simple but with the ability to transform external energy and matter into more material like itself. This time it survived, grew, and divided in two. The two divided again and then again. The spark had become a flame and evolution could at last begin. In thinking about how this monumental trial-and-error experiment must have gone on, one inevitably speculates that probably other planets in other galaxies had better luck and started sooner. Perhaps life has run its course on some while many more are still awaiting that momentus event.

The harder we look at our origins the more it seems that our answers have become questions and our facts have faded into speculations. We see that far more remains to be learned about the Earth and its life than has yet been discovered. But at least a framework has been produced which shows, in a general way, how it all fits into cosmic space and time. We see that man exists in space as an inhabitant of one of the lesser members in the retinue of a small star, one of billions of stars in a galaxy which is itself but one of billions. Man in a recognizable form has existed for perhaps 200,000 years out of the 10 billion years of the present universe. Thus man's entire span is two centimeters long in a kilometer's worth of time, one page in a book of 50,000 pages of which written history is only the last line. Obviously man has missed many events. Now science must try to fill in some of the missing details by asking harder questions and looking for answers in places not yet examined.

The best of these untapped reservoirs of information is the rocks beneath the bottom of the sea. Thus the Mohole project.

Scientific Objectives

Let us re-examine some of the questions that were raised in earlier chapters and see how undersea drilling will contribute to their solution:

The questions deal with the ages of the earth, the crust, the ocean and life; with the structure, thickness, and composition of the various layers; with the history of how these came to take their present form. Let us look at them separately, for partial answers to each may be found in samples of rocks from beneath the ocean.

What is the age of the earth? The oldest earthly rocks yet dated are about 2.7 billion years; however, meteoritic material, presumably from deep within a similar planet, has been dated at 4.5 or more billion years. This suggests that there are much older rocks on earth than those which are found on the surface. Most likely, they are either in the deep crust or the mantle. When these first hardened as the early surface of the earth was formed, the little radioactive clocks within the mineral grains were started. Now if we can find those clocks and read them, we can get a direct and more accurate age for the earth.

What is the age of the crust? If the ages of the various suboceanic igneous layers are compared with each other and with that of the mantle rocks, the rate of crustal development can be determined. These will be compared with the samples that will eventually be taken of deep continental rocks and incorporated into a comprehensive theory.

What is the age of the ocean and of the earliest sediment? The ocean did not suddenly appear on the earth's surface in anything like its present shape or volume; rather it has been growing for at least a billion years. However, the approximate date, within 100 million years, of when the early puddles and lakes joined to form a saline sea would help formulate basic theories of crustal development. Information concerning the addition of new water will be even more valuable since it might reveal something about the rate at which volcanic rocks have been reaching the surface. The first ocean or pre-oceanic lake must have had the first sediments on its bottom—sandy fragments of the early igneous rocks. It is possible that the remnants of these sediments can be found, perhaps interlayered with lava flows which can be radioactively dated.

How old is life itself? Traces of organic carbon have been found in rocks dated at 2.7 billion years. A helpful but not definitive hint, this is an isolated example followed by over 2 billion years of blackness in which only faint glimmers of the track of life can be seen—a few worm burrows and some algal remnants. The great abundance and complexity of life at the beginning of the Cambrian unquestionably demonstrates that evolutionary forces had been in progress for hundreds of millions of years. But where is the record of that development and when did it start? The continental rocks have been subjected to a thorough and unsuccessful search; the early record, if it exists, must lie in strata beneath the sea. In some subocean hole, probably not the first one drilled, there is a reasonably good chance of finding a tiny, recognizable fragment of an organism that lived over a billion years ago. Even a single, small, isolated fossil will spotlight a point in that vast empty blackness and be a tremendously valuable scientific find. Whatever its kind or age, the fossil will reveal something about the course and rate of early evolution, which is now a complete blank.

How old are the oldest soft sediments of the sea floor? There is no simple answer, for those in some areas must be much older than others. The oldest ones found so far are of Cretaceous age and in some places these may lie directly on the harder rocks below. However, since only about one-tenth of the expected thickness of soft sediment appears to be present, changes of heroic proportions may have taken place in the oceans in the last half-billion years. It is difficult to know why continuous sedimentation on the sea floor should not have occurred throughout geologic time, but evidence of breaks in the record has already been found. These suggest corollary questions of: How continuous is the sedimentary record and where could the missing sediments have gone? If they are eroded from one place, they must have been deposited elsewhere as "reworked" sediments. One possibility is that the second layer is made of hardened sediment; if this proves to be the case, geologists will heave a sigh of relief for it will mean that much of the early record has been preserved.

There is a possibility that oil will be found in the rocks beneath the sea. In some places the ocean-bottom environment seems to be much like those of continental seas where rocks were formed that now contain oil pools. Since the manner of the origin of petroleum is uncertain, no one can be sure that it has not formed beneath the ocean.

If the really ancient sediments are missing in a series of holes, either of two theories may be used to help explain why. One states that accumulating sediments, acting as insulation, cuts off heat flow from the interior to such an extent that the temperature of the deep rocks rises and the underside of the sediment is metamorphosed, perhaps melted, into a granitelike rock. The other theory is that the continental rafts, sliding sidewise over the mantle, push the sediments before them, perhaps incorporating these into coastal mountain ranges, and leave a trail of denuded oceanic crust behind. If this happened then it may be possible to track the motions of the continents by dating the oldest of the oceanic sediments. The search will be on for a nonscoured area where no continent has ever passed, for there alone will be a chance of finding a complete record. Obviously a considerable number of holes completely through the sediments will be needed to develop or disprove these theories.

What is the true structure of the oceanic crust? That is, what is the number and composition of the layers? This book has hewed closely to the present generally accepted hypothesis that there are three major layers: the soft sediments, the second layer, and the deep crust. However, these have been mapped only by the methods of explosion seismology, which depends to a large extent on preconceived ideas about the number of existing layers. If man has learned anything about geology, it is that everything is more complicated than it at first appears. Thus, it seems most unlikely that a large proportion of the oceanic floor should be composed of only three layers which are everywhere about the same in thickness and composition. Today, there is not enough information available to permit us to draw a better picture; however, no one should be surprised if it is discovered that there are ten layers of rock in some places and only one in others. Probably more complexities are covered by the superficial layers of soft sediments that we conceive today, but without the evidence obtained by direct exploration with a drill, no one can say what these are.

If we return to the assumption that there are three layers, even these pose a set of questions. What are they really made of? We have seen that there are four theories about the composition of the second layer and several more about the relationship between the deep crust, the Mohorovičić discontinuity, and the mantle. The deep crust is an igneous rock, perhaps nearly as old as the earth itself. But what is it made of and what is its relationship with the mantle? Is the Moho merely a contact where two quite different rocks touch each other? Is it a zone of gradual change perhaps representing some segregation made as the earth formed? Is it a change in phase caused by the increase of temperature and pressure with depth? Is the Moho the primordial surface of the earth? At these depths the questions come thick and fast.

It is embarrassing for a geologist not to know what kind of rock constitutes the major part of his own planet. Is the mantle composed of peridotite or dunite or eclogite or something else? If samples of rocks from the deep crust and the mantle can only be brought into the laboratory and examined, then future experiments dealing with the changes of crystalline structure and materials under great heats and pressures can be conducted on actual materials instead of on theoretical combinations of minerals. Then man will understand the meaning of the Moho.

What is the precise density of the crustal components and of the outer mantle? It is necessary to know in order to be able to determine how the total rotational momentum of the earth is partitioned among the various layers of core, mantle, and crust. Since each concentric zone contributes to the total in proportion to its mass and distance from the center, a knowledge of the density of the outer layers will make possible a more accurate estimate of the densities of the inner mantle and core.

Within the deep volcanic rocks and the mantle may lie important evidence about the source of the earth's heat. How much heat-creating radioactivity does each layer contain? What are their present temperatures? How well does each conduct heat? The answers to some of these questions may generate even more perplexing questions about the earth's heat. For example, if it is discovered that deep rocks contain very little radioactivity compared to continental rocks, the curiously even distribution of heat flow between the two will require considerable additional thought.

The residual magnetic structure of all the undersea layers—particularly those of these deep rocks—will be of great interest because this information could cast a good deal of light on the question of polar wandering and continental drift. If a sequence of precisely oriented specimens can be obtained and the directions of the magnetic particles within each compared, first with each other and second with continental rocks of the same age, the questions of whether the pole shifts and how fast may be solved. If these deep rocks are consistent within themselves on the direction of the pole but inconsistent with the continental rocks, this will indicate that the continents have shifted.

Another indication of polar shifting may come from a series of north to south holes in the sediments spaced at hundred-mile intervals which would determine the change in thickness of the oozes marking the equatorial currents. As discussed earlier, a very thick and well-defined pathway of tiny shells lies below the present equator. If the equator has shifted from some previous location, the current has probably shifted with it. If this has happened, the position of the ancient equator can probably be relocated by finding its track of shells. If such a thick line of shells can be found and matched with magnetic evidence about the position of the equator, the two will be reinforcing.

Drilling a series of holes in the Mohole project can be expected to enlighten us a little on all of these problems and questions. However, it may turn out that there are answers to questions no one has yet asked. Thus one further objective is the search for the unknown. Surely something will be found that we do not expect. The only possible preparation is to remain open-minded and ready to revise present theories if need be.

Site Selection

Given the foregoing scientific objectives, the question arises of where is the best place to drill. Selecting a site is no simple matter; many factors must be taken into account.

First, there are two general kinds of scientific interests to be satisfied: the geologists are most interested in the history of the oceans, the sediments, and life; the geophysicists are more concerned with the magnetic, gravity, and seismic properties of the rock and the thicknesses of the deep layers. The chances are small that a single site will satisfy all the requirements imposed by both groups. The geologists want "sediment holes"—that is, a series of holes that penetrate and obtain continuous samples of the sedimentary rocks. The geophysicists are eager to push on to the deep igneous rocks and the mantle—to drill a Mohole.

Next there is the question of whether the Atlantic or the Pacific should receive the first attention. And there are advantages to each.

Then the hard question of what can reasonably be attempted with drilling equipment must be weighed against probable scientific returns. For example, the ultimate depth the drill would have to reach at a geologically ideal site might be beyond drilling capabilities.

Finally, some test operations must be conducted in order to develop drilling techniques, train crews, and check the theoretical engineering studies. These will be carried on at a convenient and inexpensive site where geologically useful information is within the reach of the experimental equipment.

Taking into consideration all these factors will lead to the selection of a number of sites, each one being the optimum—the best compromise between what one would like and what is possible—for each of several situations. It is hoped that eventually all the requirements will be satisfied.

As a result, there is no such thing as "a" site. Several sites will be needed, each suitable to the step that is being taken. Many are being considered. Someday a precise spot for the first attempt to drill to the Moho will be picked. There are several promising possibilities but no decision has yet been made. That problem remains for the future.

Certain matters to be considered when choosing a site are common to each of the major objectives and to any ocean. These are the weather, the ocean currents, and the distance from an operating base.

Ocean areas experiencing freezing weather, continual rough seas, and high winds are excluded from consideration. This means that sites in near-tropic latitudes, closer to the equator than 30°, are greatly preferred as long as they are clear of the principal hurricane belts.

Areas with high-velocity currents either on the surface or at depth are to be avoided because they create additional problems in holding the ship and drill pipe in position. For this purpose high-velocity surface currents (down to 1000 feet) might be defined as those regularly over half a knot; at depth, meaning the rest of the way to the bottom, currents over a quarter of a knot would be troublesome. The surface currents are relatively well known, having been long observed by both mariners and hydrographers, who are concerned with how these currents influence the navigation of ships. Outside of the belts of broad currents which make up the principal oceanic circulation, the surface currents may be quite variable, changing direction and velocity with the wind, the tides, and the season. Even less is known about the deep currents. In the entire Pacific less than fifty measurements of them have ever been made, not a fraction of the number required to establish continuity or major patterns. These deep-current measurements have produced one important fact: the highest velocity yet found in the Pacific is about 7 cm/sec or 0.15 knots. The average is about half that. In some areas currents appear to completely reverse direction within a matter of weeks and, at various levels, sometimes move in different directions—a situation called current shear. Low velocity and current shear are both helpful since they mean that the forces on the drill pipe are small and tend to counteract each other.

Measurements of the deep Atlantic currents by Dr. John Swallow of Woods Hole Oceanographic Institute suggest that they are stronger than those in the Pacific although there is too little data in either ocean to permit any sweeping conclusions. Swallow has found that just south of Bermuda at depths of 2000 to 4000 meters the deep-current velocities ranged up to 14 cm/sec with marked variations in forty miles of distance and two weeks of time.

As sites are tentatively selected, deep-current surveys will have to be made to determine just how strong and how variable currents are at that site in the intended drilling season.

The other principal environmental data on winds, waves, swell, and surface currents needed for site-selection purposes is much more readily available from sources such as the U. S. Hydrographic Office. However, these must be treated in a statistical manner. The result is a set of figures which tell how often any combination of wind and wave conditions will occur. Based on such a set of figures, a ship must be designed to withstand all but the very worst conditions; on these a calculated risk must be taken. For example, there is always a chance of having winds over sixty miles an hour or waves over twenty feet high at any site even though such winds and waves may never have been actually observed there and do not show in the statistics. The chance that these violent conditions will arise is very small, but provision must be made so that if they do, the drilling ship will survive. This ship must remain continuously prepared for such a contingency by having the ability to abandon the hole and return to it later, and by receiving six-hour forecasts of winds and waves in order to prepare for heavy weather and to put itself in the most favorable position.

Distance from a good operating base, preferably with an airport nearby, is also an important factor. Heavy supplies will have to be brought to the site for transfer to the drilling ship; drilling and scientific crews will be periodically exchanged; and dockside repair work may need to be done. A site more than about five hundred miles from a suitable port is relatively impractical for holes which require extended drilling. This does not automatically rule out mid-ocean sites, but logistics difficulties and the consequent additional expense would help to tip the balance in favor of sites nearer to a port.

Having looked at the operational and environmental criteria for a site, we can now consider the geological reasons for selecting places to drill "sediment" holes. The principal objective of such holes will be to obtain a continuous sequence of cores all the way through the sedimentary materials of the sea floor, meaning not only the soft sediments but whatever other harder stratified sediments may be beneath them. Since the nature of the second layer is unknown and will remain so until after one or more holes actually penetrate it, it must be assumed to be at least partly sedimentary. Therefore, we must be prepared to drill the first sediment holes well into the second layer. In fact we must be prepared to find that the entire concept of three major layers is wrong and that there are five or ten layers of which several are sedimentary.

The first criterion for a sediment hole is that the sediments must be predominantly pelagic—true deep-sea deposits—and that they must be representative of some substantial part of the ocean bottom. Unusual geological conditions will be avoided as far as possible; otherwise, the cores will represent only a very specialized situation. In order to get reasonably pure pelagic sediments the site will have to be several hundred miles from shore, preferably on a gentle rise, so that there is relatively little likelihood that turbidity currents flowing along the bottom from the continental margin have contributed much land sediment or disturbed the original material.

The question of whether it is advantageous to have a thick section of soft sediment if a thin section spans the same amount of time in unbroken sequence has not been decided. The geologists and paleontologists want the most complete record that can be obtained but they feel there is no particular advantage in having it spread vertically through a full kilometer of sediment if similar information is contained in strata only 100 meters thick. On the other hand, a larger amount of material increases the chance of finding valuable fossils and of being able to distinguish sublayers. In most areas, a long (10-meter) oceanographic core can probably be used in advance of drilling to determine the nature and approximate rate of sedimentation at any site. Beyond the actual penetration of that core barrel, there can only be guesses as to whether the record is complete and how far back in time it goes.

As discussed earlier, a series of sediment holes properly located might be used to develop new knowledge bearing on deposition by currents that once flowed under the equator and the wiping away of large areas of sediment by shifting continents. However, an array of holes drilled to test any particular theory will require much specifically directed thinking, planning, and surveying in advance.

The site for the Mohole itself will depend largely on the answer to the question: Where does the mantle come closest to the surface of the sea? For the reach to the Moho—the ultimate hole—is limited by drilling capabilities. Just getting to the shallowest point of the mantle will extend these to their utmost. Table X-1, which gives the depths to the various layers at five promising sites, shows the expected depth is at least 28,200 feet (plus or minus about 300 feet).

Once they are located, places where the mantle is reasonably close to the surface must be examined to determine which is the most favorable as far as the weather, the currents, and the logistic situation are concerned.

There are also important geophysical matters to be considered in Mohole site selection. Among these is the need to drill in an area geologically significant or at least representative of a substantial part of the earth's crust, so that the samples obtained will be of maximum value. Such an area is determined in a negative way. The usual geophysical measurements of seismic velocity, gravity, magnetism, and heat flow will be made in prospective areas and if any anomalous conditions are found, that area is eliminated. Obviously it would be unwise to drill in unusual topography, or in an area adjacent to a fault or sea mount, or in an area with special magnetic conditions or high heat flow. Samples from a hole in an anomalous area would prove little—at least not until the "normal" condition had been thoroughly explored.

The heat flow is one of the most important of these measurements from the point of view of drilling operations. As noted before, the

TABLE X-1

Reach of Drill String Required to Achieve Various Objectives

| | PACIFIC | | | | | | | | ATLANTIC | | | |
| | Guadalupe Island Area 28°—45'N 117°—31'W | | Clipperton* Island Area 10°—53'N 105°—09'W | | Capricorn Station C-25 5°—47'N 123°—59'W | | North of Puerto Rico 20°—40'N 66°—30'W | | Bermuda Rise 30°—0'N 65°—0'W | |
	Km.	Feet	Km.	Feet	Km.	Feet	Km.	Feet	Km.	Feet
Depth of Water	3.5	11,500	3.1	10,200	4.3	14,000	5.5	18,000	4.9	16,100
Depth to bottom of sediment	3.7	12,100	3.3	10,800	4.8	15,700	6.0	19,600	5.3	17,400
Depth to bottom of second layer	4.8	15,700	4.2	13,800	5.5	18,000	8.0	26,200	7.3	24,000
Depth to Moho	9.4	30,800	8.6	28,200	9.7	31,800	9.6	31,500	uncertain	

* Site of high heat flow

Pacific data from R. W. Raitt and others, Scripps Institution of Oceanography

Atlantic data from Maurice Ewing and others, Lamont Geological Observatory

average heat flow through the ocean floor is such that Moho temperatures of only 150° C to 200° C are expected, which is less than those often encountered in holes drilled for oil. However, beneath points on the ocean floor where high heat flow has been measured, the mantle temperature may be as much as 500° C to 800° C—enough to cause insuperable drilling problems. Therefore, ocean-bottom hot spots must be avoided. This probably will eliminate the Clipperton Island site, where the Moho comes closest to the surface.

So it is evident that these two objectives may cause the suboceanic drilling projects to follow increasingly divergent paths. One is to investigate thoroughly the history of the oceans and of life as revealed in the upper layers of sediment; the other is to go much deeper, probing the ancient igneous rocks, the Mohorovičić discontinuity, and the earth's mantle. The first of these will eventually require many shallow holes at widespread sites; the second perhaps only one in each major area. The Moho project, as presently conceived, will move toward these objectives. It will start by testing methods of deep-sea drilling, proceed to the drilling of the first sediment holes, and wind up reaching for the Moho and the mantle.

Site Surveys

Three general kinds of surveys are needed before a site can be selected. These might be called library surveys, reconnaissance surveys, and specific surveys. The first of these is made by accumulating and restudying all existing oceanic knowledge in the light of the objectives of the hole and the capabilities of the drilling equipment. Large "provinces"—areas of geologically or topographically similar ocean bottom—can be sorted through rapidly. Continental shelves, volcanic ridges, ocean deeps, and areas of known high heat flow are rejected at once. The areas having weather that is too cold and too stormy, currents that are too strong, and excessive seismic activity are eliminated next. Excessive distance from bases in the continental United States narrows the field even more. For example, off Norway and off Fiji there are places where the crust is believed to be thin, but weather and distance from the United States make it seem unwise to seriously consider either site for a first attempt.

Geologists at scientific laboratories on both United States coasts have for some time been actively accumulating data on Atlantic and Pacific undersea geology and plotting it on master charts. The more that is learned about the ocean, the more complicated these charts become—in other words, the complexities are proportional to the amount of surveying that has been done. The more carefully the ocean floor is investigated, the more difficult it becomes to find a geologically significant open space between the sea mounts and faults and trenches. The ocean floor is about as complicated as the continental surface and three times as large. Imagine trying to decide on a place on land where one significant exploratory hole should be drilled.

The second kind of survey is a reconnaissance of an area of ocean to see what sort of structure exists beneath the sea floor. Once the available data is plotted so that the broad geological features and relationships begin to be apparent, additional reconnaissance surveys are needed to develop trends or areas which appear to be of special interest.

The 1953 Capricorn Expedition of the Scripps Institution of Oceanography made such a reconnaissance of a virtually unexplored area of ocean. The ships would run at night, arriving at a new station early in the morning, at which time seismic refraction surveys would begin. While the seismic work was going on, the piston corer would be lowered from the listening ship to take a bottom sample; when the corer came back, a temperature probe would go down. By evening the measurements would be complete, the gear would be hauled in, and the ships would begin the run to the next station, taking continuous echo soundings and towing a magnetometer behind as they went.

This routine was followed for weeks and when the ships returned to San Diego a series of pinpricks on a great white chart of the Pacific, each indicating a station along a route 10,000 miles long, showed at once how much had been learned and how little was known. Five of the present AMSOC group sailed on that expedition, all returning with a new respect for the vastness of the Pacific basin, of which we had seen only a tiny fragment. These were Roger Revelle, expedition leader; Russell Raitt, seismologist; Arthur Maxwell, heat-flow measurement man; Walter Munk, wave and current specialist; and myself, senior scientist on one of the ships.

Many other reconnaissance surveys have since been made and the number of pinpricks in the master chart continues to grow. However, if one divides out the area of the Pacific by the number of seismic stations, each one would represent, when evenly spaced, about a million square kilometers of ocean floor. Only the barest beginning has been made; even so, it gives the oceanographer an idea about how to proceed.

Equipped with general information about the undersea structure off the Mexican and southern United States coasts that had been obtained by such reconnaissance surveys, AMSOC asked that the Scripps Institution of Oceanography make additional surveys to secure the details necessary for the selection of drilling sites. In the summer of 1959 Russell Raitt and H. W. Menard, Scripps scientists who serve on technical panels of the AMSOC Committee, sailed on cruises into the waters between Guadalupe and Clipperton Islands. They determined that there was a considerable area where the crust was thin, the sedimentary section suitable, and the heat flow moderate. This general area soon became the first choice for a place to start because it was near to the port and drilling-supply facilities of Southern California and because it has a reputation for fine weather.

The third kind of survey is a detailed study of a site about which a good deal of information is already available. If an area can be found which seems promising and where many of the site requirements are met but where uncertainties about geologic structure or heat flow or ocean currents remain, it is necessary to send an expedition to make additional measurements that will clear up these points before a final site decision can be made.

Such an expedition sailed north from San Juan, Puerto Rico, in May 1959 to resurvey an area which was already one of the best known in the Atlantic Ocean. Although the ships were engaged in work relevant to the Moho project, its primary purpose was to try multiple-ship seismic refraction surveys. Until that time most United States seismic surveying had been done by only two ships, but rumors had been heard of Russian successes with several ships listening simultaneously and Maurice Ewing was determined to duplicate these and perhaps do a bit better.

Accordingly, Ewing proposed making detailed surveys east and west of the old survey line which ran due north from San Juan. This would give a three-dimensional picture of a block of crust instead of a single profile. AMSOC encouraged this plan because the Moho was known to be reasonably close to the surface in this area and Dr.

Ewing was sponsored in this venture jointly by the National Science Foundation and the Office of Naval Research.

Vema, the Lamont Observatory's flagship, carried expedition leader Dr. Jack Nafe and it was followed by the *Hidalgo* of Texas A & M, the *Bear* of Woods Hole Oceanographic Institution, and the *Gibbs* of Hudson Laboratory. For nearly a month this little fleet crisscrossed the area north of Puerto Rico, each ship making geophysical measurements, taking cores, and doing general oceanographic work. *Vema* alone was capable of collecting Carbon-14 water samples and of making continuous gravity-meter and magnetic measurements as well as taking piston cores. The other ships had fewer geophysical instruments but each measured the things its scientists were interested in. Mainly, the ships made seismic-refraction surveys of the thickness of the various layers beneath the bottom. When four ships are used, three are spaced out along the line being surveyed as the fourth runs down it, firing shots every few minutes. The sound waves from each shot are picked up and recorded at three widely-spaced positions. As a result, certain correlations can be found in records which greatly improve on the accuracy of surveys made with only one listening ship.

Although the Puerto Rico area is under consideration as a possible Mohole site, it has certain drawbacks. For one thing, the water depth at the place where the Moho seems to be shallowest is around 18,000 feet. Whether or not great water depth is an advantage is still uncertain. The amount of rock that would have to be penetrated to reach the Moho is greatly reduced and that is to the good. About 14,000 feet of actual drilling probably would suffice at the Puerto Rico site. On the other hand, the deep currents in the area have not yet been measured; unless they turn out to be small, the site may have to be rejected. Certainly it would be difficult to hold 18,000 feet of laterally unsupported drill pipe in position against any substantial current. As more surveys are made in other areas the Puerto Rico site will be re-evaluated relative to other possibilities.

In the summer of 1960 a detailed survey was made of an area in the Pacific between Guadalupe Island and the Mexican coast with the Scripps Institution of Oceanography's ship *Orca*. Led by the author, scientists from Scripps, from the AMSOC staff, and from the Alpine Geophysical Associates intensively mapped a promising drilling site that had been discovered the year before. First we anchored a position-marking buoy in the center of the area so that a careful survey of the bottom topography 12,000 feet below the keel could be made. Currents were measured both at the surface and 6000 feet down, cores were taken, and the bottom was photographed.

Seismic reflection surveys were made using RASS (repeatable acoustic seismic surveying) equipment for the first time in deep water. These determined that a major reflecting surface—presumably the top of the second layer—lay about 500 feet beneath the sea floor.

Finally we landed on Guadalupe Island, partly to pay our respects to the local commandant and partly to see the herds of goats and sea elephants for which the island is famous. We returned to San Diego with renewed confidence. Here was a piece of ocean we understood; just the place for test operations.

The selection of a drilling site for any of the three situations—experimental work, sediment holes, Mohole—is a complicated business and AMSOC has formed a technical advisory panel on Site Selection headed by Harry Hess to get expert advice on the matter. This panel will continue to sift through the mass of evidence and to ask for additional surveys until they are assured that, considering all factors, the locations eventually selected are the best possible.

PLATE V *Harbormaster* 250-hp diesel-powered outboard motor, similar to those which will be used to power *CUSS I* during the experimental drilling. The engine is fixed but shaft and propeller can turn to exert thrust in any direction.

PLATE VI *CUSS I* during the Guadalupe Island experiments, April 1961. It successfully held position and, for the first time, drilled into the deep-sea floor.

PLATE VII a. *Navy-owned ARD's* (floating drydocks) in mothballs at Long Beach, California. This inside-out hull seems to have many of the characteristics that will be needed in a Mohole-driling ship.

PLATE VII b. *Looking aft inside the ARD*. In normal usage the gate at the far end is lowered and the dock filled with water so that ships can enter. All the machinery and living quarters are in the "wing walls." On the left horizon is the large German crane which is propelled by cycloidal propellers.

PLATE VIII. *The sea floor* at the Guadalupe Island test site is 12,000 feet deep. The bottom is a soft brown mud, the home of many small animals including tube worms (lower margin), brittle stars, a small fish, and an unidentified animal looking something like a tulip.

XI

Modern Oil-Well Drilling

Because the Moho project will draw heavily on the techniques developed by the oil industry in the past hundred years, this chapter describes how deep oil wells are drilled. Drilling holes on land to depths of 18,000 feet has now become almost routine and one hole has reached over 25,000 feet. In order to achieve these depths, complicated machines have been invented and tested, and a great deal of know-how has been accumulated.

The AMSOC Committee—which also plans to drill through about 18,000 feet of rock, but beneath the ocean—intends to make the maximum possible use of the experience of the oil drillers. Thoroughly tested equipment will be chosen in preference to untried inventions which would require much development because we believe that if the best of existing methods and materials—not necessarily those in the most general use—are assembled, the Moho can be reached.

There are many ways to drill an oil well and this is by no means a comprehensive account of how it can be done. Rather it is a simplified explanation of one set of methods generally regarded in the industry today as conventional for deep drilling.

The basic problem of the oil driller is to dig a hole to a rock formation containing oil or gas that can be profitably produced. Once he starts drilling, he's primarily interested in "making hole" and getting down to where he thinks there is oil. The faster and cheaper the hole goes down, the better he likes it—especially if he's the first to drill in a new area where risks are great. Remember that today's best scientific prospecting methods in advance of drilling only locate "structures" where oil is most likely to be found, not the oil itself. A hole drilled into a structure where no oil has actually been found is a "wildcat." "Only the bit proves the presence of oil," is the saying. The odds are one to eight against the wildcat producing oil. The seven failures are called "dusters"—dry holes.

AMSOC's project to drill in almost entirely unknown material beneath the sea bottom is a type of scientific "wildcat." Scientific prospecting gives clues about the structures beneath the sea, but only actual cores and measurements can tell what is really there.

Drilling a deep hole for oil is a fascinating process. In simplest terms, the conventional method uses a long pipe to rotate a weighted bit which chips and grinds away the material in the hole. The rock chips or cuttings are washed away from the bit and brought to the surface by a thin mud that circulates down inside the drill pipe and up around the outside. All this is accomplished by the rotary drilling rig, a large and complex machine.

The Rotary Rig

The most obvious feature of a drilling operation is a derrick standing against the skyline, the symbol of the oil business. One form of derrick is a four-legged pyramidal framework of structural steel about 140 feet high. A remarkable structure, it must be able to withstand 125-mile-an-hour gale winds and support working loads of three hundred tons or more. Inside the tower at the base is the derrick "floor," where the driller and his roughneck helpers work, and at its summit is the "crown block" which carries the weight.

The crown block is the upper half of a huge block-and-tackle arrangement; the lower half or traveling block hangs from it and moves up and down inside the derrick tower carrying the "hook" which supports the load. Everything going into or coming out of the well is raised and lowered by these blocks. This is massive equipment. In a heavy-duty outfit each block may weigh six tons and have five pulleys four feet in diameter. When cable is strung through all pulleys on the two blocks, this gives a mechanical advantage of ten to the draw works. In other words, a 300-ton hook load requires only a 30-ton pull on the cable.

The cable is wound on a spool which is part of the draw works. The draw works is the oil man's name for the big winch which winds in and pays out the cable that moves the traveling block and raises and lowers the drill pipe in the hole. The cable-storage spool and its brakes, clutches, and controls are all mounted on the derrick floor where the driller can operate it and at the same time be close enough to supervise his crew of helpers, called roughnecks.

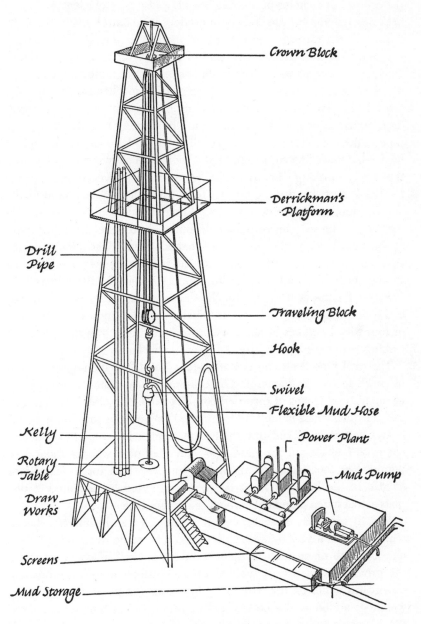

Fig. XI-1 The Rotary Drilling Rig

Directly in front of the driller's control levers are a series of dials which indicate how much weight is being supported on the hook. Since the driller has a choice of hoisting speeds and a very efficient hydraulic braking system, he has remarkably delicate control over his huge tools and can raise or lower them an inch at a time.

The drill pipe is turned by means of a rotary table, a massive round steel plate with a square hole in its center that occupies the center of the derrick floor. Beneath the floor is a drive mechanism for rotating the table at speeds up to 200 revolutions per minute. This rotating table transmits motion to the drill pipe by turning a square length of pipe called the "kelly" which can slide up and down in the square hole. Anyone asking to "see the hole" would be shown the hole where the "kelly bushing" fits into the rotary table. Everything, including the largest size drilling bit, has to fit through it. Rotary tables have another job, not quite so obvious. When the drill pipe is being assembled ("run in") or withdrawn ("pulled"), the weight of the pipe in the hole is supported on wedge-shaped "slips." The pipe's weight tightens the slips against the sides of the hole in the rotary table. This means the table must be able to support several hundred tons.

Power for the drilling—to run the draw works, rotary table, pumps, and a dozen smaller machines—is usually supplied by a bank of three or four diesel engines of 500 horsepower each. It is transmitted to the drilling machines by a system of gears and chains.

The drill pipe itself consists of 30-foot "joints" of high-quality steel, often 4½ inches in diameter. The bottom of one connects to the top of the next by means of threaded couplings or "tool joints" so that they can be quickly assembled and detached. When the drill pipe is not in the hole it is racked upright in the derrick in "three-joint stands" about 90 feet long. Four-and-a-half-inch steel pipe weighs about 16.6 pounds per foot in air or about one hundred tons for a 12,000-foot length. In the hole, where it is partly supported by the mud it displaces, that much pipe might weigh thirty tons less.

A drill pipe has such remarkable flexibility and slimness that a scale model of a 12,000-foot length of it can be made by hanging a wire one-sixteenth of an inch in diameter from a twelfth-floor window to the ground. Obviously it would not be sensible to drill by pushing downward either on the wire or a pipe of similar proportions. Instead weight is added at the bottom to hold the pipe in tension and push the bit against the bottom of the hole. This weight consists of drill collars, extra thick-walled pipe joints assembled into sections several hundred feet long, weighing two to forty tons. By placing this extra mass at the bottom, the hole is kept straight and the rotational motion is evened out. Moreover, the resultant wavelike motions which run up and down the drill pipe causing "whip"—a tendency to slap against the sides of the hole—are greatly reduced. Besides, the collars strengthen the drill string at a critical place where there is the greatest likelihood of its twisting in two.

The top of the drill pipe is coupled to the square kelly which slides up and down in the rotary table and continuously imparts rotary motion to the pipe below as the bit goes deeper and deeper.

When assembled, these pieces comprise the drill string and screwed to the bottom of the lowest collar is its business end—the bit. It is the bit that actually makes the hole by chipping, cutting, and wearing

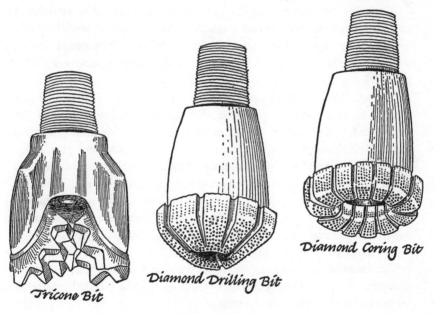

Diamond Coring Bit

Diamond Drilling Bit

Tricone Bit

Fig. XI-2 Drill Bits

away the rock as it is rotated. Most ordinary drilling is done with some version of the tricone or roller bit. These bits resemble cone-shaped gears with sharp teeth and when they are rolled around under the weight of the drill collars, they act like an endless train of small chisels striking in quick succession.

The entire weight of the drill pipe and collars is not permitted to rest on the bit; if it were, the pipe would wear itself out against the sides of the hole and the hole would tend to go crooked. Therefore, the weight on the bit is constantly and carefully controlled by the driller who watches the weight indicator.

The connection between the traveling block, which does not rotate, and the kelly, which does, is made by a remarkable piece of hardware called the swivel. The upper part of the swivel is attached to the hook and remains stationary while its bottom part turns with the kelly. This means that its bearings must be able to support a hundred tons or more of pipe while rotating rapidly. Since the drilling mud enters the drill pipe via a flexible hose leading to the nonrotating part of the swivel, the bearings must be tight against high-pressure leaks. Otherwise the drilling platform beneath the swivel will be under a continuous shower of mud.

When first learning about drilling, newcomers are often astonished to find that the success of the operation may depend on muddy water (respectfully called "the mud") being mixed and pumped into the well. Since the same mud is used over and over again, we might benefit from following it on one round trip.

The working supply of mud is stored in tanks where pumps pick it up and force it, at high pressure, through the flexible hose into the top of the swivel. Down it goes inside the kelly, the drill pipe, and the collars at a rate of up to 1000 gallons per minute and at a speed of a couple of hundred feet a minute. When it reaches the bit, nozzles squirt the mud at high velocity against the cutting teeth and the bottom of the hole. Then, loaded with cuttings and rock fragments, it rises around the outside of the drill pipe to the surface. Discharged across a vibrating screen to remove the rock chips, the clean mud is returned to the original tank for re-use.

This circulating mud serves several important purposes. First, it prevents the pipe from becoming stuck in a mass of rock chips by flushing the rock chips and cuttings to the surface. Second, it cleans and cools and lubricates the bit. Third, the mud seals off the walls of the hole and helps prevent caving.

Drilling mud is usually fresh water to which materials such as bentonite, a clay which swells when it gets wet and seals up pores in the rock, and barite, a heavy mineral which raises the density, have been added. The spinning pipe plasters a layer of mud against the sides of the hole. The high density of the column of mud causes it to exert considerable pressure against the walls of the hole and this, along with

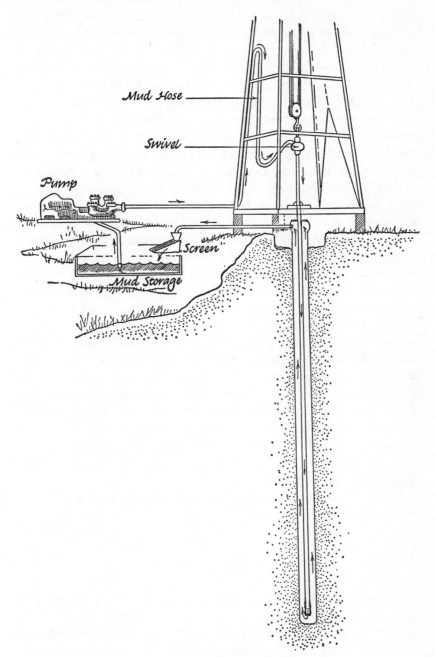

Fig. XI-3 Mud Circulation

the rubbing of the turning pipe, forms a mortarlike mud cake which helps keep the hole from caving. Moreover, the weight of the mud column tends to prevent high-pressure gas or oil from "blowing out" unexpectedly.

Muds are rated by their density, usually stated in pounds per gallon. A good mud has the consistency of chocolate pudding and can hold the rock chips in suspension when drilling temporarily stops.

Another important function of the mud, keeping the broken fragments out of the way of the bit, allows the energy to go into deepening the hole instead of grinding up chips that have previously been broken loose. For maximum efficiency each rock chip broken loose should be removed before the next tooth of a rotary bit reaches it. This obviously requires a high-pressure, fast-moving mud stream.

Experiments have shown that bits cut faster if plain water is used, so, whenever the hole walls will stand without high-density mud, drillers gladly dispense with the expensive heavy additives. Holes over 18,000 feet deep have been successfully drilled using only sea water as the drilling fluid, and in areas where there is not much underground water, excellent results have been obtained with compressed air as the drilling "fluid."

The crew on an oil rig usually consists of a "tool pusher," as the foreman is called, a driller who has a number of helpers called roughnecks, and some maintenance mechanics. The driller stands at the controls of the draw works, directing the work on the drilling floor. Close by are two or three floormen who, when a drill string is being assembled, guide the pipe into place, twist it on, and tighten the joints securely with tongs. High in the derrick on a platform opposite the top end of the drill pipe stand is the derrick man who latches pipe in and out of the elevators.

Having considered the major pieces of machinery, let us see how the drilling is done.

Drilling a Hole

On land the hole begins with a stake marking the hole's location. Somebody is gambling a lot of money that beneath it there is oil. At that spot the hole is "spudded in"—often with a special small drilling rig—and a "conductor" pipe, about two feet in diameter and perhaps one hundred feet long, is set. The purpose of the pipe is to conduct the drilling fluids through the unconsolidated surface material so that they will not cause it to cave in and to conduct the bit from the derrick floor to the hard rock where it can go to work. Remember the conductor pipe. Installing its counterpart for a deep ocean hole will be a difficult operation.

After the conductor is in place and the rig's foundation is built, the derrick is quickly erected, the machinery installed, and the mud tanks filled. Then drilling begins.

Hanging from the swivel is the square kelly, the first joint of pipe, the drill collar, and a bit, attached in that order. The rotary table starts to turn; around goes the kelly and the drill string. The driller releases the brake on the draw works, lowering the bit slowly until it touches the rock and bites in. He keeps just enough weight on the bit so it drills most efficiently. If too little pressure is put on the bit, the chips are small and progress slow. If too much weight rides the bit, it will embed itself in the rock and the chips cannot be thrown free, or else the hole may go crooked.

The pumps have been started and soon the drilling mud, forced down inside the drill pipe, wells up around it. At the wellhead, the mud flows into the return pipe, over the screens, and back to the mud-storage tanks. Circulation has been established.

The driller is making hole. Before long the drill has deepened the hole until the top of the kelly is almost down to the rotary table, making it necessary to add another length of pipe. So the kelly is withdrawn until the top of the drill pipe can be held with slips at the rotary table. Then the kelly is unscrewed; a joint of pipe is picked up from the pipe racks, centered over the hole, and lowered until it can be screwed onto the top of the pipe below. The slips are removed and the elevator lowers the top of the new joint, now supporting all the pipe below it, to the rotary table, where it is again held by the slips. The elevator releases the pipe, the kelly is attached to the top of the drill string, and drilling resumes.

After a number of joints have been added and the hole is down a few hundred feet, the bit will be dull. Then all the pipe will have to be pulled out of the hole, disconnected in three-joint stands, and racked in the derrick. At every stand the slips must be set, the pipe unscrewed and swung out of the way, and the elevator lowered to pick up the pipe. Finally the worn-out bit is retrieved. Then with a new bit, the drill string goes back into the hole, one stand at a time, reversing the process. The entire cycle is called "round-tripping."

A round trip with 4½-inch pipe in three-joint stands from 5000 feet may take three hours; from 20,000 feet ten hours. It's a long and tedious operation in which a mistake by any member of the crew can result in loss of life as well as the pipe string.

How fast does a drill make a hole? There are said to be limestones so tough that progress of ten feet a day is considered good. However, the record is 3459 feet in eight hours, drilled in Venezuela in soft shales. A 10,000-foot well was drilled in the same area in six days, including time for setting casing, logging, and coring; and the Kerr McGee Oil Company drilled 10,000 feet from a Louisiana offshore platform in four days twenty-two hours. The average time for a complete 10,000-foot hole in the soft sediments of Mississippi is about twenty-five days; in the considerably harder California coast rocks, ninety days.

Casing

Casing is heavy steel pipe that is used to line the hole. It serves several purposes. First, it prevents cave-in of the walls where the hole passes through soft and poorly consolidated sediments such as clays or shales. Second, it prevents the loss of drilling fluid which might seep away through porous or fractured rock. Third, the casing can prevent unwanted water or oil from entering the hole until the operator is ready for production. Normally, every hole drilled for oil or gas has at least one string of casing and since the casing is the largest single expense—often one-third the entire cost of the well—it receives close attention.

The size of the hole drilled depends on the size of casing that the operator expects to use. Usually the hole is sufficiently larger than the outside diameter of the casing to permit it to slide easily down the hole. Since the inside of the casing determines the size of the drill bit that can be used, installation of casing is delayed as long as possible. There is a limit to how small a bit can be used and the driller doesn't want to reach that limit sooner than necessary by setting casing too often. However, it's not unusual to have four strings of casing in a well, all supported by the casing-head-assembly at the surface.

This means that the hole in the rock gets smaller in steps as it goes down. But since each casing string runs all the way to the surface, small ones being telescoped inside large ones, the hole inside the casing is the same size from top to bottom.

It is customary to attach a "blowout preventer" to the casing at the wellhead. Then, if the drill should suddenly encounter a zone of high-pressure oil and gas, a pair of sliding gates inside the blowout preventer can be quickly closed around the drill pipe, sealing off the space between it and the casing. These effectively prevent "gushers," as blowouts were formerly called.

Joints of casing pipe, usually 30 or 40 feet long, are assembled with threaded couplings much like the drill pipe. Each joint is picked up by the casing elevators and screwed into the joint already supported by the slips; the string is then lowered until the upper end of the new joint is just above the derrick floor and another piece is added. On the bottom of the casing string is a special shoe which helps it cut through minor obstructions that may be encountered as it is lowered.

If a long string of casing were lowered without the proper precautions, its own weight might pull it in two. To prevent this, casing is "floated" into place—this means that the driller makes it float in the well just like a steel ship does in the ocean. He makes a bottom for his "ship" by putting a concrete plug—a float shoe—at the lower of the casing. Now when he lowers the casing, it is buoyed up by the fluids in the well; thus, the strain on the pipe and on the derrick is greatly reduced. The weight of the casing string can now be adjusted by filling the inside with water or mud. When the casing is a few feet off the bottom, the driller stops lowering and prepares for cementing.

In order to hold the casing firmly in place, the space between it and the rocky walls of the hole need to be filled with thin, fast-setting cement. Cementing experts are called in and they calculate just how much cement will be required to fill the annulus between the casing and the hole walls. Then they prepare the cement and put it in the hole, followed by a barrier plug that just barely slides inside the casing. Water is pumped in behind the plug under high pressure. This forces the plug downward, driving the cement ahead of it. When the cement reaches the bottom, it is squeezed around the end of the casing shoe and back up the outside, filling the space between the rock and casing. The expert carefully watches the pump pressure. When it jumps suddenly, he knows the plug has reached the bottom of the casing and all the cement is in place. He signals the driller to finish lowering the casing to the bottom of the hole and, maintaining the pressure to hold the cement in place, they wait for it to set.

With the casing solidly in place, drilling resumes, beginning, of course, with drilling out the plugs and the excess cement in the bottom of the hole.

Coring

It is necessary for the drillers and geologists to keep track of the rock formations being drilled because they started the hole expecting to find oil in a particular kind or age of rock. There are several ways of doing this. One is for the geologist who "sits on the rig" to routinely examine the rock chips that come up in the drilling mud. By inspecting these carefully for foraminifera or other small fossils whose geologic age is known, he can usually tell where in the stratigraphic section the bit is working. If the geologist is uncertain which formation the drill is in, or if the hole is approaching the depth at which they hope to find oil, it is customary to take a core—a cylindrical sample of a rock.

When coring is done, a special open-centered bit and a core barrel are attached to the lower end of the drill string. Inside the core barrel is a second piece of tubing—an inner core barrel—and the drilling mud circulates between the two. As the bit wears away a ring of rock, a column of rock a few inches in diameter and maybe ten or twenty feet long enters the inner core barrel. At the bottom of this barrel is a device to break the rock off and just above that is a "core-catcher" with springy metal fingers to prevent the core material from falling back into the hole when the bit and core barrel are lifted off the bottom.

Like virtually everything else in the drilling process, the method used in coring and the degree of success depends on the rock. In soft formations, core recovery ordinarily averages 70 per cent—that is, for every ten feet of hole drilled seven feet of core are extracted. The other 30 per cent is washed away by the drilling fluid. However, new and improved tools, such as the Christensen rubber-sleeve core barrel, have made it possible to get nearly 100 per cent recovery even in unconsolidated sediments. In hard rocks 95 per cent core recoveries are not unusual with conventional methods. There are wide variations in core recovery but if the driller's technique is good and if he is lucky, it is possible to get an almost continuous sample.

When the drill has advanced far enough to fill the core barrel, the pipe is pulled and the inner core barrel is removed and turned over to the geologist. The most satisfactory cores are made with a diamond bit whose doughnut-shaped end is studded with small diamonds and grooved with spiral slots through which the mud can flow. Although the cost is great (up to $6000 for a bit), it's usually worth it. The faster cutting saves time and cores 60 feet long have been taken on one round trip. It would be nice to have continuous cores. Unfortunately, this is expensive, because in order to attach the special bit and core barrel—and to retrieve the core after it is taken—it is necessary to "round-trip" the pipe. Taking apart and reassembling all that drill pipe twice for 30 feet of hole entails a lot of extra work, so there is understandable reluctance to take a core unless it's really necessary. If the geologist insists, the driller will take cores on every second bit change, since he has to make one of the round trips anyway, but rarely is the drilling crew enthusiastic for coring when they are trying to "make footage."

However, if an extended sequence of cores is to be taken and a coring bit is already in place, cores can be taken without pulling all the pipe, by means of what is called "wire-line coring." Wire line is the oilman's name for cable or wire rope.

In wire-line coring, the inner core barrel is inserted in the drill pipe at the surface and pumped down with the circulating mud until it seats itself just behind the coring bit, where it is held by the pressure of the flowing mud. Drilling resumes until enough hole has been made to fill the barrel; then a latching clip is lowered on a wire-line which captures the core barrel, permitting it to be retrieved. By repeating this process, it is possible to take continuous cores as long as the coring bit will cut them, without round-tripping the drill pipe. In some experimental holes drilled in Nebraska in 1952 a light portable rig with a diamond bit used this method to make a 4½-inch hole to 4800 feet and recover continuous cores 1¾ inches in diameter. An operator in Utah cored for 2418 feet with 95 per cent recovery. The round-trip time for drill pipe from 7000 feet was five hours but the wire-line trip time from the same depth averaged seventeen minutes.

After the hole is drilled, but before the casing is set, samples can be taken from the walls of the hole at any desired depth by using a side-wall sampler. This tool, consisting of a dozen small "guns," is lowered on a firing cable to the level desired. The guns, simply short pieces of tubing held horizontally in the hole, have hard, sharp cutting edges and are backed by explosive chambers. When the charge is fired electrically from the surface, one tube is hurled into the wall by the

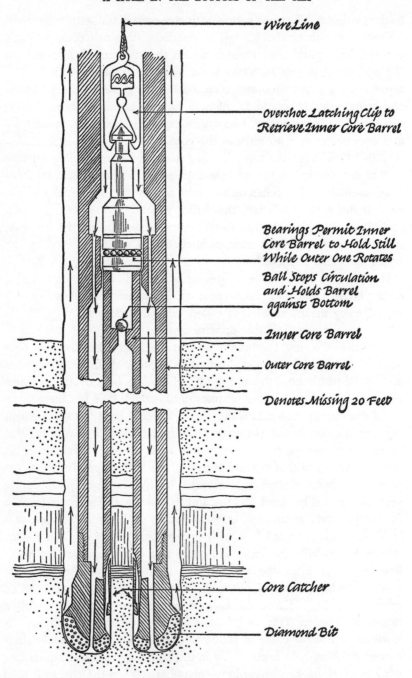

Wire Line

Overshot Latching Clip to
Retrieve Inner Core Barrel

Bearings Permit Inner
Core Barrel to Hold Still
While Outer One Rotates

Ball Stops Circulation
and Holds Barrel
against Bottom

Inner Core Barrel

Outer Core Barrel

Denotes Missing 20 Feet

Core Catcher

Diamond Bit

Fig. XI-4 The Standard Wire-Line Core Barrel with Diamond Bit

explosive. Each core tube is attached to the main part of the tool by a short wire and when the tool is retrieved, the cores dangle from it. A series of cores ¾-inch in diameter and 2 inches long can be quickly obtained from the walls of the hole.

Fishing

Fishing, for an oil driller, is no sport. He must fish when tools or pipe or casing are accidentally, but not necessarily carelessly, dropped into the hole. Getting them out requires patience, ingenuity, and money. At best, progress is halted until the articles are recovered; at worst, the hole is abandoned.

If it's "junk," the driller's word for small broken parts of bits or tools, electromagnetic fishing devices may be able to recover them. But very likely the problem will be more difficult. One of the major oil companies is rumored to have a battered pipe wrench mounted on the wall in its main office. It looks like any other old pipe wrench except that it is gold-plated. Underneath is a price tag: $28,000, the cost of bringing it up from the bottom of a well.

Occasionally a string of drill pipe will be twisted in two or the threads will pull apart at a joint. The pipe was under strain when it parted. Now that the circulation has stopped below the break, the heavy ingredients in the drilling mud have settled to the bottom and mired the broken piece in place. Getting it out sounds like an impossible job. Well, it is—almost.

The driller may decide to make his first try with a tool called a spear. He wants to spear the pipe—that is, he hopes to jam the tool down inside the open upper end of the lost pipe. He lowers the spear on the drill pipe and, if he's very lucky, he spears the pipe on the first try. As the tool penetrates the upper end of the broken pipe, loosely fitting "slips" slide down inside the pipe. When the driller tries to retract the spear, its wedge-shaped centerpiece forces the slips outward so they grip the lost pipe. The harder he pulls, the tighter they get. Once he has a firm grip, he "circulates" for a few hours by pumping mud down the pipe to loosen it before he pulls. Then slowly he takes up the strain. The whole drill pipe becomes an extension of his sense of touch. A thud and shiver goes through the rig, the gauge showing tension on the pipe drops, and a disgusted look crosses the driller's face. He dropped it.

He'll start again, perhaps using different fishing tools which, he hopes, will grip the outside of the lost pipe. Fishing is no fun.

Logging

A log is simply a record of a hole at every stage from top to bottom. The driller knows within a foot or two how deep the bit is working because he keeps track of the length of pipe in the hole and notes the drilling progress like a captain logs a ship's progress. The drilling speed is a measure of the formation's hardness; the loss of mud indicates porosity; the color of the mud and the size of the rock chips it carries are direct evidence of the kind of rock. A driller can tell other things about the formations thousands of feet below from the behavior of the drill, the pump pressure, and the condition of the bit when retrieved.

The geologist also takes notes on the hole's progress but from a different point of view. He microscopically examines the chips that come from the bottom of the hole, recording the length of time between changes in their character. Then, by comparing notes with the driller, he can establish the thickness of a limestone layer, for example; the fossils present tell him its geological age. As the hole deepens, the strata through which it passes are carefully recorded on a geological diagram. When the geologist examines a core sample of the layered rocks instead of mere fragments, he may have a lot to write in the log.

From time to time, or when the hole is complete, an instrument will be lowered which records the slope and direction of the hole at all levels. From this the position of the hole's bottom can be determined and often it is a long way from being under the derrick. Since a vertical hole is usually desirable, the driller will want to take corrective action as soon as possible. Moreover, if the hole is close to a property line, the man next door does not want this hole taking oil from his property.

Logging in the modern sense usually means a survey by one of several geophysical methods. The kind most often used measures electrical resistivity.

Electrical logging, originally developed by Conrad Schlumberger (pronounced Slumber-J), a French physicist, was brought to the United States in the 1930's by the company bearing his name. Now when somebody says, "We ran a Schlumberger," you know he made an electrical log. Today, of course, there are many companies in the logging business and many varieties of logs. In a number of fields nearly every well has been logged by this method, for once the electrical characteristics of a set of strata is known, the sedimentary strata can easily be correlated from one hole to the next by comparing records of resistivity or other changes.

The principle is a simple one based on the fact that some rocks are better conductors of electricity than others, depending on how much moisture they contain. This means the rock's resistance to the flow of electricity is a good measure of its relative porosity since water usually fills any open spaces. The idea then is to lower a pair of electrodes and create an electrical field in the rock around the hole. By measuring the field's electrical potential with another pair of electrodes, the resistivity of each layer of rock can be determined.

Hard dense rocks such as granite, basalt, or limestone have high resistivities; soft porous ones like sandstone and shale have low ones. Usually, however, it's the pattern of changing resistivity made by a sequence of layered rocks that is most useful in correlating the depths of beds between holes.

Resistivity logging cannot be used if steel casing or salt water are in the hole but similar information about porosity or changes in strata can be obtained with either of two radioactive logging methods.

The first method senses the nuclear radiation of minerals and rocks which contain minute quantities of radioactive elements such as radium, uranium, thorium, or radiopotassium. For reasons not entirely understood, these are often concentrated preferentially in certain strata. Shale usually has more radioactivity than sandstone; quartzite and limestone have least of all. Since these elements continually emit gamma rays which penetrate all substances, a sensing device such as an ionization chamber, lowered slowly down a well, will detect the differences in the rock through which it is passing and provide information for a gamma-ray well log.

A variation on this device is the neutron log. If certain materials containing hydrogen compounds such as water or oil are bombarded with fast neutrons, they become temporarily radioactive and give off gamma rays. So a neutron source is lowered down the well which temporarily induces gamma-ray activity in these materials present in nearby rock. If a device sensing and recording this induced radiation follows the capsule, the result is a profile indicating the amount of hydrogen in successive formations. Thus the neutron log is another

231

means of obtaining data on the porosity of rocks and the likelihood of their containing oil.

There are many kinds of logging sondes, as the instrument package is called, used to measure other physical properties of the rocks or the hole. Some are in general use, others have only been tried on an experimental basis. These are mentioned to show that considerable thought has gone into direct "in-hole" measuring devices and that existing techniques and instruments can be used or modified to obtain scientific information in the bottom of a hole. Among these are instruments for logging: (1) inclination—slope and direction of the hole; (2) sonic velocity—direct measurements of the compression-wave speed in the rock; (3) rock density; (4) magnetic field intensity; (5) temperature; and (6) pressure. Some of these qualities can now be measured with more than one type of instrument. Other properties of the deep rocks, such as the value of gravitational force or the direction of the magnetic field, require the development of more sophisticated sondes.

Many complications in the drilling of deep holes cannot be covered in this brief account. There are, however, a few questions about cost and depth and feasibility that should be answered before going on to the problems of drilling at sea.

What does it cost to drill an oil well? Obviously there are many factors. It depends, for example, on the nearness of the hole to a supply center, on the depth of the hole—each additional foot being more expensive than the previous—on the hardness of the rock, on the amount of casing to be set, and on other things, including luck. The accidental loss of a tool in the well may require a long fishing job, the casing may collapse, or too much water may enter the hole. Any of these things can greatly increase the cost of a hole.

In 1959, the cost for drilling on land in the United States with standard techniques averaged $12.35 per foot. Offshore drilling costs in the Gulf of Mexico during the same period approximated $42.19 per foot. In the deeper reaches of record holes, costs are considerably greater, as we shall see.

Deep, Deep Holes

How deep can a hole be drilled? That question has no final answer. New materials, techniques, and ideas will always be forthcoming. But a provisional answer can be found if we pool the best drilling talent and machinery and attempt a deep objective. When 25,000 feet was first reached in September 1958, the *Oil and Gas Journal* said, "Based on past performance it will be 7 to 11 years before 30,000 feet is

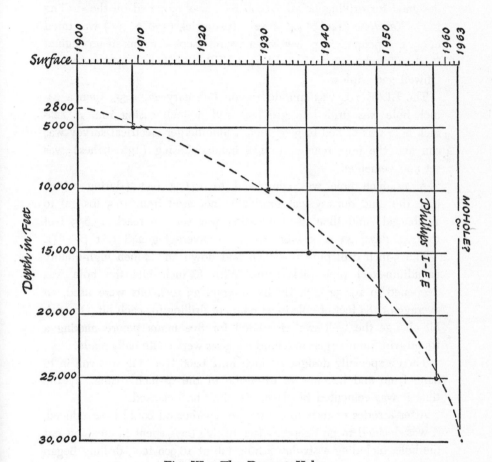

Fig. XI-5 The Deepest Holes

reached." However, since profitmaking possibilities grow dimmer with depth, the best reason to drill really deep is a scientific project such as the Mohole.

We might make a beginning on the interim answer by looking at the case histories of two deep holes. The accounts are technical but from them you can glean the flavor of big-time drilling.

THE RICHARDSON AND BASS-MECOM-FREEPORT-HUMBLE LL&E
STATE 2414—WELL NO. 1-L[*]

The hole named above was drilled to a world's record on the flank
of a salt dome thirty-five miles southwest of New Orleans. The rig,
designed for drilling below 20,000 feet, was mounted on the drilling
barge *Keystone* (140′ × 54′ × 12′). Its derrick (136′ × 30′) was rated
at 952,000 pounds; its power was a 2750-horsepower Ajax steam engine:
its draw works was a National 3410 FEB; and its main pump was an
Oilwell 320 triplex.

The LL&E 1-L was spudded in on February 27, 1955; then a 24-
inch hole was drilled to 310 feet and 20-inch casing run. A 12¼-
inch hole was drilled to 3007 feet, a Slumberger electrical survey was
run and the hole reamed to 17½ inches. Casing (13⅜ inches) was
set and cemented.

A 12¼-inch hole was completed to 13,655 feet (during which
time the mud density was gradually increased from 10.5 lbs/gal to
13 lbs/gal) and then 9⅝-inch casing was set. To reach 13,655 feet
took 48 days; 43 rock bits were used averaging 248 feet per bit.

The 5-inch drill pipe was then laid down and 4-inch high-quality
vanadium-steel pipe picked up. With 8¾-inch bits the hole was
deepened to 19,752 feet. In this interval 33 rock bits were used, an
average of 184 feet of hole in 34 hours of drilling for each bit. On each
bit change the well was circulated for five hours before making a
round-trip. Slumbergers and mud analyses were continually made.

Then a specially designed 7-inch liner 6266 feet long was run in to
hang from and become an extension of the 9⅝-inch casing. By the
time it was cemented in place, 130 days had elapsed.

After a series of tests to determine whether oil could be produced,
it was decided to go deeper. After twelve days spent in cleaning out
the hole, including a six-day fishing job at 16,900 feet, drilling began
again.

Below the 7-inch liner, 2⅞-inch drill pipe was used, reducing the
hole size to 6 inches. Bits, run 15 to 40 hours, were pulled out while
they still had appreciable life left to avoid the possibility of a failure
that might leave junk in the hole. As before, the drilling rate was
kept below 10 feet per hour. Generally, 48 hours were needed from

---

[*] The following account was abstracted from a paper presented to the American
Petroleum Institute at Dallas, Texas, in March 1957, by R. M. Zimmerman, T. H.
Terrell, and E. T. Nagle, Jr.

the time drilling began with one bit until the drilling commenced with the next. This included 28 hours drilling, 11.5 hours for a round-trip, and a total of 8.5 hours of circulation before and after making the trip. In the opinion of the operators the 2⅞-inch drill stem could be used to drill below 25,000 feet.

At 20,652 feet an electric log was run and at 20,729 feet a 24-foot core was cut showing signs of oil so encouraging that coring was continued to 20,791 feet. Drilling resumed, using 18.5-lbs/gal mud. On the 256th day, the old depth record of 21,482 feet was passed and on the 315th day the hole bottomed in shale at 22,570 feet for a world's record. The date was January 7, 1956.

A special feature of the 5-inch liner set in the lower part of the hole was that it used a radioactive compound in some of its joint connections. This was to insure that any oil zones found could be positively identified. Temperature at the bottom of the hole was 326° F (163° C).

Eventually oil was produced from Miocene shales at a depth of 20,740 feet. Although today this is the deepest known production, the operators believe that someday oil will be found below these depths. This well cost over $3¼ million and it is questionable whether the oil produced will repay the investment. However, the hole did result in increased knowledge of deep drilling. The drilling costs, especially during the deep-drilling phase, are of interest here.

To drill from 20,000 to 22,570 feet took 115 days and cost approximately $335 per foot. Daily cost averaged $7500, including $2000 a day for the rig and $3000 a day for the mud. In short, 2500 feet of deep hole in sandy shale cost about $850,000.

THE PHILLIPS PETROLEUM COMPANY'S I-EE UNIVERSITY

Records are made to be broken and in June 1958 the I-EE in Pecos County, Texas, passed the record of the LL&E 1-L. By September 23 the new champion reached 25,000 feet and almost two years from the day it spudded-in, reached maximum depth of 25,340 feet—the world's deepest hole at this writing. A National 130 draw works rated at 18,000 feet by the makers, Le Roi L-4000 gas engines for power, and a National G-700 pump were the main items of equipment.

The drill pipe was a tapered string: 10,200 feet of 3½-inch internal flush, 6000 feet of 3½-inch slim hole, 8500 feet of 4-inch flush joint, and 300 feet of 4½-inch drill collars. To round-trip it from below 25,000 feet took 12 hours and when that depth was first reached, Phillips, as a precaution, pulled the pipe to inspect it. The top 10,200 feet was specially handled in the hole by a hydraulic shock-absorber unit and dual elevators.

Near the bottom where the hole is 5¾ inches in diameter, the average bit life was 33 hours and average deepening per bit was 70 feet. The temperature was 165° C (340° F).

In some ways the drillers were fortunate. The hole walls stood up well and muds of only 11.8 lbs/gal were used at depth. In fact, two auxiliary world's records were set because of these favorable circumstances: (1) at one time there was 12,000 feet of open hole, and (2) a string of 7-inch and 7⅝-inch casing 22,919 feet long was run-in.

There were difficulties too. For example, a fishing job at 21,400 feet resulted when the drill pipe parted with the bit 3600 feet off the bottom. The drillers, after they "recovered fish" to 20,000 feet, decided to bypass the broken pipe in the bottom by using a whipstock to divert the hole around it. On the first attempt the pipe twisted off but on the next try they went on past to break the record.

Five miles is a long way down but it is by no means the limit of our technology. As a Phillips official said, "The science of deep drilling is outstripping that of production; we could go deeper but we'd have to have a really good well to make it pay."

So much for holes already drilled. It is clear that 25,000 feet can be reached on land. But to return to the original question, how deep can a hole be drilled?

Not long after the Russian geophysicist at the Toronto IUGG meeting had boldly claimed that his country was ahead of the United States in drilling technology and that the Soviet Union had equipment capable of making a hole ten miles deep, a panel of United States experts had a special meeting to ask themselves that very question. The petroleum group of the South Texas section of the American Society of Mechanical Engineers met in Houston in January 1958 to discuss the problem. Annoyed by the boast, they conceded nothing to the Russians. They believed the United States could drill a 50,000-foot hole if there was an incentive, but it would require some research on materials.

According to the American engineers, the principal problem would be created by the high temperatures encountered at depth. They guessed 470° C at 50,000 feet. They suggested that special muds, cooled at the surface, would be needed, that drill bits would soften, that electrical insulation in logging cables would become inelastic and conducting, and that cementing would be difficult.

Another problem would be keeping the hole large enough to permit a drill bit to work effectively and these engineers noted that the smallest practicable roller bit is about 5¾ inches in diameter, although diamond bits can work in smaller holes.

The drill string could be tapered high-tensile-strength pipe decreasing from 4½ inches to 3½ inches to 2⅞ inches. It would hold together if handled properly but special slips would have to be developed to support the pipe without damaging it while the drill string was being made up or taken apart. Round trip time from 50,000 feet was estimated at 24 hours.

As for casing, they felt that P-150 pipe, which has already been used experimentally, would be satisfactory: at 21,000 feet a string of 10¾-inch casing could be used; at 30,500 feet a string of 7⅝-inch; then a 5-inch liner to total depth.

Derrick, draw works, pumps, and accessories in existence appear to be adequate for the job. Logging instruments, as well as the insulated cable on which they are lowered, would probably require additional development, and the metallurgy of all highly stressed parts could stand improvement.

So there is an answer. After completing the necessary development work, the oil experts believe they can reach 50,000 feet on land. The Mohole planners, who only need to go 31,000 feet, and that beneath the sea where high temperatures are not expected to be encountered, find this opinion encouraging.

XII

The Oil Rig Goes to Sea

We have seen how deep oil-well holes are drilled and no doubt 31,000 feet—the depth to the suboceanic Moho in a thin spot—could be reached on land by minor modifications and careful usage of existing equipment. However the depth to the mantle on land is around 100,000 feet and this is decidedly beyond the capabilities of present technology. Moreover, since samples of oceanic rocks would not be obtained and since the temperatures at the continental Moho would be excessive, the idea of deepening one of the deep land holes was quickly and firmly abandoned by the AMSOC Committee. The deep-drilling technology of land must be moved out to sea if the Moho is to be reached.

At first glance oil rigs appear to be seaborne already on any of the dozen varieties of offshore platforms. These platforms, however, only permit drilling in very shallow water on the continental shelves. No drilling has yet been done in the ocean. Nevertheless much has been learned from these offshore operations which is valuable to the Mohole project and their development marks an important step in the history of deep-drilling operations at sea.

History of Offshore Drilling

The offshore story begins in the 1930's with two almost simultaneous developments—one in California, the other in Louisiana. The driving force was the search for new oil fields, for oil had long been produced close to the shore in both areas. Geophysical prospecting had located some promising structures under the tidelands and shallow coastal waters. The problem was: How can this underwater oil be produced?

The solutions were quite different. At Elwood, California, piling piers a thousand feet long were built out into the ocean and derricks installed on caissons at the extremities. The water was only twenty feet deep but the operators felt very daring to be drilling while surrounded by waves. From a single spot as many as a dozen holes could be drilled, some being slanted out even farther under the ocean by directional drilling techniques. Many years later, in 1957, the Richfield Oil Company carried this offshore drilling method to its logical conclusion at Rincon, California, by building a quarter-mile-long trestle out over the shallow coastal waters and constructing an artificial island at its end. Great concrete tetrapods protected the island from wave erosion and palm trees beautified it. The drillers, although well out from the main shore, were also a long way from the deep ocean.

In Louisiana, drillers were confronted with the problem of operating in the great marshy areas and bayous of the Mississippi River delta. Because the land was too soft to build roads or erect derricks and the water too shallow for any ordinary ship, the tidelands barge was developed. These wide, flat-bottomed barges, equipped with complete drilling outfits, floated in three to six feet of water and at high tide could be towed to a drilling site. Then, by driving piles around the perimeter to hold it in place or by flooding some of the barge compartments so that it would settle to the bottom, a firm drilling platform could be established. Roberty Flaherty made the prize-winning documentary movie *Louisiana Story* about one of these rigs.

It was a beginning. The drillers were becoming accustomed to working on water.

The next step was to go after the salt-dome oil structures lying beneath the open waters of the Gulf. The tidelands barge could not operate there even though the water was shallow. The solution was to build a solid base by driving just enough pilings to support the derrick and draw works; everything else would stay on a small ship, a tender, anchored alongside. The tender housed the drilling crews as well as the mud pumps, power plant, and supplies. But driving piling in the presence of waves, even though they were small waves, was not easy, especially when the piling often penetrated 120 feet into the soft mud bottom. So the template, a structural-steel form containing guide holes, was devised. Piles, inserted in the holes, were driven in precisely the right position. Then, after completion of the driving operations, the template was raised to the top of the pilings well above the water to become the drilling platform. The heavy and unwieldy templates had to be equipped with buoyancy tanks before they could be floated to the drill site.

Hurricanes took their toll of these first platforms. After one big blow in 1947 the crew returned and found no trace above water of what, a few days before, had been a complete drilling outfit. Pilings, platform, derrick, and tender had disappeared completely, necessitating the use of surveying equipment to find the place where the structure had been and a magnetometer to locate the wreckage in the mud. From such experiences came new ideas and more rugged structures.

As the technology developed, the equipment increased in size and complexity. The flotation tanks became larger and more elaborately compartmented until eventually there was room for all the necessary machinery, supplies, and crew quarters. The driven pilings were replaced with three to twelve large tubular legs. After the structure had been floated to the drilling site it could lower the legs until they touched bottom and then, using hydraulic jacks invented by Colonel L. B. De Long, raise itself well above the water. This general arrangement for establishing an offshore platform became known as the "Texas Tower." Although a great many varieties finally were built, the most famous are the three-tubular-leg type used by the military for radar warning stations on shoals in the North Atlantic.

Offshore drilling now entered the age of mobile platforms. The equipment became so expensive, with some units costing over five million dollars, that the oil produced at any one location could not pay for it. A rig was needed that would move in, drill several holes at one site, and then move to a new location leaving a steel skeleton behind for production purposes. These were floating rigs only in the sense that they floated from place to place. When they drilled they were solidly fixed to the bottom.

The mobile platform, produced by the Le Tourneau Company since the mid-1950's, is a triangular platform having triangular structural-steel legs in each corner that are raised by a system of gears and electric motors. Since the legs can be individually canted, these platforms "walk" and that is how they are launched at the company's Mississippi River plant. With these rigs holes of 18,000 feet have been drilled in water over 100 feet deep and the company is willing to build one which will drill in 600 feet of water; in other words, anywhere on the continental shelves.

In contrast to these "self-elevating" rigs, another form of offshore oil-drilling platform called "submersibles" uses the opposite method to establish a solid foundation. Instead of raising the flotation compartments above the water, they are flooded and settle to the bottom. From the corners of the main barge, four large caissons and various other columns extend upward to support the drilling platform. When the barge arrives at the drill site, the lower compartments are flooded so that the base sinks gently to the bottom, leaving the drilling platform above the water. This kind of rig is rarely operated in water more than thirty feet deep.

In the course of building and using the various mobile platforms several concepts developed, the most important being the completely packaged rig. No longer do supply ships bring pieces to be assembled on the site over a period of weeks. Recent versions have left port completely equipped and ready to go with all the drill pipe, casing, mud, cement, and commissary equipment aboard. Within a few hours of reaching the site and getting firmly planted on the bottom, drilling operations can begin.

Labor intelligently recognized the special problems of offshore work and agreed to an unusual set of hours. The rigs, of course, must run twenty-four hours a day, often at a considerable distance from shore so that commuting is impracticable. Therefore, the crews live aboard many of the rigs. Offshore, crews work twelve hours a day for seven days, then have a full week off. Near-shore units may use crew boats or even helicopters to transfer men but the trend is to keep the men on board and treat them like elite sailors.

The growth of offshore drilling has been attended by the development of many offshore specialty services. Schlumberger, the biggest of the well-surveying companies, has a "standard offshore logging unit" which consists of a spool of its special cable and a blue-and-silver cab containing the instruments and recording apparatus. Permanently installed on the mobile platforms, these units are manned by the company whenever the operator wants logs made.

Haliburton, the best-known well-cementing company, also has its characteristic red-painted equipment installed and ready to go. After the operator calls in by radio telephone, only a few hours pass before the cementing crew arrives. Other specialty companies stand ready to supply mud products, housekeeping supplies, radio and helicopter services.

The result is that in the last few years a whole industry, with a two-billion-dollar investment in offshore work, has developed on the

U.S. Gulf Coast alone. The close of 1959 saw more than fifty offshore rigs busy drilling for oil. All of the fixed and mobile varieties of drilling platforms are, of course, limited by the depth of the water, the deepest location so far being 140 feet. The next step, somewhat reluctantly taken, was to try drilling from a floating platform.

Floating Platforms

Successful drilling of production-sized holes from floating vessels anchored in several hundred feet of water has now been repeatedly demonstrated. Not very long ago, however, the suggestion of such a possibility was scoffed at. Oil men liked their rigs firmly planted on the sea floor and as far out of reach of the waves as possible. In the early days they worried about what might happen if a rig responded to the motion of every wave that passed. Although their reasons were good, the problems they feared most have been satisfactorily solved.

The development of the present techniques for drilling from floating platforms dates from about 1953. Starting in 1946, various oil companies had been doing seismic surveying in the Santa Barbara Channel off Southern California and using converted mine sweepers to take geologic samples of the sea floor. Until 1953 there were two sampling methods, darting and jetting. The former was done by dropping a short, weighted, dart-shaped pipe to take a punch core. This pipe contained a camera which photographed a compass, thereby obtaining oriented specimens in areas where the geologic formations were exposed. The jet tool, a modification of the dart, was used in areas having silt atop the formations. From the surface, sea water was pumped down a rubber pipe through the jet pipe to blast the silt away. When harder material was encountered beneath the silt, the tool was picked up a few feet and dropped to take a punch core. With this simple method, over a hundred feet of soft overburden has been successfully penetrated.

In 1953 the first rotary drilling machine was mounted on a ship— a 173-foot ex-Navy patrol craft named the *Submarex*. For the first time holes were drilled in the sea bottom from a floating vessel. This little ship was owned by the CUSS group, which took its name from the initials of the Continental, Union, Shell, and Superior oil companies who sponsored it.

The CUSS group had originally been formed as an engineering

study committee to keep these California oil operators abreast of off-shore drilling developments and to determine the direction that their research and experimentation should take. The committee soon decided that the geography, economics, and hard-bottom conditions of the West Coast made the offshore practices of the Gulf Coast unsuitable. They felt that a floating vessel would be a better solution than a fixed platform if certain problems could be solved, such as: (1) how do you hold a ship steady enough to drill in spite of tides and waves; (2) how do you re-enter a hole, change bits, and perform other necessary drilling operations; (3) how can a closed-circuit, mud-circulating system be provided; and (4) how can blowout preventers be installed?

With the *Submarex* the CUSS group set out to find some of the answers. They rigged a 42-foot drilling mast overside on the afterdeck and, using a 2⅞-inch drill string, drilled a series of experimental holes which showed how these problems could be solved. While moored in shallow water between four anchors, holes as deep as 2700 feet were drilled and cased. Closed circulation was accomplished by sealing the space between the drill pipe and the casing with a rubber packer and by using hoses to return the drilling fluid from the annular space to the ship. Two parallel guide lines, stretched between the ship and fittings on the bottom, had a sliding crossbar to guide the bit so that the hole could be re-entered at will. The equipment that was mounted on the bottom at the top of the hole included a "circulating head and a remote latching mechanism" manufactured by the Shaeffer Tool Works of Long Beach.

Since the *Submarex* has only a 23-foot beam and drilled overside, it was not unusual for the landlubber drill crew, intent on some such job as freeing a stuck drill pipe, to pull until the ship listed a 20° or more. This caused the ship's captain some bad moments but it dramatically demonstrated the ability to drill from a decidedly nonrigid platform. Eventually the *Submarex* drilled a total of 300,000 feet of hole, including one hole beneath 1500 feet of water.

Once the CUSS committee was satisfied that a floating drilling platform would work, a more formal organization was created to design a full-size drilling ship, the *CUSS I*.

While this design was being worked out, construction on the next generation of ships was already under way. This was the conversion of LSM (landing ship machinery) hulls left over from World War II amphibious campaigns. In the years 1954–57 three of these ships were modified to do exploratory drilling for geological data. They drilled through a center well with light drilling rigs originally designed to drill 1500 feet on land. These small ships and rigs worked so well that the drillers grew increasingly bold. By the end of 1958 each had drilled holes as much as 6000 feet deep in water 250 feet deep and each had completed a total of 150,000 feet of hole without serious mishap. One of these ships, Richfield's *Rincon,* spent many months drilling off the coast of Peru in open water exposed to the winds and waves and currents of the Pacific. Another, Humble Oil Company's *SM I,* has drilled a number of holes off Point Conception, California, in waters considerably rougher than those for which the ship was intended. By this time it was apparent that drilling at sea from a floating vessel was a better method than its early proponents had predicted.

John Marriner, principal naval architect for Craig Shipbuilding Company of Long Beach, California, deserves considerable credit for the development of this class of drilling ship. He is undismayed when clients ask him to cut a large hole in the center of a ship, remove its propellers and seal off the shafts, or make other radical changes. Somehow he can do these things and still keep the ship afloat. One of his LSM drilling-ship conversions was launched only four months after he was approached with the problem. With this valuable background, he became one of the AMSOC Committee's special consultants.

In 1958 other floating drilling vessels appeared. Some, like the *Venmac III,* are merely flat barges with a standard oil derrick erected in the center. *Venmac* drills off the California coast for Phillips Petroleum under the direction of W. O. Roberts, an AMSOC drilling-panel member. It makes few concessions to the ocean; the barge compartments are tightly sealed and never entered. A standard drilling rig is mounted on the deck much as it would be on the Texas prairie. In a half hour one forgets he is at sea. It is rather a jolt, therefore, to hear the call "Thar she blows" and see the whales playing in the blue water between the derrick and the shore. *Venmac* and its counterparts do the job they were designed for very well, but they are not true drilling ships capable of supporting a crew for a long term far from shore.

Another type of drilling ship is the *Nola.* A converted drilling tender, it drills over-the-side in the Gulf Coast area. This means that the derrick is not centered over a well but cantilevered out over the vessel's side. On the opposite side a sponson 8-feet square runs most of the length of the ship. In order to counteract the changing loads on the off-center derrick, water is pumped in and out of the sponson. This arrangement has a great advantage, from the oil man's point of view, since a well can be "completed"—made ready to produce oil—above water. The eccentric position of the derrick makes the ship look exceedingly unstable but the *Nola* has drilled holes 12,000 feet deep in water 50 feet deep.

An early task of the AMSOC staff was to survey existing drilling ships and platforms. After carefully examining the characteristics of the offshore drilling rigs discussed above, it reported that *CUSS I* seemed the most suitable for drilling preliminary test holes in deep water.

Eighteen months were required to design and construct the *CUSS I* and it was launched in early 1957 at a cost of 2.7 million dollars. For most of the first year its operations were kept as secret as possible in the highly competitive oil business where lead-time and know-how mean money. In the early days small boats with "sight-seers" would circle for hours watching the operations through binoculars and photographing with telephoto lenses. Occasionally, the men aboard the *CUSS* would look back with their own binoculars and identify friends who worked for rival oil companies.

The observers saw a war-surplus Navy freight-barge hull (known as a YFNB) with an extra-heavy-duty derrick amidships. This particular hull resembles those used as tenders alongside the piling platforms in the Gulf of Mexico. These YFNB's, which are not self-propelled and so must be towed from place to place, are the largest barges the Navy has built. They are 260 feet long, 48 feet wide, and draw about 15 feet when loaded. Their particular virtue is their strength, low cost, and uninterrupted space, which can be easily modified to suit the new owners' needs.

The heavy-duty derrick on *CUSS I*, a mere 98 feet high compared with the standard derrick height of 140 feet, has been designed to drill through a center well so that the ship has maximum stability and minimum chance of derrick failure in a heavy sea. Inside the derrick are two long vertical girders called "guide rails" which prevent the six-ton traveling block from swinging with the roll of the ship. Two other major items of equipment are a National 80-B draw works, capable of lifting 475 tons, or 20,000 feet of 4.5-inch pipe, and National G-700 pumps, capable of moving 800 gallons per minute at 3500 psi.

The unique pipe-racking machinery, located on the drilling deck just aft of the derrick, is a particularly interesting feature of the *CUSS*. In virtually all drilling operations the pipe is racked in three-joint units 90 feet long which stand upright inside the derrick. *CUSS I*, however, has a racking arrangement where pipe doubles—60 feet long—are stored horizontally on a pair of endless sprocket chains just aft of the derrick. When a section of pipe is needed, the driller operates a switch and a piece of pipe is deposited in a narrow conveyor belt aligned with the center of the derrick. Automatically, the pipe is carried toward the rotary table and the end raised about six feet so that the elevator can be conveniently attached. As the elevator rises, the pipe swings into a vertical position above the rotary table, where it can be added to the drill string. This method, not quite as rapid as vertical racking, has two shipboard advantages: it keeps the ship's center of gravity low and it avoids the danger of the pipe shifting when the ship rolls.

On the main deck beneath the drilling platform and pipe racker is an open work area where equipment to be lowered through the center well can be assembled. Forward of the work area are the living quarters and galley. The hold, below the main deck, contains the pumps, motors, and mud-storage tanks.

The *CUSS I* holds its position in several hundred feet of water by means of a cat's cradle arrangement of six mooring lines running out, almost horizontally, from the ship to large floating buoys a thousand feet away. The buoys are, in turn, connected by heavy chains to anchors dug into the sea floor over a thousand feet beyond. Three winches at the bow and three more at the stern are used to keep these lines taut and to correct for changing wind and current conditions. Since it is usually best to keep the ship aligned with the swell, the mooring cables are rigged in such a way that the ship can be rotated a quarter turn in either direction if need be. This permits the ship to take the waves with a pitching (fore-and-aft) motion rather than the more annoying rolling (side-to-side) motion.

Having anchored itself in position, *CUSS I* prepares to drill by rigging a "landing base" in the center well. The landing base, a hexagonal steel structure about fifteen feet in diameter and six feet high, serves as a foundation for the equipment on the sea floor. Attached to the top of this landing base are the blowout preventers; below it is a piece of casing perhaps 200 feet long. While the landing base is hanging in the ship's well, the drill pipe with the bit attached is lowered through the base and casing until the bottom is reached. Wherever the bit touches, drilling begins. When several hundred feet of hole have been made, drilling is stopped and the drill string partly withdrawn until only a hundred feet remain in the hole. The drill pipe serves to guide the casing into the hole when the landing base is lowered to the bottom. Cement is then pumped down the drill pipe to seal the casing and landing base in place. When the cement has set, the drill pipe is withdrawn and from then on the hole can be re-entered by means of the guide cables which lowered the landing base to the bottom. Using a method similar to the one originally tried on the *Submarex*, a sliding crossbar guides a piece of conductor pipe into place.

This conductor pipe, almost reaching from the blowout preventers on the landing base to the surface of the ocean, is known as the "riser pipe" to offshore operators. Its upper end is independently supported beneath the ship by a cylindrical buoy so that the hole can be left temporarily and regained again. As an additional precaution against losing the hole if the ship has to leave in an emergency, the two guide cables from the landing base are attached to the ship by small constant-tension winches in such a way that they can be quickly detached and buoyed off. Once the riser pipe is in, return mud circulation can be established via a flexible pipe to the surface and the drilling can proceed.

From this point on, the drilling methods are almost identical with those employed on land. One exception results from the up-and-down motion of the ship caused by waves. The problem faced by all the floating drilling operators was: How can the bit be kept in contact with the bottom at the correct pressure for drillings? The solution is the bumper-sub. The bumper-sub, a special double-walled piece of pipe, is inserted amid the drill collars near the bottom. By means of a telescoping motion between the sub's inner and outer sections, its length can change by as much as four feet. At the same time, because the two sections are geared together by splines, it can transmit rotation from the pipe above to that below. The drill collars serve two purposes: they weight the bit so that it can drill, and they keep the drill pipe in tension. When drilling from a moving ship, it is common practice to use one set of collars for each purpose and put a bumper-sub between them. That is, if 10,000 pounds of bit pressure is desired, that weight of collars is permitted to rest directly on the bit. The rest of the drill collars, which may weigh another 10,000 pounds, hang from the ship and keep the drill pipe in tension. Between the two sets of collars is a bumper-sub which slides in and out as the ship rises and falls on the waves and permits each set of drill collars to do its proper job.

In order to keep an eye on bottom operations, especially in water too deep for divers to work, *CUSS I* has an underwater television camera which can be lowered down the guide cables. The image is seen on a TV screen in the pilothouse and on occasion it has been very helpful in showing the driller just what is happening below.

After a few months of trial and practice, the *CUSS* and her crew became a very efficient drilling machine. They could move to a new site, drill a 5000-foot exploratory hole, seal it off, and move on again in about eleven days.

This was the state of the drilling art in May 1958 when A. J. Field, general manager of Global Marine Exploration Company, showed motion pictures of the *CUSS I* in action to the assembled geophysicists in Washington on the occasion of the first general discussion of the Mohole project.

Holding a Ship with Anchors

The shallow-water operations of *CUSS I* gave great encouragement to the AMSOC Committee members, who saw that these indicated a method of drilling in deep water. Even the severest critics of drilling at sea had to admit that maybe reaching the Moho underwater was not quite as crazy as it had at first sounded. But even though the *CUSS I* held great promise, no one, even in a burst of enthusiasm, was so optimistic as to believe that it could drill to the Moho. We hoped that *CUSS I* could be used for experimental operations in deep water and perhaps during those operations it would obtain the first deep cores in the soft oceanic sediments. How far into the bottom *CUSS* might be able to drill was completely unknown when the AMSOC staff began to make plans.

Although the designers and operators of *CUSS I* had solved many of the problems of drilling from a floating platform—enough to make it a very successful oil-drilling operation—a great deal remained to be done if it were to be used beyond the edge of the continental shelf. The most important question to be solved was: How can a ship be held still enough to drill? By oil-drilling standards a hundred feet of water is deep water but by oceanographic standards deep water means beyond the bottom of the continental slope—10,000 feet deep or more. Oceanographers usually hold a ship still in deep water by anchoring with the dredging-winch cable. Then they measure the slope of the cable and use the ship's propeller and rudder to keep the cable as vertical as possible. On analyzing this method it was found that within the smallest angle that can be measured, the ship may move as much as 2000 feet off station. Obviously a better method of station-keeping in deep water would have to be developed for drilling operations.

The first question to be answered was: How much can the drilling ship be permitted to move about? The problem arises because if the ship is not almost exactly over the hole, severe bending stresses may be imposed on the drill pipe. As we will see later, those stresses must be calculated precisely in order to determine how much the ship can be permitted to move about. The shallow-water drillers guessed that their ships moved away from the "station," a point directly over the hole, by as much as 10 per cent of the depth of the water. There were no precise measurements but they believed that in 150 feet of water a fifteen-foot sidewise motion of the ship was acceptable; beyond that the riser pipe might be damaged or the drill pipe overstressed. In order to make preliminary calculations of various methods for holding the ship on station in deep water until we could determine exactly how much sidewise ship motion a drill pipe would stand, we selected what seemed to be a conservative figure of 3 per cent of the depth. But how do you hold a drilling ship within a circle of only 360-foot radius in water 12,000 feet deep?

First, the forces acting to move the ship must be examined. These are, of course, the winds, which exert a force on the derrick and the part of the hull above water, and the ocean currents, which tend to drag the pipe and the underwater part of the hull along with them. The general rule of hydrodynamics is that objects in the water tend to do what the water does. If the water moves, anything in it tends to move along with it. This concept is particularly important in thinking about the effect of waves on the ship.

In a previous chapter we examined the mechanism of ocean waves in deep water and found that the surface particles of water move in circular orbits which are equal to the height of the passing waves. If a wave four feet high passes, a floating piece of driftwood will describe a four-foot circle in a length of time equal to the period of the wave. If there are no winds or currents acting on it, after a dozen waves have passed, the driftwood will still be at the same place. The wave forms have passed beneath it. A ship acts the same way. This means that the net effect of wave forces acting to move a ship in deep water is zero and therefore waves need not be considered in the problem of holding position.

Thus the forces which the ship must be prepared to resist, if it is to hold position at sea, are caused primarily by wind and current. When an area is selected for drilling, the records of years of observations by sailors must be studied and reduced to a set of statistics. The engineer examines the statistics and calculates just how much force the combined winds and currents will exert against the ship. Then he must design a means of holding the ship against all except maximum storm conditions. To have to resist the worst storm of the year would make the problem unsolvable or at least would require methods that would be inefficient for any ordinary situation. So the engineer makes one assumption—if an exceptionally strong gale arises, the ship can temporarily desert its station, returning when the winds and waves have abated.

Another force acts on the ship if it is supporting pipe that is rotating in a current of water. There are deep currents in the ocean and although their velocity is low compared to those of the surface currents, they range from 5 to 10 cm/sec or 0.1 to 0.2 knots per hour. This current exerts relatively little drag force on a slender pipe which is holding still. However, if the pipe is rotated at considerable speed, as a drilling pipe will be, the streamlines of the water flowing past are piled up on one side. A region of high velocity and consequent low pressure, develops so that the pipe tends to move in the direction of the low pressure. This force is called the Magnus effect. Fortunately these currents generally are small and pipe-rotational velocities during coring are low, but under some circumstances the Magnus effect may be important, as we shall see later on. Of course, if a riser pipe— a casing from bottom to surface—is installed, it shields the pipe from the current and the Magnus force is eliminated.

The first method suggested for holding a drilling ship in position against these various forces was to anchor it, and rather elaborate calculations were made for various sizes and numbers of anchor lines. The Global Marine Exploration Company, owners of the *CUSS I*, made a study of a deep-water anchoring system for their ship that could be used during the early phases of test drilling. Like their shallow-water system, it would have used six heavy cables from the ship to surface buoys and six cables from the buoys to large anchors

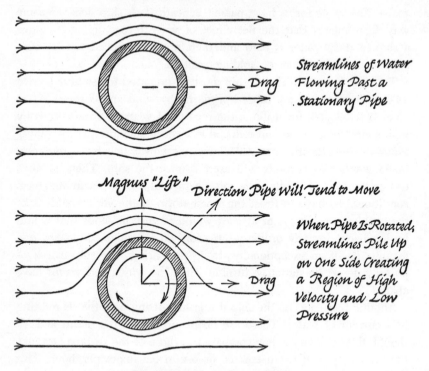

Streamlines of Water Flowing Past a Stationary Pipe

Drag

Magnus "Lift"

Direction Pipe Will Tend to Move

When Pipe Is Rotated, Streamlines Pile Up on One Side Creating a Region of High Velocity and Low Pressure

Drag

Fig. XII-1 The Magnus Effect

on the bottom. They proposed using a riser pipe, and at first this seemed to have numerous advantages. A riser pipe would eliminate the Magnus effect, make it possible to circulate drilling mud and to re-enter the hole. In this anchoring system both the ship and the top of the riser pipe would be held by similar networks of cable so the ship and the pipe would move together. If a large storm arose the ship could slip the lines to the buoys and leave, returning to pick them up and resume drilling through the riser pipe when the seas quieted down. After careful analysis we decided against this plan in spite of these advantages.

The design of a deep-sea anchoring system suitable for holding a drilling ship is much more difficult than it at first appears. Very few of the many people who have suggested anchoring deep-sea drilling platforms have ever made even the most casual calculation of the forces involved. The minimum "scope" of an anchor line—the ratio of the horizontal distance to the anchor to the depth of water—is about one to one. Large ships anchoring in shallow water commonly have anchor-line scopes of five to one. In 12,000 feet of water with a scope of one to one—considering the added length because the lines sag— each anchor line would be about three and a half miles long. Together the six lines would total twenty-one miles of wire. If 1¼-inch wire lines were used for this job, they would present a surface to the ocean currents of about 14,000 square feet. Larger wire or longer scope increases the area and the drag force. The result is that even modest currents can exert a force of many tons against the moorings. Any change in current velocity or direction at depth would cause the ship to move far from its desired position. Another hazard is that each cable would have a certain amount of tension in it that would have to be resisted by the cable on the opposite side of the ship. The more rigidly one tries to hold the ship with this system the higher the tension in the lines. Consequently, if one cable were to break, the cable on the opposite side of the ship would pull the ship far out of position, probably causing the failure of the drill pipe that the rigidity was intended to prevent.

The main difficulty arises because the cable, like any suspended line, sags in a curve called a catenary. This means that if the mooring system is called upon to resist changing forces on the ship at the surface, the first thing that happens is that the sag is pulled out of the catenary. It is impracticable to keep enough tension on the wire to keep the sag out of it. As a result, the new forces cannot be effectively resisted until the ship moves. For most mooring designs the ship would move so far before the tension increased sufficiently to restrain it that damage would be done to the drill pipe.

This is a fundamental difficulty of wire-line moorings but several means have been proposed for overcoming it. One is to put a series of buoys along the anchor cable to support the sag. These would straighten the line considerably and cause it to hang in a series of small catenaries instead of one long one. The trouble is that such buoys increase the drag area and add considerably to the difficulty and danger of installing the anchoring system. The danger arises because the underwater buoys need to be filled with a buoyant fluid in order to keep them from collapsing under pressure. Most buoyant fluids, such as gasoline, are flammable and cause a serious fire hazard on the ship that handles them.

Another way of overcoming the sag is to make the cables out of some light material such as nylon which is much closer to the density of water. Aside from the facts that no large-size nylon lines are readily available, although they can be specially manufactured, the nylon has a serious problem. It stretches, as do other similar neutral-density fibers, and depending on the amount of force applied, the stretch may be as much as 20 per cent. This means that a mooring rope three and a half miles long could stretch half a mile. Thus, although nylon might solve the catenary sag problem, its stretch would permit the ship too much freedom. The cost of nylon rope for such a mooring system was estimated at half a million dollars.

There have been suggestions for using coated magnesium rods or other exotic materials that are light and strong for mooring cables. Although this might be possible, the risk would be great because very little is known of the properties of such materials in tension under high pressure in a corrosive medium like salt water. The problem of how fittings would be attached, how such a piece of rod would be handled at sea, and what it would cost, introduce such major uncertainties that these materials were eliminated from consideration.

So, although it undoubtedly would be possible to use some form of an anchoring system, AMSOC rejected the idea of anchoring for several reasons. First, the installation of buoys and cables and anchors clearly would be a very expensive and difficult operation. It did not seem to be worthwhile to spend over a million dollars on the anchoring system and riser pipe that the ship's owners felt would be required. With the anchors, lines, casing, and buoys, there would be a substantial investment in underwater equipment which did not appear to be recoverable, or to be resalable for much more than the cost of salvage even if it could be recovered.

AMSOC believed that experimental drilling could be done without the riser pipe and that substantially as much information would be obtained for a great deal less money. We felt that a more flexible system for positioning the ship would be needed if we were going to drill a series of holes in the soft sediments at several locations. An array of wires and anchors would be difficult to move and once these were placed the project was committed to drilling at that particular site. It would be a great advantage to be able to change location easily and to move to a new site after the sediment in one place had been cored. If the test methods worked as well as we hoped, this drilling ship would be an invaluable tool for coring the sediments in many parts of the ocean.

The clinching argument against anchoring for the test-drilling operations was that we believed the ultimate ship—the large one that will some day be designed to drill to the Moho—would have to be held in position without anchor lines and we wanted to make a smaller-scale test of how that would be done. Thus it was decided to use a dynamic positioning system, one in which the thrust of constantly rotating propellers is balanced against the natural forces, to hold the ship in place.

Dynamic Positioning

The concept of holding an unanchored ship at a precise position in deep water by sensing its position with respect to fixed markers and maneuvering it to maintain that position by means of "steering screws" is one of the author's own contributions to the Mohole project. Immediately before joining AMSOC to work on the Mohole feasibility study, I was serving as staff director for the Maritime Research Advisory Committee, also of the National Academy of Sciences. That committee was charged with the problem of advising the U. S. Maritime Administration on the direction that its research program should take. Many forward-looking and unusual ideas for improving the U.S. merchant marine were reviewed, ranging from hydrofoil ships to cargo-handling methods. One problem of particular interest was that of maneuvering ships in the restricted waters of canals and harbors by means of various kinds of special propulsion devices. These included steering screws, large outboard motors, and cycloidal propellers which are something like horizontal paddle wheels. Each can be a very effective mechanism for propelling and maneuvering a ship if it is properly used.

We had not studied AMSOC's deep-sea positioning problem for very long before I became convinced that it would be much better to hold a ship in position by using these propellers to constantly maneuver it against the winds and current. They have a great advantage over ordinary propellers in that they can be used to exert quickly whatever force is necessary in any direction. This opinion was soon confirmed and refined by Robert Taggart, a naval architect and expert on propulsion devices who joined our staff.

The problem of maintaining a ship precisely above a point in deep water is composed of two major parts: (1) How do you know where that point is; and (2) how do you overcome the various forces of the sea to stay at that point? The propulsion devices mentioned above solve only the second part. Grant for a moment that they can be used to maneuver the ship on station while we consider the first part.

There are many ways which might be used to determine a ship's position but the original suggestion for ringing it with deep-moored buoys is one of the simplest. The ocean has a vast surface and any point on it looks very much like every other point. The deep-moored or taut-line buoys give a reference point and the ship's pilot can maneuver by them as well as he can by channel-marker buoys in shallow water.

In 1952 as a part of a project to measure the waves produced by the first big hydrogen-bomb explosion, the author devised and built the first deep-moored buoys. These buoys were used to support wave meters in deep water north of Eniwetok atoll. They were cheap and simple, being composed of an anchor weight made from an old San Diego trolley-car wheel, an anchor line made of steel music wire only a tenth of an inch in diameter, and the buoy itself, which was a surplus bomb case about thirty inches in diameter.

The buoys floated a hundred and fifty feet beneath the water surface so that the pressure-measuring devices they supported could detect the waves above but not be moved about by them. This was possible because the underwater buoys exerted enough upward force to keep the slender anchor wire very taut. The small area that this wire presented to the water kept the drag of passing currents at a minimum. As a result, the underwater buoy changed position only if the velocity and /or direction of the current acting against the buoy changed. The buoys swayed but they stayed almost directly above their anchors. From the underwater buoy a slack line led to a surface float which contained the recording mechanism and was equipped with a radar reflector and a light so that it could be located day or night.

The forces that act on taut-line buoys and the resultant displacement of the buoys can be calculated so that it is possible to determine how much they will move about under various oceanic conditions.

Where the currents are low, as they are at some of the proposed drilling sites, a modernized version of these buoys will make a reliable and accurate position marker. For example, in a surface current of 0.3 knot (15 cm/sec) and a deep current of 0.1 knot, an elliptically shaped buoy six feet in diameter and three feet thick which pulls with 3500 pounds of tension on a 7/32-inch cable 12,000 feet long, is displaced no more than 40 feet from a point above its anchor. This

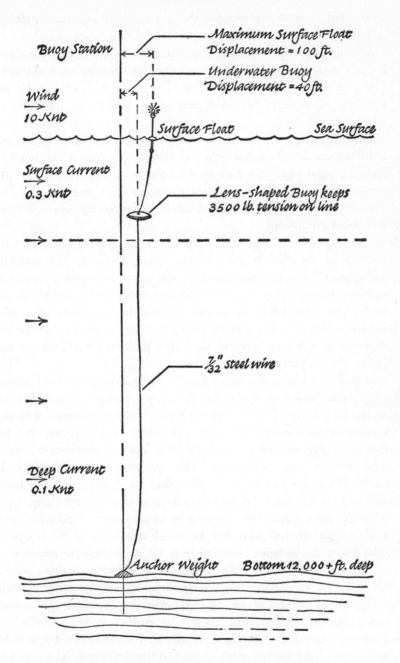

Fig. XII-2 The Deep-Moored Buoy Design

means that a complete reversal of the currents would produce a change in buoy position of only 80 feet.

A doughnut-shaped surface float—attached to the underwater buoy by an elastic cord—will support a radar reflector and a night light. The cumulative inaccuracies in this buoy system results in an uncertainty of position for each marker of about 100 feet for the current stated.

Thus, if a ring of these deep moored buoys were installed around a drilling site, a pilot could hold a drilling ship within a few hundred feet of a point above the hole in the bottom by simply observing the marker floats. This might be satisfactory; however, the accuracy and convenience of this visual method can be improved by means of radar and sonar equipment.

Radar (radio direction and range) can be used to determine the position of the ship relative to the circle of floats. The standard technique of scanning the sea with radio waves in search of reflecting surfaces would easily detect the corner reflectors mounted on the floats. The information so obtained would be presented on a fluorescent screen as a series of dots with the ship in the middle. In this way a pilot can keep track of the ship's position even if fog or rain makes the visibility zero.

In a similar manner, a sonar (sound navigation and range) system can be employed to determine the ship's position relative to the underwater buoys. In order to do this a sonar transducer, a device for sending and receiving underwater sound signals, is mounted beneath the ship so that it can be rotated like an underwater searchlight with a beam of sound. The underwater buoys will make excellent targets; that is, they will reflect the "pings" and the transducer can detect the echo. Just to make sure that this returning signal is amply strong, transponders—devices which receive a ping and send back a signal of their own—will be attached to some of the buoys. In pilot house the distance obtained from the travel time of sound from the ship to the buoys and back will be presented on another screen. The pilot can then check the sonar position against the radar position.

Or, any of several of the long-distance-radio navigational systems might be used which are known by curious names: LORAN-C, LORAC, Raydist, Decca. These require shore-based radio-transmitting towers and have various advantages and disadvantages. The principal objection to all of these schemes is that they are more complicated and expensive than the methods that AMSOC proposes to use.

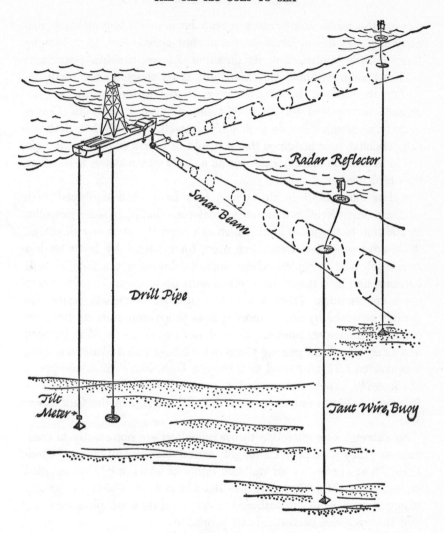

Fig. XII-3 Drilling Ship and Buoys

Having established that the position of the ship can be accurately determined, we can return to the maneuvering mechanisms needed to maintain that position.

Most large merchant ships have a single propeller at the stern with a rudder immediately behind it. When the ship is underway, a slight change in the attitude of the rudder deflects the thrust of the propeller and changes the ship's course by moving the stern of the ship to one

259

side or the other. Rarely does a ship have to do any delicate maneuvering and this is fortunate, for at slow speeds and when backing there is little control over its direction. At sea a ship's position is seldom known within a mile and there is no concern over small deviations in position; in a harbor or restricted waterway, tugboat assistance is required for all except the simplest maneuvers. Consequently, although ships do their job very well, probably few deep-sea skippers have ever imagined that it would be useful or possible to hold a ship in position in mid-ocean within a circle whose radius is less than the ship's length.

A few ships built to do special jobs have been equipped with auxiliary omnidirectional propulsion devices. That is, an extra propeller in addition to the usual kind, which can exert thrust in any direction. Such extra propellers have been used, for example, by buoy tenders whose job it is to replace channel-marker buoys in the face of swift currents, and by a luxury liner which must dock in remote ports where there are no tugs. There are also a number of vessels which are entirely powered by one or more special propulsion units so that they can easily maneuver sidewise, skewed, or in circles, as well as forward and astern. Among these are German-built tugs called Water-Tractors, a converted LST now used as a ferry, a U. S. Navy mine sweeper, a U. S. Army beach lighter, and a powered barge which is used to transport drilling mud to some of the offshore rigs in the Gulf Coast area.

So although omnidirection thrust propellers are not exactly in common use, they have been thoroughly tested under many kinds of situations. There are two major varieties, either of which might be installed on a drilling ship. These are the steering screws, which are greatly enlarged versions of the outboard motors used on small pleasure craft, and the cycloidal or vertical-axis propellers.

The steering screw is manufactured by Murray and Tregurtha of Quincy, Massachusetts, under the trade name of Harbormaster. Harbormasters are powered by diesel engines of as much as 600 horsepower. This power is transmitted down a vertical shaft through a gear box to an ordinary screw propeller. Unlike the small outboards in which the entire engine turns to change the direction of thrust, the diesels hold still; only the shaft and propeller change orientation.

Harbormasters produce about 20 pounds of thrust per horsepower at low ship speeds. If four 200-horsepower units were attached to opposite "corners" of a drilling ship the size of CUSS I, enough thrust

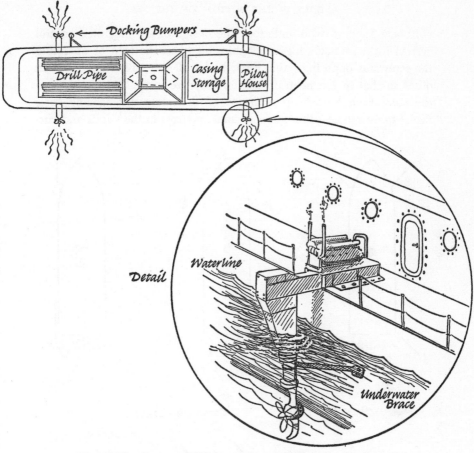

Fig. XII-4 Proposed Harbormaster Installations on *Cuss I*

could be produced to hold the ship in position against all but the worst storms. Of course, the amount and direction of the thrust of each engine would have to be controlled by a pilot at a central position on the bridge.

Although a man probably could learn to operate individual engine controls satisfactorily, this would require considerable skill and would be fatiguing for extended operations. A simplified system for controlling four engines simultaneously had to be designed. One problem was that diesel engines must be kept running, and since they have no clutches, the idling propellers are constantly producing thrust—more than is needed when winds and currents are low. This thrust had to be opposed by some force, otherwise it would be necessary to constantly flip the direction of the screws from side to side to keep the excess thrust from moving the ship off station.

Robert Taggart, who undertook the design of an integrated control system for a four-steering-screw ship, hit upon the idea of operating the screws as opposing pairs. First, he let all the screws oppose each other so that in the neutral position they are all pushing inward on the ship; then he set up a means of delicately unbalancing their thrust to overcome either large or small changes in the winds and cur-

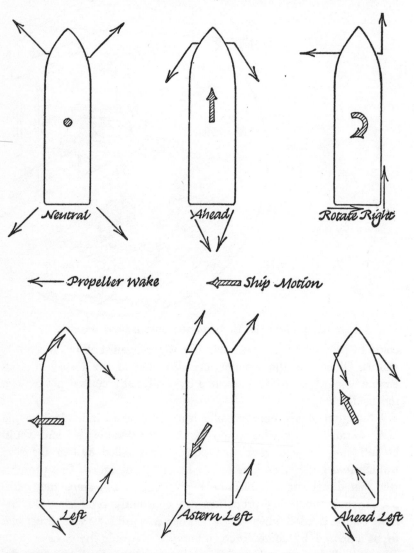

Fig. XII-5 Direction of Thrust of Centrally Controlled Propellers to Achieve Various Ship Motions

rents. The thrust directions of the screws required to give the major kinds of motion are shown in Figure XII-5.

With Taggart's integrated control system the pilot will have only a single lever to manipulate which will be something like the "joy stick" of early aircraft. If he wants the ship to move ahead, he pushes the lever ahead; the farther he pushes, the faster the engines run and the more thrust they produce. If the ship is to be moved in a skewed fashion—that is, in any direction, but remaining parallel to its original heading—he pushes the lever in that direction. If the ship is at the correct position but must rotate to be more directly headed into the swell, he turns the steering wheel. In order to accomplish these operations there are various electrical linkages, differential gears, and servomotors but the mechanism is not excessively complicated. Under special conditions of storm or if one engine should break down, it will be possible to control screws individually.

The great advantage of such a system is that the motion of the lever corresponds directly with the intended motion of the ship and with the picture presented by the sonar. No complicated procedures for maneuvering will be necessary. As a result, it is believed that no great amount of pilot-training will be necessary and that under all but the worst conditions of sudden gusts of wind and abrupt changes in current the ship can easily be held within two hundred feet of a point above the hole.

Another propulsion device which produces omnidirectional thrust is the Voith-Schneider or cycloidal propeller. It consists of a turntable which is flush with the flat bottom of the ship and which constantly rotates about a vertical axis. Along its perimeter are mounted six equally-spaced vertical blades with hydrofoil sections. As the ship moves through the water the blades trace out a cycloidal-shaped curve. The angle of attack of each blade is automatically regulated so that it has a sculling action on the fore and aft sides, a pushing action away from the direction of the ship motion, and a feathered stroke as it travels with the ship.

In the version by J. M. Voith, a German company, engine speed and turntable speed are constant but the amount of blade pitch for any direction of thrust is controllable. Thus it is possible to vary thrust from nothing to full ahead in any direction almost instantaneously since no mass of machinery needs to be accelerated. Maneuvering is done directly from the ship's bridge and since no rudders are needed, the engine controls are operated by the helmsman.

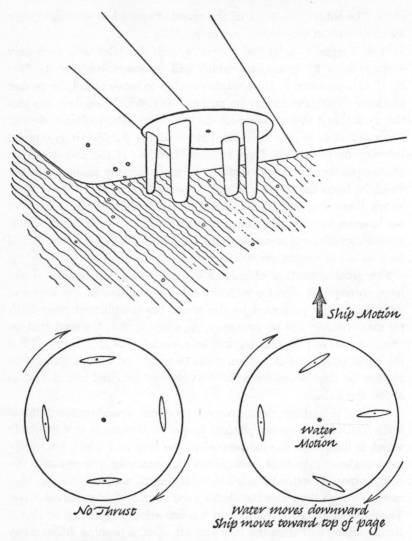

Fig. XII-6 A Voith-Schneider Cycloidal Propeller as Seen from Below. Constantly rotating propellers can be instantly adjusted to exert thrust in any direction.

Although over a thousand Voith cycloidal units are in use in Germany and Japan, only a few have reached the United States. One of these is a German-built floating crane, (YD-171), the largest in the world, which was captured by the Allies in World War II and is now used in the Long Beach, California, naval shipyard. It is equipped with three 700-horsepower Voith-Schneider units powered by individual electric motors which make it self-propelled and completely maneuverable. With its great crane of structural steel this vessel is curiously similar to a floating oil derrick, although its hull is much smaller and the derrick much larger than that of a drilling ship would be.

The efficiency of vertical-axis propellers is not as great as that of screw propellers on a ship under way at sea. However, at lower speeds the efficiencies are comparable and, for maneuvering, the cycloidal type is greatly superior. Voith units come in sizes up to 1250 horsepower which have six blades six feet long on an orbit diameter of twelve feet. Since about 22 pounds of thrust per horsepower can be safely assumed, each 1250-horsepower until would produce 27,500 pounds of thrust. An integrated control system even simpler than that to be used with the Harbormasters could be worked out for a group of these propellers. Therefore, cycloidal propellers appear to be an ideal means of providing omnidirectional thrust for a drilling ship. However, they are precision-made to order and delivery time is long. Moreover, the ship on which they are installed must have a suitable hull shape so that they will operate efficiently. So Harbormasters are more practical for experimental work.

We have examined the two major parts of the ship-positioning system: the instruments for locating the ship's position and the maneuvering propellers for counteracting the forces of winds and currents. Figure XII-7 shows a pilot's eye view of the controls on the bridge. All the information needed to guide the ship, night or day, is displayed on PPI scopes (polar position indicators). These scopes, both sonar and radar, indicate the relative positions of the buoys and of nearby ships—the drilling ship is in the center. In addition, the gyrocompass gives a check on the ship's heading so that it can be kept headed into the swell at night.

It is necessary to keep the ship as close to its station as possible to reduce the bending stresses in the pipe where it enters the bottom. When the pipe is vertical the stresses are minimal. Thus a continuous direct measurement of pipe slope at the sea floor would be the most useful information the pilot can have.

It might be possible to measure directly the slope of a rotating pipe at the sea floor but that would be difficult and it is not necessary. Instead the AMSOC staff has designed an analogue of the pipe which is much more manageable. It is simply a steel cable containing electrical conductors which extends vertically from the ship to an

anchor on the sea floor. If the cable is kept at the proper tension it approximates the reaction of the drill pipe. Just above the anchor, mounted on a universal joint, is a short piece of pipe containing an inclinometer. If the ship moves off station, the cable pulls a tilt into the inclinometer which is immediately recorded on the control panel in front of the pilot indicating which way the ship must go to straighten the cable. If there are substantial deep currents, the ship would have to take a position slightly upstream of the hole in order to keep the meter vertical and to have the pipe enter the bottom vertically. Therefore this kind of position indicator gives the *best* position for the ship rather than the position directly above the hole.

After a little practice a pilot should be able to manipulate the control lever so as to hold the ship within a few dozen feet of the position indicated by the instruments. The combined uncertainty caused by buoy wander, sonar error, and piloting difficulties under the conditions specified should be less than 200 feet—well within the original goal of 360 feet. Whether or not this is good enough depends on the strength of the drill pipe. The next step is to examine stresses in the drill pipe and determine how large a positioning error the pipe will permit. Finally, when the theoretical work has been completed, it will be necessary to try out the ideas at sea—to do some experimental drilling in deep water.

XIII

Experimental Holes in Deep Water

From the beginning it was clear even to the most optimistic AMSOC members that it would not be sensible to try drilling to the Moho without taking any intermediate steps. Drilling a hole over 30,000 feet deep on land would be a difficult job. The drilling of even a shallow hole in the bottom of the deep ocean would be an equally great undertaking. But to start by attempting the world's deepest hole in its most difficult environment would be out of the question. It would be necessary to obtain some actual data on the forces and stresses on drilling ships and drill strings at sea before Mohole-drilling equipment could be designed. Moreover, some oceanic drilling "know-how" was needed.

The AMSOC Committee had reported to its sponsor, the National Science Foundation, in September 1959 that the drilling of the Mohole was within the range of U.S. technology. But how, exactly, should the work begin?

A considerable amount of information had been accumulated about possible drilling sites both in the Atlantic and the Pacific. We were becoming familiar with the capabilities of the various floating vessels; we had some ideas about how to hold a ship in position in deep water; we had done enough engineering on the drill pipe to establish that a standard drill string could be used for shallow holes in the deep-sea floor. But we needed a specific plan that described in detail how preliminary work should be carried out. Moho drilling would have to wait until basic engineering studies had been made and tested at sea.

The Special Staff Study Group

In order to plan a set of drilling experiments that would develop this know-how, a Special Staff Study Group convened in Washington in December 1959. The participants were AMSOC's regular staff members plus about fifteen experienced engineers borrowed from the staffs of oil companies, equipment manufacturers, and metal makers. The group was asked a series of closely associated questions. How should an oceanic drilling program begin? What specific problems of drilling can be resolved by shallow holes before deep-drilling methods can be designed? How can an existing drilling ship be used to obtain the maximum engineering and geological information for the least money?

In order to get the discussion started I proposed a tentative plan for doing experimental drilling with *CUSS I*. It was not very different from the plan finally adopted, but it sounded so wild to the visiting experts that at the end of the first day most of them retired to a nearby bar to commiserate with each other for having come so far to hear such foolishness. The whole idea of drilling in water two and a half miles deep seemed quite mad. Nevertheless, they returned to the meetings each day for a week. The sessions were devoted to "brainstorming," with the group divided into sections on ship positioning, drilling procedures, and instrumentation—headed respectively by Robert Taggart, Jack McLelland, and Phillip LaHue, regular AMSOC staff members. Each section discussed matters within its special area of competence but as the days passed they departed further and further from the pathways of tried-and-true drilling practice. As a result of boldly relying on engineering which, though sound, was most unusual and reached well beyond actual experience, some novel suggestions for drilling beneath the ocean were made.

Once these men were released from the usual requirement that drilling show a profit, their imaginations soared. The original scheme quickly evolved into a workable plan and reluctance changed to enthusiasm. At the end of a week the group had not only agreed that drilling in deep water was possible but it had formulated a fairly specific program of experimental work to try it out. The out-of-town experts returned to their home companies, leaving AMSOC's permanent staff to complete the designs, make the refined calculations, and write the report.

The plan that finally evolved was this: *CUSS I*, owners willing, would spend about a month at sea drilling shallow test holes beneath deep water. The ship would keep track of its position by sonar-ranging on deep-moored buoys and would maneuver to stay there by means of Harbormaster steering screws. It would simply lower the drill pipe to the bottom and, wherever the bit touched, drill. There would be no riser pipe or other means of hole re-entry. If the bit were once withdrawn, the hole would be lost; when the bit wore out, the hole would be finished. Diamond bits, wire-line coring, sea-water circulation would be used.

It sounded so simple. Just lower the pipe to the bottom and drill. At that time some of us were very naïve but in looking back I am inclined to believe that it was a good thing. If we had recognized all the problems that lay ahead, we might not have had the nerve to proceed. Fortunately we stumbled upon the difficulties one at a time over a period of weeks. But at least we knew where we were going.

There were to be three holes, each with different objectives, which would give basic data on ship positioning, on stresses in a long drill pipe subjected to the forces of the ocean, on logging holes beneath the sea, and on diamond-drilling and wire-line coring in very soft and very hard rocks. When the holes were completed we hoped to return to port triumphantly, laden with new information, and start designing a really deep-drilling rig.

The point of beginning was the *CUSS I*, which after a study of the other floating drilling rigs, we believed would be uniquely able to do the experimental drilling. It looked as if it could be modified and stretched beyond its usual capacity to drill holes a thousand feet into the bottom in deep water. In order to be sure we carefully studied its potentialities.

Naval architects Robert Taggart and John Marriner huddled over the ship plans with Hal Stratton and Ray Hobbs, the engineers who represented the ship's owners. They debated ship stability, how much weight could be added, and how the ship would be held in position. The last of these questions caused the most argument, the problem being whether the shallow-water mooring-line system should be transplanted to deep water or whether steering screws should be used. If steering screws were to be used, how many? And should there also be anchor lines to reduce the maneuvering? Ultimately all anchor lines were rejected in favor of four steering screws, arranged as previously described, large enough so that if one should fail the remaining three would be able to hold the ship against maximum winds and currents at the drilling site. The question of how powerful these propulsion devices should be depended on the natural forces they would have to oppose at the site selected.

Picking a site for experimental drilling was at least as difficult as finding a site for the ultimate Mohole, for we were limited by time, equipment, and funds. Although our eventual objective was to get as much geological data as possible, the immediate one was to get

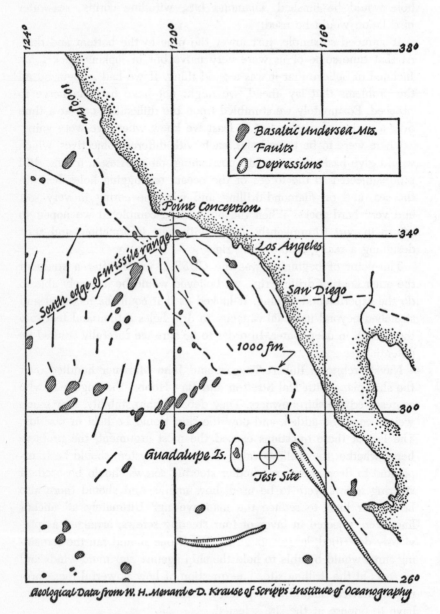

Fig. XIII-1 Test Site 117°-30' West 29° North

basic engineering information and drilling know-how. Because the *CUSS* was based in the Los Angeles area, we wanted to stay within two days' towing time of that port—about 300 miles. Second, we wanted the water depth to be about 12,000 feet—a depth much less than that would not stress the pipe sufficiently to make the tests meaningful; a depth of much more than that would put a thousand-foot hole beyond the stretch capacity of *CUSS*'s drill rig. Our problem was to find a place to drill that simultaneously fulfilled all these criteria.

We began by adding the geological data obtained from the Scripps Institution of Oceanography to a navigational chart, with the result shown in Figure XIII-1. The site would have to be south of the Point Mugu missile range (north of the range the weather was likely to be bad), beyond the edge of the continental slope (indicated by the 1000-fathom line), and in a geologically significant area. This last requirement was more difficult than we had expected. The sea bottom southwest of Los Angeles, which had seemed like a logical place to drill, turned out to be creased with faults and dotted with large undersea basaltic mountains. The map was so crowded with geological complexities there was scarcely room to drill a hole. Nevertheless, we eventually settled on a site between Guadalupe Island and the Mexican coast at 117°-30' W, 29°-0' N. The bottom seemed to be reasonably flat, the weather was believed to be favorable, and the area had been surveyed both by geologists and seismologists, who were of the opinion that the sediments were about 700 feet thick.

With a site definitely selected it was necessary to assemble statistics on the waves and winds and currents that would be encountered. These were gleaned from the records of the U. S. Navy Hydrographic office and reduced to usable form by Robert Taggart. Wind velocity at the chosen site was found to be less than 20 knots 97 per cent of the time, less than 15 knots 84 per cent of the time, and less than 10 knots 60 per cent of the time in all seasons. Similar statistics for surface currents and waves at the site are given in Table XIII-1. They showed that the weather in the Guadalupe area is about as mild as any that could be expected in the ocean, that winds and waves are uniformly from the northwest, and that the best weather is in the late fall months.

Two additional assumptions were built into the plan. First, the drilling program would be designed to fit the conditions that existed about 95 per cent of the time. If the winds or waves or currents

TABLE XIII-1

Statistics on Winds, Currents, and Waves
in the Guadalupe Island Area

	Jan Feb Mar	Apr May Jun	Jul Aug Sep	Oct Nov Dec
WINDS (11,578 Observations)				
% of time less than 10 knots	68	60	71	72
% of time less than 15 knots	87	84	92	90
% of time less than 20 knots	97	97	98	98
Average velocity for season	10.1 kts.	11.0 kts.	9.6 kts.	9.2 kts.
(From the northwest about 90% of the time)				
SURFACE CURRENTS (from H. O. 570 Atlas of surface currents)				
% of time less than 0.1 knots	35	5	78	81
% of time less than 0.2 knots	70	43	98	98
% of time less than 0.3 knots	99	98	99	99
Average velocity for season	0.17 kts.	0.23 kts.	0.12 kts.	0.11 kts.
(From the northwest about 90% of the time)				
HEIGHT OF WAVES AND SWELL (3,026 Observations)				
% of time less than 2 ft. high	24	22	27	27
% of time less than 4 ft. high	50	55	69	62
% of time less than 6 ft. high	73	82	90	87
% of time less than 8 ft. high	88	92	97	96
(From the northwest about 70% of the time)				

Compiled from U.S. Navy Hydrographic Office data by R. Taggart

exceeded those conditions, the ship would simply pull in the pipe and abandon the hole, returning to the site to start a new hole when the bad weather abated. Second, the ship would always be kept headed into the deep-sea swell to minimize roll. This implied that the largest drag forces—sidewise winds and currents—might be acting broadside on the ship part of the time. Fortunately the chances of this happening appeared to be small since winds, waves, and currents usually all came from the northwest.

Armed with these data and assumptions about the natural forces at the drilling site, it was a relatively easy matter to work out the sizes of steering screws required. Three 225-horsepower Harbormasters would hold the ship in all but the very worst weather; four would be installed in case one should fail.

John Marriner, the other naval architect on the study group, re-examined the stability and additional weight-carrying capacity of the *CUSS I*. In shallow water its drilling record showed it to be unques-tionably stable; however, some of this stability was attributed to the taut anchor lines and the excess of drilling mud which it carries for ballast.

Therefore, Marriner recalculated the metacentric height of *CUSS I* for several conditions of drilling far more severe than those the study group contemplated. Metacentric height is used as a measure of the tendency of a tilted ship to right itself; the larger it is, the more stable the ship. He found that if *CUSS I* were loaded—all water, fuel, mud, and cement tanks full and 13,500 feet of drill pipe in the racks—the metacentric height would be about eight feet. However with the weight of the drill string hanging from the crown block at the top of the derrick—a severe and improbable circumstance since much of the weight of the drill string is transferred to the rotary table at deck level as the vessel rolls—the metacentric height would be five feet. This compares favorably with the two-foot height of many large pas-senger liners, including the *Independence* and the *Constitution*. The *CUSS I*, Marriner concluded, is stable under the worst conditions and could even take on another hundred tons of weight if that were necessary.

The method to be used in determining the precise position of the ship during the experimental drilling was described in the previous chapter. First a ring of deep-moored buoys would be installed. Then sonar devices hanging beneath the ship would measure the distance to the underwater buoys; radar devices on deck would measure the dis-tance to surface floats; an instrument panel on the bridge would present the pilot with all the information needed to operate a cen-tralized steering unit. The steering unit would, of course, control the thrust of the four steering screws.

While this design was being thrashed out, the drilling-procedures group was working on the design of the drill pipe—the critical element in the system. We could not be sure that the chosen method of ship positioning was good enough until we knew more about the strength of the pipe. The question was: How far could the ship move off station before the pipe would break?

The Drill String

In order to make definitive calculations, a specific drill string had to be designed. The water depth would be 12,000 feet, the maximum hole depth 1500. So the problem was to decide what combination of alloys and strengths and sizes of pipe should be used as components in the 13,500 foot total length of the drill string. The decisions about sizes and characteristics of pipe were made after considering and rejecting many possibilities.

This is not a tremendous length of pipe by comparison with that used in the deepest oil wells but, if you can imagine a pipe 4½ inches in diameter laid out along the ground from your house to some point two and a half miles away, you can appreciate how little stiffness the experimental drill string will have. Dangling beneath a ship this pipe will be as limber as a wire in a wind. No longer will it have the guidance and lateral support of the sides of a hole; it will be subject to the whims of the ocean's currents.

Thirteen thousand five hundred feet of 4½-inch drill pipe, including the heavy section of drill collars at the bottom, weigh about 125 tons. This is a considerable weight of pipe to be supported by its own strength at the top but since standard strength E-grade pipe can support about 200 tons before yielding, this seemed safe at first. After all, such lengths and weights are commonly used by oil well drillers. E-quality pipe would be adequate if the pipe were not also subjected to bending at the top. However, the tension caused by the bending adds to that caused by the weight and the combined load could cause the pipe to break.

In ordinary oil-well drilling ashore the derrick remains vertical and the pipe does not bend; previous drilling from floating rigs had not reached to great enough depths to put sufficient tension on the pipe to endanger it. But our deep-sea drilling ship might roll as much as five degrees while the upper end of the pipe is supporting 13,500 feet of its own weight. Calculations indicated that pipe under this amount of tension could safely permit only half a degree of bending at the top. If the ship rolled more than that, the derrick would act like a gigantic lever to bend the pipe into a sharp kink at the rotary table and $100,000 worth of pipe might end up on the bottom of the Pacific.

A partial solution was to use G-grade steel, which is about 25 per cent stronger than the standard E-grade. This helped by increasing the strength of the pipe but this was still not enough to prevent failure if the pipe was bent sharply. We worried over this problem for a few days until Edward Horton, petroleum engineer on the staff, devised a trumpet-shaped "guide shoe" which, in effect, spread the five degrees of bending along a greater length of drill pipe and prevented kinking at the rotary table.

The guide shoe is simply a flared tube with a circular cross section which extends downward from the bottom of the rotary table for about forty feet. The curve of its inside is an arc corresponding to half a degree of bend. The drill pipe hangs inside it and when the

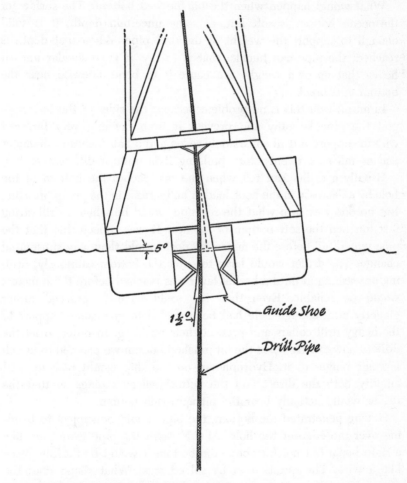

Fig. XIII-2 The guide shoe, which is rigidly supported in the drilling well, is a smooth funnel which prevents excessive bending in pipe when ship rolls and/or is displaced from its station.

ship rolls five degrees the pipe is supported in a smooth curve by the shoe. Thus any short section of pipe can bend only half a degree.

Another source of bending comes from the displacement of the ship away from a point over the hole. Even with a calm sea, if the ship moved 600 feet off station, the maximum we had decided to allow, this would cause the pipe to bend another degree and a half. So the 5-degree guide shoe was made a little longer to accommodate 6½ degrees of bending. The solution, a novel one, was reassuring and we proceeded more confidently to the next problem.

What would happen when the bit touched bottom? The surface of the ocean bottom is soft but, at some uncertain depth, it is solid enough to support the weight of the drill pipe. When that depth is reached, the pipe can buckle; that is to say, it is so slender and so heavy that its own weight can cause it to bend sidewise near the bottom and break.

In an oil well this is no problem because the sides of the hole support the pipe laterally and prevent it from bending very far. But with unsupported drill collars only seven and a half inches in diameter and as tall as a twenty-story building it is quite a different matter.

Usually a driller can tell when the bit reaches the bottom of the hole by a decrease in the hook load or an increase in the pump pressure. But no one was sure what the reaction would be when a drill string first touched the soft bottom of the sea. It was conceivable that the pipe would fail before the meters on deck would show any substantial change. The driller would have to enter the bottom cautiously, drilling or washing in until a harder layer was reached before these meters would be reliable. Even then he would have to proceed rather gingerly until enough hole had been drilled to give some support to the heavy drill collars and prevent their buckling. In order to let the driller know exactly when the bit touched bottom we planned to attach a sonar pinger to it. Hydrophones on the ship would pick up and amplify both the direct and the bottom-reflected pings so that the driller would actually hear the bit approach bottom.

Having penetrated the bottom, the pipe would be subject to bending over the edge of the hole. At that point the pipe would act like a rigid beam but not far above the bottom it would be flexible, more like a wire. The question to be solved was: What shape does the pipe take under various conditions? We found it would form what engineers call a beam-connected catenary on a more heroic scale than had ever before been contemplated. Luckily we had the advice and assistance of Arthur Lubinski, theoretical drilling expert of Pan American Petroleum Corporation. His own special set of equations, worked out over a period of years, were brought to bear on the problem and after repeated conferences and consultations with him, the staff learned how to work out the shape of the pipe for any situation that was likely to exist.

It was discovered that a major limiting factor in deep-sea drilling would be the bending of the pipe where it enters the hole. A series of factors contributed to this bending, the most important of which was the distance the ship is displaced from its station. Other causes of bending were the sidewise force of deep ocean currents and the Magnus force, either of which would tend to bow the pipe even if the ship were exactly on station.

In order to spread out this bending in the pipe at the point of entry and prevent kinking, we could have designed a guide shoe like that at the upper end of the pipe; however, a better solution was found.

No one knew in advance whether a hole in the beds beneath the sea would stand without caving. If the walls collapsed with a thousand feet of pipe in the hole, the pipe might be stuck. It was not likely that this would happen as long as the pipe was rotating and water was being circulated at high pressure; however, when these motions stopped—while a wire line was being run to retrieve a core, for example—the hole might easily collapse.

It was decided that the upper hundred feet or so of the hole should be cased. This would prevent caving in the softest zone and would afford a temporary refuge for the pipe while circulation was stopped. If the casing projected above the surface of the bottom, then the drill cuttings could not fall back into the hole.

Now if this casing, which ordinarily is heavy and rigid, were tapered where it projected above the bottom so that it became increasingly pliable toward the top, like a hollow fishing rod, it would lead the drill pipe in and out of the hole in a gentle curve.

The idea was a simple one, but the theoretical design of a tapered casing which permitted the drill pipe to bend just a safe amount and no more turned out to be a very difficult problem. Eventually Francois Lampietti, staff theoretician, solved it with the help of M. Ludwig of the Standard Oil Company of California and an I.B.M. computer.

The entire casing, both the bottom section which held the hole open and the upper tapered section, was to be lowered to the bottom

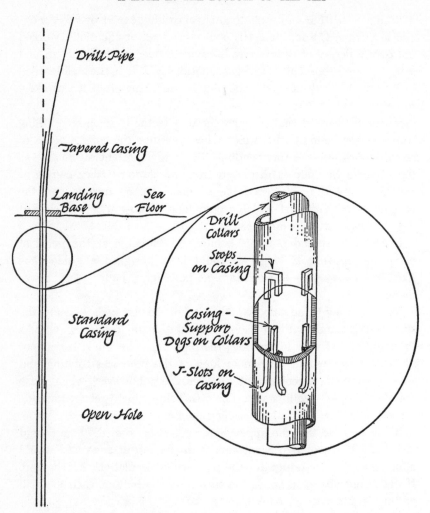

Fig. XIII-3 Casing for Experimental Holes

on the drill pipe by means of a pin-and-slot arrangement and drilled into place. Separating the two sections was a flat bearing plate which was to seat itself on the sea floor. Once the casing was drilled into place so that the bearing plate rested on the sea floor, the drill pipe could be detached from the slots supporting the casing and the drilling could proceed in the normal fashion.

The tapered casing was designed to permit the pipe to bend as much as 8° where it entered the bottom. With 30,000 pounds of drill collars holding the pipe in tension, even with maximum currents and Magnus force, the pipe would be safe even if the ship wandered 600 feet from its station. This was the figure we had been looking for; they made it clear that a positioning system which would keep the ship within 200 feet of its station gave us an ample margin of safety against possible human errors.

The final hurdle to be crossed in the design of a drill pipe is that of the vibrational stresses in the pipe. These dynamic stresses are difficult to estimate accurately in advance of actual drilling. They come from two main sources.

The first of these vibrations could occur when the drill pipe is simply hanging beneath the ship. Since steel is a very elastic material it tends to act like a long spring and longitudinal compression waves can run up and down it. In fact, a soft tension spring, such as a "Slinky" toy, can be used to make a reasonable facsimile of these vibrations. Hold one end, allowing the rest of the spring to hang down and come to rest. Then make a small vertical motion at the top, returning to the original position. You will see a wave travel down the spring, reflect off the bottom, and return to your hand. Now if you make a second motion at the top just as the first wave returns, the second wave you send down will be reinforced and amplified by the reflection of the first wave. If this sequence is repeated several times, a small motion at the top can become a very large motion at the bottom.

A similar resonance can be created in a springlike drill pipe by a ship that heaves and falls in response to the passing ocean swell. If several consecutive motions of the ship should coincide with the travel time of a wave down the pipe and back again, the pipe could tear itself in two.

The AMSOC staff computed the spectrum of waves in the test area, the response of the *CUSS I* to those waves, and the natural resonant frequency of 13,500 feet of drill pipe. Eventually we decided that for this length of pipe and this ship, a dangerous resonant condition does not appear to be likely. If longitudinal compression waves should become a problem later on when a longer pipe is suspended from a drilling ship which responds differently to the waves, it will be possible to put a number of rubber discs on the pipe and "damp out" this motion, reducing it to safe proportions.

Another form of vibration, commonly known in the oil business as pipe "whip," comes from rotating a pipe without the restraint of hole walls. Small eccentricities in the pipe start a series of waves

running up and down the pipe following patterns which are too complicated to calculate.

Fortunately for the AMSOC group, Henry Woods, an engineer at
Hughes Tool Company in Houston, Texas, had investigated this problem. He made a model of a drill string to find out how fast pipe
can be rotated without excessive whip. His model is 75 feet long,
of which the upper 60 feet is ⅛ inch in diameter (representing
4½-inch drill pipe) and the lower 15 feet is 3/16 inch in diameter
(representing the drill collars). The model pipe is a special plastic
weighted with tungsten dust representing the density of a steel drill
string. It hangs in a case that protects it from disturbing air currents
in a five-story stair well at the Hughes plant in Houston. This length
represents only a 3000-foot length of pipe since a full-length model of
the oceanic drill string (scaled to an eighth of an inch in diameter)
would be twenty stories high.

In the model the pressure on the bit and the rotational speed can be
varied. As these are adjusted to simulate the underwater conditions,
some very complicated waves run up and down the drill string. Some
waves are as long as the model; others have a wave length of about
fifteen feet; imposed on both are short waves with a length of about
three feet. Some seem to stand still; others move so fast that it is a
frustrating experience to try to measure them. However, the result
was that Mr. Woods advised us that vibrations probably would not be
excessive if the drill pipe rotated at speeds less that 60 rpm. This is
slower than optimum for drilling but a sacrifice that anyone who has
seen the waves in the model would willingly agree to.

There actually may be an advantage to having these transverse
waves in the drill string. It is possible that they will break up the
streamlines which cause the Magnus effect and reduce that force to
zero; this will in turn reduce the amount of thrust needed to hold
the ship in position and decrease the pipe bending. The only way
to be sure is to run the experiments.

Test Operations

The special study group was, happily, unaware of many of these
complications when it proposed a test drilling program. The members
felt that several holes should be drilled, each a little more difficult than
the previous one, each to try out a new technique.

The program would start with the modification of the *CUSS I* in some Los Angeles shipyard to prepare it for the experimental work. Four Harbormaster steering screws would be added and central controls for them installed. Radar and sonar devices would be attached to the ship; arrangements for racking another mile of drill pipe made, and drilling and housekeeping supplies loaded aboard. After leaving the outfitting site the ship would proceed to a nearby shallow-water navigational test site for a trial of the positioning and maneuvering procedures.

The plan was to establish a practice range about eighty miles south of Los Angeles harbor where the water is about 3000 feet deep; then, if trouble developed on the trials, the ship could return to port for further modification.

This practice range would be composed of a ring of underwater buoys complete with surface floats which would be approximately like those at the Guadalupe drilling site. This would permit the pilots to be trained, the electronic ranging equipment to be tuned, the steering screws to be tested and adjusted, and some of the pipe-handling equipment to be tried out. After several days and nights of practice during which the ship would be held at various orientations to the wind and waves, the pilots would be expected to have mastered the technique of holding the ship by maneuvering. Then the drilling crews would be brought aboard and the ship moved to the drilling site.

During the practice period an oceanographic ship will be working at the Guadalupe Island site remeasuring currents and installing deep-moored buoys. Wind and wave forecasting will have begun, probably in co-operation with the Mexican weather observatory on the south end of the island. Scientists will converge on San Diego, where a scientific ship will be ready to transport them to the drilling site.

When the drilling ship arrives at the site and enters the waiting ring of marker buoys, the positioning instruments and the maneuvering propellers will be rechecked. If the weather forecast is favorable, drilling operations can at last begin.

The drill string will be made up, starting with the diamond bit; above it come collars, bumper-sub, more collars, and drill pipe of three qualities—all as shown in Table XIII-2. The drill string will be assembled slowly, joint by joint, and lowered through the ship's center well. It will not carry a casing. As this drill pipe goes down for the first time, it will be accompanied by a rising level of excitement

TABLE XIII-2

The Experimental Drill String

	Minimum yield strength of steel (p.s.i.)	Length (feet)	Nominal weight per foot (pounds)	Weight per foot under water (pounds)	Total weight of section in water (pounds)
Kelly (round)	100,000	45′	—	—	—
Drill Pipe* 4½″ internal flush	105,000 (G grade)	1,500	20.0	18.5	27,750
Drill Pipe 4½″ internal flush	95,000	3,500	16.6	15.5	54,250
Drill Pipe 4½″ internal flush	75,000 (E grade)	8,000	13.7	12.8	102,400
Drill collars	120,000	300	117.3	100.0	30,000
Bumper subs	100,000	15 feet of travel	—	—	—
Drill collars	120,000	60	117.3	100.0	6,000
Diamond bit	—	1	—	—	—

Total Length 13,421 feet

Dead load 220,400 lbs.
Acceleration load 31,600 lbs.

Total hook load 252,000 lbs.
(126 tons)

* The uppermost pipe has a cross-sectional area of 5.5 square inches and can support a load of 530,000 lbs.; therefore, the safety factor is about 2.

The entire string except the kelly has a 3½″ clear internal diameter.

aboard the ship. The pipe will have been engineered as thoroughly as possible, but there is always the possibility that some important point was overlooked in the theoretical work. In a few hours the watchers on deck will know.

The pipe will be lowered through the water until the bit almost touches bottom. Then a survey of pipe slope at all depths will be made by running a directional log down the inside of the pipe. The results obtained will be correlated with current measurements to determine the effect of ocean currents on the pipe. Then the bit will be lowered to the bottom with constant circulation in order to find out if there will be a change in pump pressure and drill-string weight when the bit penetrates the soft material. The question to be answered is: Can the driller detect the bottom with his usual instruments?

Having touched bottom and entered it a little—the weight of the collars and the jetting action of the circulation can be expected to produce 50 feet of easy penetration—the pipe will be rotated cautiously at increasingly faster speeds, drilling deeper into the bottom all the time. At this stage the questions will be: What is the maximum pipe speed at which there is no harmful vibration, and does the Magnus effect cause a substantial amount of thrust or do the spiraling waves in the pipe cause it to cancel itself out?

Next the tests will learn about the "drillability" of the soft sediments. How fast will the bit penetrate? Is the bit carrying the proper weight of drill collars? At what depth do these unconsolidated strata become competent so that the hole will stay open without casing? And at what depth is the really hard rock of the second layer encountered?

The actual drilling in this operation will be continuous and, if the sediments are soft, 500 feet will be reached in a few hours. Most of the remainder of the estimated 32 hours spent on the first hole will be devoted to round-tripping the pipe. It is expected to take ten hours to reach bottom and another ten to return. While all these operations are going on, the pilots will be practicing holding the ship in position; the oceanographers on the nearby ship will be measuring winds and waves and currents and checking this information against the forecasts; the drillers will be "getting the feel" of deep-water operations; and the AMSOC Committee will be "sweating it out." As soon as this first test hole is completed and the bit retrieved, the drilling crew will immediately begin preparations for the next hole. If all the machinery works as planned and if the pipe vibrations are not dangerous at reasonable rotational speeds, everyone will feel much better about the chances for success. We will be ready to go deeper.

On the second test hole, casing will be set to protect the drill pipe from being stuck when circulation and rotation are temporarily stopped. This casing will be long enough to reach to a competent layer

—determined by the previous hole—beneath which the hole walls will stand without support. The upper end of this protective casing will be attached to the bearing plate, and tapered casing and the whole mechanism will be lowered on the drill pipe. The casing will be drilled into place so that the bearing plate is firmly grounded; then the pipe will be disengaged to drill deeper.

In this second hole the drilling will continue until the bit is dull or until the entire 13,500 feet of pipe is assembled. At that time the center of the doughnut-shaped coring bit will be retrieved with a wire line. The drill pipe will be withdrawn until its lower end is even with the bottom of the protective casing and the hole will be filled with high-density fresh-water drilling mud to help prevent caving. Then logging sondes will be run down the inside of the drill pipe, out thru the now-open bit and into the uncased hole below to measure various characteristics of the strata.

Most of the usual varieties of measuring sondes, including electrical, radioactivity, and sonic velocity logs, can be reduced to a size that will pass through the 3½-inch hole in the pipe. It may also be possible to lower hydrophones that can listen to explosions in the water at some distance and thus make a direct measurement of the travel time of seismic waves in the ocean bottom. A caliper survey of the size of the hole will be run in an attempt to find out how much the hole walls have been eroded by the hydraulic action of the drilling fluid. In future holes this information can be used to help determine proper pump pressure, necessary length of casing, and bit design. Finally, it may be possible to make a direct measurement of temperature in the bottom of the hole. It is hoped that this first cased hole will penetrate well into the hard second layer. If it does, the combined evidence of drilling rate and the various logs will give the scientists aboard a good clue as to its composition.

When the logging is completed, the drill pipe (and perhaps the tapered casing) will be retrieved. If all goes according to schedule and weather is favorable, the second hole will have taken less than five days.

By this time the pilots should be expert at holding the ship in position; the idiosyncracies of the interaction between the drill pipe and the ocean will be known, and the crews will be accustomed to their various tasks. They will be ready to tackle the third and most important experimental hole.

The third drilling experiment is designed to try out wire-line coring procedures in very soft and very hard rocks. This will be the first attempt to actually obtain core samples of the deep sediments and the second layer. This hole will begin as did the second one with the lowering of the casing on the drill pipe, utilizing the experience of the previous hole as much as possible. Once the casing is in place, an attempt will be made to take continuous cores to the greatest possible depth.

If the sediments are soft, as they may be for some distance below the bottom of the casing, punch cores will be taken. That is, a special core barrel will be hydraulically forced downward into the sediments for about ten feet through the center hole in the core bit. The core barrel is left in place while the hole is drilled down around it, after which the barrel is retrieved on a wire line. Then another core barrel is pumped down the pipe. This cycle of punching, drilling, and retrieving will be repeated until the strata becomes too hard to permit satisfactory penetration. When that point is reached, cores will be drilled in the usual fashion, in which the advancing bit leaves a core standing inside a regular core barrel. The barrel will be retrieved by the standard wire-line coring procedures which were described earlier.

There is always the possibility that the hole walls may collapse and the pipe will stick if the driller stops rotation or circulation for too long a time. Since the process of running in the wire line and recovering the core barrel may take two hours or more, precautions will be taken to prevent the hole walls from collapsing and sticking the pipe while circulation is stopped. When the core barrel is to be picked up, the hole will be filled with drilling mud and the drill pipe withdrawn until its lower end is even with the bottom of the casing. This will protect the drill pipe and maintain its position in the hole while the wire line is lowered and the core barrel retrieved. After the core barrel has been replaced, the bit will be lowered to the bottom and the drilling will resume. The estimated time required to core to maximum reach is approximately fifteen days. By this time the bit, which is actually drilling only about one-fifth of the time, will be worn out.

One point must be made clear. If the pipe is removed from any of these experimental holes, there will be no way to ever get it back in again. Therefore all operations must be done by means of the drill pipe alone. On the deeper Mohole, where it will be necessary to change worn bits and pipe, a riser pipe will have to be installed to maintain circulation and to find the hole again if weather forces the ship away from its station. But in these experiments where no great sum of money is involved in any one hole, it is cheaper to lose the hole and start over again than to install a riser pipe.

The lack of the riser pipe is, in one way, a great advantage. In the early days of deep-sea drilling when no one knows what will be found beneath the ocean, it will be well to have a flexible operation. Without a permanent riser pipe the site can be changed by merely moving buoys if the first holes indicate that is a desirable thing to do.

The total time scheduled for outfitting, practice maneuvering, moving to and from station, drilling the three holes, and waiting for weather is about two months. Once these experiments start it will not be long before the results are known.

Although the engineering of these experiments has been done as carefully as possible—at the time of this writing the sea trials have not yet been carried out—the staff was well aware of the uncertainties. The first page of its report, "Experimental Drilling in Deep Water," which outlined the program, said: "There are risks involved, and although these can be minimized by careful planning, it must be recognized that certain failures are possible. However, if anyone is ever to drill in deep water, a beginning such as this must be made which is characterized by the calculated risk rather than either recklessness or overcaution. That risk stems from incalculable dynamic forces on the drill pipe and the remote statistical chance of unusual weather."

The possibility that a string of drill pipe might be lost was recognized but the report made it clear that we were determined not to give up easily: "If the pipe is lost, it is irrecoverable since fishing in the test conditions is virtually impossible. Therefore, it is our plan to have an alternate drill string, perhaps of slightly different characteristics, held in readiness on the dock in Los Angeles. If the first drill string should fail because of some unusual circumstance or should be lost in an accident, the ship will return to port and pick up the alternate one. Such a loss must not be permitted to stop the project."

The product of these experiments will be the first direct knowledge of deep-sea drilling and of the strata beneath the sea. Since the cost of this work is now estimated at about $1.5 million, AMSOC will learn a great deal for a relatively small smount of money.

When the planned holes are successfully completed, U.S. science will possess in this modified drilling ship an incomparable tool for exploring the deep-sea sediments of much of the ocean. It is possible that subsequent work with the same ship using techniques developed in these experiments will go on for many years, gradually unveiling, bit by bit, the history of the oceans. But by then, AMSOC will long since have directed its attention to the Mohole itself.

In March and April of 1961 the experimental drilling program was successfully carried out. A series of five test holes were drilled in 3146 feet of water, about 25 miles west of San Diego, California. The deepest hole at this site was 1035 feet; casing was lowered on the drill pipe and implanted in the sea floor; cores were taken. The *CUSS* was then towed to the 11,700-foot-deep Guadalupe Island site where it successfully held position for three weeks and drilled five more holes, the deepest of which was 601 feet. The soft sediments were found to be gray-green oozes, 560 feet thick, of Miocene age. Beneath the ooze, a hard basalt was penetrated for 44 feet. Several kinds of logs were run in the hole, the temperature of the sediment at depth was taken, and a wire line coring turbodrill was tested.

These experiments conclusively proved that deep-sea drilling by the methods outlined in this chapter is feasible.

XIV

On to the Moho

When the experimental drilling has been completed, the AMSOC group will be much wiser in the ways of drilling at sea. Then, using this new hard-won knowledge, it will decide upon a method for drilling to the Moho itself.

As this is written, the plans for the ship, the drilling tools, the deep-water riser pipe, and the scientific work are hazy. The main factors that will influence the design are known but a great deal of engineering remains to be done. This chapter outlines the problems and possibilities. Since many of these items have never been discussed by the AMSOC Committee or by its panels and since the ultimate method of drilling may vary considerably from these suggestions, whatever burden of responsibility accompanies long-range forecasting must rest on the author.

Deep-Drilling Tools and Techniques

The chore of sorting through the many possible ways of conducting deep-drilling operations and selecting the best ones may not be as difficult as we at first expected. It appears now that the decision rarely will be marginal; usually there are overwhelming reasons why one method should be rejected and another accepted. But in the planning phase the policy is to listen to all ideas and then subject each one to rigorous engineering study until it proves unworthy of further consideration. Those that remain are tools for the Moho.

For example, one suggestion frequently received comes in the form of a question: "Why don't you put the machinery on the bottom?" Usually the contributor believes that all deep-sea drilling problems would be solved if the entire drilling outfit were made completely automatic and set up on the sea floor. The object would be to escape from waves and storms at the sea surface and to get the machinery closer to the depth at which the bit is working. However, none of the persons who have proposed this idea have made a serious attempt to answer such fundamental questions as: What supplies the driving energy? How is the drilling controlled? How are the cores retrieved? These are left for us to solve, and if we suggest that these may be difficult, we get the airy opinion that an atomic power plant and a little ingenuity will solve these difficulties.

Let us examine this proposal in more detail. Very few of the many steps in the standard drilling operations have ever been automated even though several seem to be in need of it; for instance: the making and breaking of pipe connections, the racking of pipe, the control of pressure on the bit. Although machines have been devised which perform these simple operations automatically, the expense of developing these machines to a point where they would be generally used in the oil fields has deterred drilling companies from making a real effort in that direction. As a result, there is virtually no experience with even the simplest aspects of drilling-rig automation. The reduction of all the other complicated operations of drilling to a remote-controlled automatic system, even if it were to be used on land only a short distance from the operator, is possible but it certainly would be a major undertaking. Furthermore, constructing a machine that would operate for a long time in muddy darkness under vast pressures in a corrosive environment where there would be very complicated interactions between various metals, where existing instruments would not work, and where repair would be virtually impossible, is obviously out of the question. Finally, even if such a remote drilling machine existed today, it would be very difficult to lower it to the bottom, erect it on a suitable foundation, and control it. A ship required to lower a rig and to keep the drill operator on station at the surface above would be as difficult to build as a drilling ship.

Another suggestion for drilling in deep water is that a buoyant platform be anchored with cables so that it floats about a hundred feet beneath the surface—something like one of our deep-moored buoys—but with six heavy cables holding it down instead of one light one. Then, as with the submersible mobile platform, long caissons from the float would hold the drilling platform well above the sea surface. The object of this would be to avoid wave action, but in return for this advantage the operator would have the much more serious problem of currents acting against catenaries that was described earlier. Although it might be possible to build such a structure, the cost of its development probably would be greater than the total price of reaching the Moho from a ship. True, wave actions is a problem but it must not be permitted to weigh too heavily in the creation of an optimum design.

Still a third scheme for putting the drilling equipment on the sea bottom requires that it be installed in a special submarine. The depth to which most modern submarines go is about a thousand feet or one-tenth of the shallowest likely drilling depth. The bathyscaphe, it is true, has dived to the bottom of a deep trench—about 35,000 feet. It can reach this depth because only the small spherical gondola—two meters in diameter—where the men ride is protected from the pressure. To build a submarine, a pressure-proof "igloo," or a bathyscaphe capable of drilling in the bottom is well beyond the range of present technology. Actually, some layout sketches have been made by one company for a submarine that might be used for oil-well drilling on the continental shelf in water depths of as much as 600 feet. This undersea drilling ship would have all the difficulties of a surface drilling ship except those of wave action and of holding position, plus a lot of much stickier ones, such as how the operators get back and forth to the surface. It requires a ship to stand by on the surface above which is nearly as large as a drilling ship.

There is another way of putting the drilling machinery on the bottom which AMSOC will very likely use when the deep hard rocks are encountered. This is the turbodrill.

All previous discussion of drilling in this book has been concerned with the "standard rotary method," used for virtually all holes in the United States over 10,000 feet deep. In it, the drill pipe is rotated and this, in turn, rotates the bit. Drilling mud is pumped down inside the pipe to flush the cuttings out of the way. In turbodrilling, the pipe is not rotated; instead, the mud being pumped down the pipe is used to turn a turbine at the bottom. These turbines are long slender hydraulic motors, in which the moving fluid strikes vanes attached to a rotor that turns at a high speed. The drill bit is attached directly to the rotor.

Almost any open-minded engineer who thinks about the rotary method quickly convinces himself that there must be a better way to drill a hole than by twisting a pipe several miles long. Yet, rotary drilling has been so highly developed and is so successful in the United States that turbodrilling has never been able to compete with it economically; consequently, it has aroused little interest here. On the other hand, the oil industry in Russia and in Western Europe, which has largely developed since World War II, has favored the turbodrill. Needing greater oil production in a hurry, the Europeans placed a premium on drilling speed; this the turbine delivers, at a slightly higher price. But in the highly competitive and often over-stocked U.S. oil business, few producers are willing to pay this bonus for speed and the choice of a drilling method depends almost entirely on the cost per foot of hole.

The Europeans also had other factors to consider. They needed to drill deeper to reach oil-bearing strata; their few available rigs had to be kept working at maximum speed; and poor-quality pipe caused frequent twist-offs when they used the rotary method. All of these things affected the development of the turbodrill. The Russians, its principal advocates, now turbodrill about 90 per cent of their oil wells.

Thus today's turbodrill is primarily a Russian-French development. Americans like to recall, however, that the first patent on a down-hole turbine was issued in the United States in 1873, and the first multistage turbodrill, from which all modern designs descend, was invented by C. C. Sharpenburg of the United States in 1924.

The turbodrill unit, which is attached to the bottom of the drill pipe, is thirty feet long, eight inches in diameter and weighs about three tons. Inside there may be a hundred or more "stages"—combinations of rotors (vanes connected to the shaft that drives the bit) and stators (vanes connected to the outer barrel of the drill). As the mud is pumped down the drill pipe at high velocity, the stators deflect the flow against the movable vanes which rotate the drill. The drill and bit rotate about 1000 rpm, approximately eight times as fast as rotary bits usually turn. In order to generate these speeds, large volumes of drilling mud must be pumped at high pressures; this means that substantial pumping capability is required and that the drill pipe becomes mainly a hydraulic transmission system. Because the drill pipe need not be rotated, there is little chance of twisting it in two, although it must still counteract the torque of the bit turning in the opposite direction. Moreover, without rotation there is no pipe whip. The friction of the turbodrill pipe against the walls of the hole, which in the rotary system wastes as much as 90 per cent of the power and wears the pipe greatly, is reduced to almost nothing.

Diamond bits are much better suited to the turbodrill's high speed than the standard tricone rock bits. They last longer and there

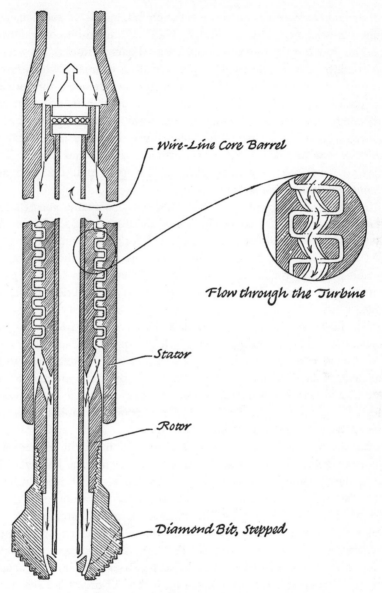

Wire-Line Core Barrel

Flow through the Turbine

Stator

Rotor

Diamond Bit, Stepped

Fig. XIV-1 The Wire-Line-Coring Turbodrill

are no bearings to wear out. The diamond-bitted turbodrill, a recent development, seems to have great promise. Experiments are now being carried out, mostly in France, to determine the best shape of bit, arrangement of diamonds, weight on bit, speed of rotation, and other factors. Some of the modern turbodrill diamond-bit combinations have drilled for two hundred continuous hours in rocks that dulled tricone bits in a few hours. Neyrpic, a French company which is the leading manufacturer of turbines, has greatly extended turbine life by introducing plastic turbine blades and a method for automatically adjusting bearings to compensate for wear. This suggests that if a turbodrill were specifically designed to use sea water as the driving fluid, the wear should be even further reduced and the driller's dream of drilling for a week without having to pull the pipe and change bits might come true.

In the years 1957 to 1959 the Shell Oil Company and Dresser Industries tested turbodrills in United States oil fields. They concluded that turbodrilling is worthwhile if: (1) the formation is hard and suitable for diamond-bit drilling; (2) the drilling fluid is not hot or abrasive; (3) round-trip time is long—if the hole is deep; (4) rig-operating cost is high; (5) adequate pumping facilities are available.

On all counts the Mohole qualifies. However, the AMSOC group wants more than a tool for making a hole rapidly in deep hard rock. Continuous cores are needed. A core 30 feet long is considered to be satisfactory in ordinary drilling operations. But to withdraw a turbodrill and all the pipe from the Mohole every time a 30-foot advance is made would be very inefficient. Cores from the Mohole must be pulled back to the surface on a wire line.

Packaging a turbine in a cylinder only 7¼ inches in diameter is quite an achievement by itself; to ask that it have a hollow space inside large enough to accomodate a core barrel might seem insuperable. Nevertheless Neyrpic has built and is now testing such a machine with bits supplied by Christensen Diamond Products of Salt Lake City, Utah. If this new drill continues to perform well as the tests proceed, it will be precisely the right sort of a tool for taking continuous cores in deep hard rocks such as the Mohole will encounter. A diamond-bitted, wire-line-coring turbodrill driven by sea water should satisfy those who think the drilling machinery should be on the bottom; it will be right at the bottom of the hole.

Since the sea water which drives the turbodrill will flow at high velocity, there will be substantial "hydraulic losses" caused by the friction of the water against the inside of a long pipe. One way to minimize these losses is to use a pipe of larger diameter. For the same amount of fluid passing down through the drill the fluid velocity inside the pipe will be lower, while that outside the pipe, which must raise the cuttings to the surface, becomes more rapid. Thus with increasing pipe size the entire hydraulic system becomes more efficient.

A large-size steel drill pipe with an internal diameter of six inches would be prohibitively heavy in the depths of the Mohole. Moreover, one of the advantages of steel pipe is its superior strength in torsion, resistance to twisting, a quality not required of pipe used for turbodrilling. So, aluminum drill pipe with steel tool joints—threaded ends for coupling pipe together—has been the subject of considerable study.

Aluminum has several important advantages over steel. It can bend three times as far without being overstressed, it is more corrosion resistant, and it is much lighter. In shallow, rotary-drilled holes these factors are not important and drillers use the less expensive steel pipe. Consequently, steel pipe was used exclusively in U.S. oil fields until September 1960. Then the Shell Oil Company, using pipe made by Reynolds Aluminum Company, successfully drilled a 10,000-foot hole near Victoria, Texas, with the first all-aluminum drill string.

In choosing a material to be used at sea the engineer's judgment is based on the strength-weight characteristics of steel and aluminum when both are immersed in sea water. He finds that underwater a cubic foot of steel weighs 424 pounds and a cubic foot of aluminum weighs only 108 pounds. The aluminum is only one-fourth as heavy. Thus even though the best grade of steel is 1.5 times as strong, the aluminum is a better material for deep-sea drilling pipe.

Another way of comparing the effective underwater strengths of these two metals is to calculate how long a piece of itself each will support. Earlier we noted that an untapered oceanographic cable (or a steel rod of any size) will pull itself in two if more than 35,000 feet are dangled over the side of a ship. But a rod of the best grade aluminum can support a piece of itself 88,000 feet long.

Aluminum pipe is not without problems; for example, there are two principal alloys, one of which is very strong, the other very corrosion resistant, but the best qualities of both cannot be obtained in the same pipe. Even so, for deep turbodrilling at sea, relatively thin-walled large-diameter aluminum drill pipe will be ideal.

On the Mohole drill string the aluminum pipe probably will be topped with a few joints of special steel pipe so that at the point of maximum bending it will be possible to take advantage of the greater strength and fatigue resistance of steel—fatigue that will result from repeated flexing of the pipe caused by the roll of the ship.

Pipe-handling operations on the Moho ship will be automated. As indicated previously, present oil-field practice is to manhandle pipe with chains, tongs, and elevators. The drilling platform is a nightmare of machinery and the procedures are, at best, clumsy and dangerous. No doubt oilmen have good reasons for so operating. However it seems clear that the assembly and disassembly of a drill string is an often-repeated operation that should lend itself admirably to automation.

Two groups, one in the United States and the other in Britain, have drawn detailed plans of machines to perform these operations. The British group, led by Hew Fanshawe of the National Research Development Corporation have devised a method for making and breaking drill pipe *while it is in motion*. They believe that their equipment, which is still on the drawing board, will be able to pull pipe or run it into the hole as a continuous operation and they estimate that round-trip time will be reduced by as much as 75 per cent.

International Drilling Machines of Dearborn, Michigan, has designed an even more sophisticated drilling machine. By adapting the concepts and techniques of the mass production machine tool industry, I.D.M. is well on the road to automatizing completely drilling procedures. Their engineers are not oil men and so are uninhibited by present drilling practices. They asked themselves fundamental questions about what it is necessary to do to drill a hole in the ground. As a result their "rig" has few points of similarity with those now in use. There is no structural steel derrick, no draw works, no tongs, and no rotary table. These are replaced, respectively, by a short and solid derrick tower, a hydraulic lifting unit, a "knockerchuck," and a "drillhead." Single joints of pipe are stored in horizontal racks from which they are seized and erected by a "transfer carriage." The pipe ends are then automatically aligned and spun to a tight joint with exactly the right amount of torque. The lone driller sits at a control console watching instruments that tell him exactly what weights and speeds and pressures are being applied. With dials and push buttons he controls the drilling. The high costs that will be incurred in developing these designs into generally useful trouble-free machines has made the oil industry reluctant to accept these ideas. However, the increasing cost of drilling may force automation on the drillers within the next decade.

An automatic pipe handler might work as follows: Disassembled, the individual pipe joints will be stored horizontally in tiers below deck. When pipe is to be run-in to the hole, the conveyors will pick up a joint and move it past automatic inspection equipment that will reject any pieces with flaws. The moving pipe will then be seized by grips that will bring it erect over the previous joint of pipe already descending. While both pipes are moving downward at the same speed, the new joint will be threaded and tightened to the one below. The grips release the lower one, take the next joint out of the conveyor, and raise it so that there is a continuous hand-over-hand assembly. Coming out of the hole the process will be reversed, perhaps with the addition of a step in which the threads are automatically cleaned and greased before the pipe is returned to its racks.

On shipboard there are even better reasons to handle pipe and heavy machinery with an entirely mechanical system. Men at sea should not be required to work around heavy objects that may move erratically with the roll of the ship. For safety's sake, everything that might be moved by the ship's acceleration should be "secured for sea." That is, round objects such as pipes must be held firmly so they cannot roll and hanging objects like the traveling block must be guided so they cannot swing. These can be kept from moving dangerously by a system of special racks and guides such as those used by present drilling ships. A better plan is to devise a system in which a rigidly mounted machine firmly grips the pipe and tools, and mechanically transfers them from place to place.

On a drilling ship there will be essentially unlimited space, weight-carrying capacity, and power. Therefore, designing an automatic rig to work on a ship will be simpler than making one to work in the oil fields, where it must be disassembled and moved after every hole is completed.

The Riser Pipe

In order to obtain certain basic geological and engineering data rapidly and inexpensively, the experimental drilling program skirted some difficult problems which must be solved before any really deep drilling can be done. Foremost among these is the design and installation of a riser pipe. The riser pipe is the special piece of casing that extends from the bottom of the sea almost to the surface. Without it, hole re-entry and return circulation of drilling mud cannot be accomplished. And without the capability for re-entering the hole, the total depth that a drill can reach is limited, as it was in the experimental work, by the distance one bit can penetrate before wearing out.

The principal job of the riser pipe, therefore, is to lead the bit and the drill pipe back into the hole in the sea bottom. The shallow, relatively inexpensive test holes could be permanently abandoned without great loss if the drilling ship was forced off station by a storm. But for the deep hole to the Moho, which will have a great deal of time and money invested in it, there must be a means of finding the hole again if the ship is required to leave the station temporarily.

Another good reason to have a riser pipe is that at some stage in the drilling, strata requiring some special kind of drilling mud may be encountered. This mud may need to have high density or heat capacity, or some other special characteristic. With a consumption rate of over five hundred gallons per minute, even the cheapest additive material would soon seem intolerably expensive if it were merely expended on the ocean floor. This means that a closed, continuous circulation system will be necessary to return the drilling mud to the ship.

A riser pipe is required, a fixed pipe between the sea floor and the sea surface, which is self-supporting and which will hold its position independently of the ship. This pipe must be firmly attached to the bottom and must rise 12,000 feet or more almost to the surface of the ocean. It must have an internal diameter of approximately fourteen inches to take the largest bit and tools needed for deep drilling. It must be strong enough to support itself in tension while being lowered, in compression and buckling while being installed, and against the bending forces of the ocean currents while in use. It must resist corrosion, electrolysis, and the attack of marine organisms.

The riser pipe cannot be supported by the ship. If it were, the hole would be lost when the ship left the station and a major purpose in having the riser would be defeated. The riser pipe must stand alone, being held in a vertical position by means of large underwater buoys so that its upper end reaches to within about a hundred feet of the surface. From the top of the riser to the ship a flexible pipe will carry the mud back to the ship. Guy wires, which can be released quickly and buoyed in time of emergency, will be used to steady the top of the riser with respect to the ship. Conceptually the riser will be much like the deep-moored buoys used for positioning the ship, except that instead of a slender wire a 14-inch pipe must resist the lateral forces of the ocean currents. This will be difficult to do, for pipe weight, current drag, buoyancy, and anchoring capacity must be carefully balanced, one against the other.

In addition, the riser must meet other requirements. For example, if high-density drilling mud is used it will tend to burst the pipe by creating an excess of internal pressure at the bottom of as much as 3000 psi. If the pipe is made of metal it must be able to withstand electrolytic action and corrosion of sea water for the useful life of the hole, which may be two years or more. And the riser must withstand the frictional wear of drill pipe, the logging tools, and the diamond bits which frequently will be run in and out of the hole.

Only a very remarkable pipe will resist all these forces for so long a period of time, but AMSOC is confident that it can be designed. Our ideas about the details of what it will be like are just starting to take shape. First, a suitable material must be selected.

Of the metals, the most promising possibility is an aluminum alloy which would have the good qualities of aluminum drill pipe—lightness and flexibility. Aluminum pipe is made by an extrusion process in which heated ingots are squeezed out through dies by huge hydraulic presses. This means it is possible to get any desired cross section and a pipe produced in this way need not be round; it could be made with side chambers as shown in Figure XIV-2. If these chambers were filled with gasoline and sealed at every connection, the result would be a continuously buoyant pipe. With this built-in buoyancy, the main supporting buoy at the top would not need to be so large and the additional walls of the chambers would contribute greatly to the strength of the pipe. One serious objection to aluminum is that comparatively little is known about its corrosion characteristics in the deep sea, especially when it is being continually flexed and subjected to corrosion fatigue.

Nylon or some similar synthetic substance might make a good riser pipe. A recently tested process makes it possible to join sections of nylon pipe together in the field in such a way that the connections are as strong as the factory-made pipe. With this method a riser pipe could be assembled as it is lowered from a ship. Nylon supporting buoys filled with gasoline could be added during the assembly as an integral part of the pipe. Since nylon is nearly weightless in water, the principal function of the buoys would be to hold tension in the pipe against the drag of the currents. The wall thickness would be designed to have proper strength at each level; near the bottom, for example, the walls would be extra thick to withstand bursting. Nylon's

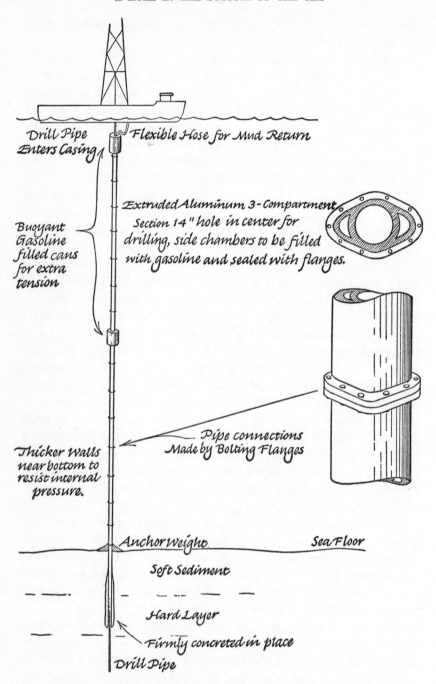

Drill Pipe Enters Casing

Flexible Hose for Mud Return

Extruded Aluminum 3-Compartment Section 14" hole in center for drilling, side chambers to be filled with gasoline and sealed with flanges.

Buoyant Gasoline filled cans for extra tension

Pipe connections Made by Bolting Flanges

Thicker Walls near bottom to resist internal pressure.

Anchor Weight   Sea Floor

Soft Sediment

Hard Layer

Firmly concreted in place

Drill Pipe

Fig. XIV-2 Aluminum Riser Pipe

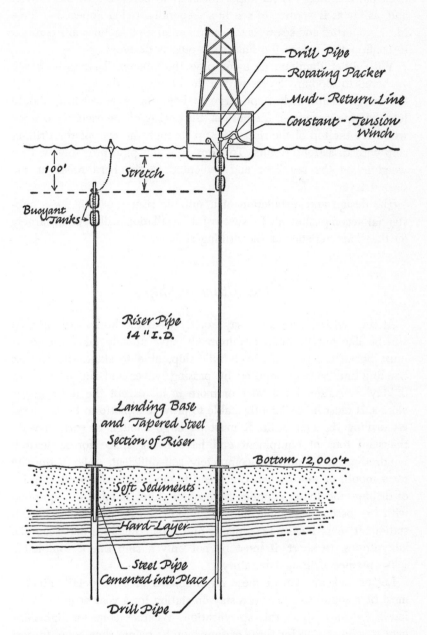

Fig. XIV-3 Elastic Riser Pipe of nylon-like plastic floats on buoys beneath surface when ship is not on station. During drilling, pipe is stretched up into well by constant tension winches.

principal advantage is its imperviousness to corrosion, to electrolysis and, as far as is known, to sea life. Generally, nylon appears to have ideal properties and sea tests of experimental pipe sections are planned to confirm this before the final riser pipe is designed.

With either aluminum or nylon pipe, the pipe will have to be firmly anchored to the hard layers within the bottom. If the upward pull of the buoys, deliberately kept large to hold the pipe vertical, should tear the pipe loose from the bottom, the energy of the excess buoyancy will drive the top of the riser pipe up through the well of the drilling ship with disastrous results. To avert this, the pipe probably will be weighted at the sea floor and cemented to the hard rocks of the second layer.

The design and installation of a suitable riser pipe will be a substantial accomplishment. Its successful installation will depend largely on the characteristics of the drilling ship.

The Ultimate Ship

At this writing we cannot say exactly what the Moho drilling ship will be like but its main requirements have already taken shape. It must be an exceptionally well-built ship, able to stand the endless bending and racking imposed by passing waves and rugged enough to stay on station for a year or more in all except the most severe storms. It must be sufficiently stable to provide a platform for the largest drilling rig ever built. It must be large enough to carry several thousand tons of equipment and have living space for at least a hundred men. It must be completely self-sufficient, able to operate for a month or more when the ocean is too rough to permit transfer of drilling and living supplies from other ships. It must be equipped with the best navigational and propulsion devices for remaining on station. It must have power plants and repair facilities and scientific laboratories. In short, it must be not only a ship but a completely self-contained drilling laboratory.

Let us look at each of these requirements in more detail. First, it must be a sound ship that can stay on station for a year or more. Very few ships must meet this specification. Weather ships or lightships may stay on station for three or four months before they come to port for inspection and repair but most ships spend a good part of their lives in harbors. If they are in protected waters and a storm comes up, they need not put out to sea or, if they are at sea, they can avoid storm areas. But the Moho drilling ship will be expected to stay on station and ride out all but the largest storms. We will select drilling sites where the weather is as favorable as possible and have a riser pipe to mark the hole if the ship is driven off by a gale. Even so the requirement that a ship remain on station for a year or more at a time is a difficult one.

Large ships look rugged but in some ways they are surprisingly fragile. An ordinary freighter scaled down to a three-foot model would have a skin as thin as this paper. Excessive flexing, caused by the passing swell, or "racking," caused by the ship being at an angle to the waves, can produce failures in the skin or in the structural members. All ships must be constructed to withstand this kind of wave action and much of their strength is in the keel. But the Moho ship will have a large open drilling well amidships which will reduce the structural strength at the place where it is most needed.

The most critical problem of hull design is keeping the roll and heave of the ship at a minimum so that the least possible motion is transmitted to the drill pipe. Captain Harold Saunders, USN (Ret.), for many years director of the David Taylor Model Basin, thinks that these motions might be greatly reduced by the addition of very deep bilge keels with heavy weights at the lower extremities. Small bilge keels are commonly used to reduce ship roll but ones of the size he proposes have never been constructed. The resistance that such keels would offer to ocean currents may outweigh the improved roll characteristics. Or perhaps they will not be needed; no one can tell without more calculations and model experiments in a wave channel. At any rate the naval architects will have to carefully adjust the metacentric height of the drilling ship so that the best compromise is reached between stability—tendency to remain upright—and comfort—tendency to roll easily. A too stable ship will act like a floating plank and rapidly adjust its slope to each passing wave so that it "snap rolls." This makes a most uncomfortable ship motion and in a drilling ship could produce unacceptable accelerations of the derrick.

The Moho ship will need living facilities aboard equivalent to those of a modest hotel for over a hundred men, including the drilling crew, the ship's crew, the maintenance crew, the specialty service crews, the scientists, and their visitors. It must have ample facility for making fresh water and storage for a month's supply of food. And there must be hospital and recreational facilities.

The ship must carry a complete stock of the supples required for drilling: pipe, mud, cement, spare parts. Furthermore, to insure that all the machinery is kept running, a complete heavy-duty shop with lathes, drills, milling machines, a welding outfit, and a supply of metal stock will be needed.

The ship will require a set of maneuvering propellers—probably four Voith-Schneider 1200-horsepower cycloidals set in special wells and driven by electric motors. It will be equipped with precision sonar and radar position-sensing equipment in duplicate so that when one fails, another can instantly be put in operation.

A completely automatic steering device will maintain the ship in position by using signals from one or more of the position indicators to adjust the direction and amount of propeller thrust. This device will replace the pilot, who, in the experimental drilling, watched the sensing system and personally manipulated the controls of the propulsion system. A man will still be required to preside over this pilot-house automation and make certain it is operating properly but many of the risks of human failure will be replaced by the lesser risk of mechanical failure.

Finally, the naval architect must consider the space and weight requirements for the drilling machinery and integrate these into the ship design. It is possible to say in a general way what kind of equipment will be needed. Any more detailed description will require a good deal of engineering study.

The actual drilling will be done, as previously indicated, by a turbodrill driven by a battery of heavy-duty, high-pressure pumps which will be heavy but require little space. However, the drill pipe and the machinery that handles it will be bulky, requiring as much room as a good-sized house.

The riser pipe will require a lot of space but since it is installed in the first days on station, the pipe sections can be carried in temporary racks. The bulky and heavy casing for lining the hole will have to be stacked in several sizes so as to be readily available when needed.

The other drilling facilities, equipment, and tools probably will be similar to those used on deep holes and drilling vessels today. There will be concreting equipment, fishing tools, special mud ingredients, and so on, carried aboard and ready for use at all times. With relative ease they can be fitted into the various cubbyholes that honeycomb a ship.

The ship designer is more concerned with how the large underwater equipment will be handled. For example, the large buoys supporting the riser pipe must be assembled, fastened to the pipe, filled with gasoline, and lowered cautiously. This work must be done through a large center well, perhaps twenty feet in diameter, beneath the derrick.

The center well must have high enough walls so that water does not slop over into the ship, and there must be at least twenty feet of clearance between the top of the well and the derrick floor so that the large buoys can be moved in under the derrick. The well will be equipped with a movable cover or decking that rolls on special tracks. Then the buoys and other heavy fittings can be assembled on top of the well cover, rolled in under the derrick, picked up by the hoist, and lowered through the well after the cover is rolled out of the way again. This well cover will be sturdy enough to support casing strings while they are being made up and tight enough to seal off the opening in case of a storm. During drilling operations a guide shoe or some similar device will be installed in the well to prevent kinking of the drill pipe caused by the roll of the ship.

The derrick itself will be of unusually rugged construction in order to resist the violent acceleration forces that may occur while handling heavy loads in a seaway. It probably will have the usual draw works and hoisting blocks, but much of the raising and lowering of the pipe will be done with hydraulically operated elevators. The actual drilling will very likely be done with automated machinery like that previously described.

Power for the draw works, the propellers, the pumps, and virtually everything else on the ship will be furnished by a bank of large diesel generators. These will be furnished by the Electro-Motive Division of the General Motors Corporation as a contribution to science.*

The requirements just listed are formidable enough to make even the most intrepid naval architect pause. Probably no one had ever required so much of a single ship before; nevertheless, one had to be found. After examining the plans of many kinds of ships, we reached the conclusion that no ordinary hull could be modified for our purpose. The trouble with most ships is that the keel, the propulsion machinery, and the living quarters are amidships, right where the

---

* GM Vice-President N. C. Dezendorf, on hearing Gordon Lill speak at the Undiscovered Earth Conference in Birmingham, Alabama in June 1959, was so impressed with the scope of the deep-drilling project that he made an offer on the spot to loan AMSOC a million dollars worth of generators, "for the duration."

center well and derrick should be located. Thus, to convert a merchant-man to a drilling ship would require alterations that would be more expensive than building a new ship. Of existing hulls, that of a large tanker came closest to meeting our requirements and we were considering one when John Marriner suggested that we might use an ARD.

An ARD (Auxiliary Repair Dock) is one of the many kinds of floating dry docks that the U. S. Navy built during World War II to repair ships close to the fighting zones. The reserve fleet has a dozen of these dock ships, all in excellent condition even though they have not been used for fifteen years. Four are kept at the Long Beach, California, Naval Station, where John Marriner and the author boarded one to inspect it. We were astonished by its size as we climbed down into the bottom of the dry dock. It reminded us of a floating football stadium.

The ARD is 489 feet long, 81 feet wide outside, and has a rated lifting capacity of 3500 tons. When its well deck is submerged, ships such as destroyers and LST's can be brought inside for repairs. Then the stern gate is raised and the water inside is pumped out, leaving the damaged vessel standing high and dry in a huge open room 61 feet wide and 426 feet long with walls 30 feet high.

The AMSOC Committee, although having little use for this docking capability, quickly realized that the same features needed for a dock are needed for a drilling ship. That is, the ARD is something like an ordinary ship turned inside out. Instead of having its strength in a center keel, its rigidity comes from the wing walls, each ten feet thick, which run the length of the ship. Inside these walls are the machinery and the living quarters, just the opposite of most ships. These walls converge and thicken at the bow, thus making room for a large machine shop below and pilothouse, wardroom, and boat deck topside.

We found it easy to imagine this hull converted into a drilling ship. Its great advantage is, of course, the 25,000 square feet of unobstructed docking area. A large drilling well could be cut in the center of the dock without damaging it structurally, and maneuvering propellers could readily be installed in wells at the corners.

On the upper of the two decks within the wing walls there are living accommodations for a crew of 110, including galley, mess, and hospital. The lower deck has huge pumps, facilities for making fresh water,

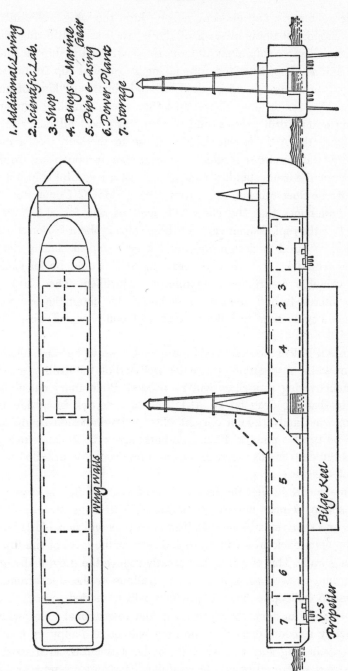

1. Additional Living
2. Scientific Lab.
3. Shop
4. Buoys & Marine Gear
5. Pipe & Casing
6. Power Plants
7. Storage

Wing Walls

Bilge Keel

V-S
Propeller

Fig. XIV-4 The ARD Converted to a Drilling Ship

electric generators, and air compressors. Atop the wing walls, mobile cranes capable of doing all sorts of chores, such as transferring materials from a supply ship alongside, run the length of the ship on tracks. The machine shop, intended for making substantial repairs on war-damaged destroyers, could be used to build almost any kind of hardware needed for drilling. There are lathes, presses, milling machines, welding outfits, drill presses, and a supply of stock, all ready to go.

In short, the ARD is astonishingly close to the ship that a naval architect, starting from scratch, would design for deep-sea drilling. Perhaps by the usual standards an ARD is not a beautiful ship but the sight of one does quicken the hearts of the AMSOC Committee. We have fond hopes that the Navy will lend us one for a few years.

Because the replacement value of these ships is about $6,000,000 and the time required to design and build a new ship of similar characteristics would be at least two years, an ARD would be an exceedingly valuable contribution. Optimism is justified. The Navy has shown interest in both the search for knowledge about the ocean and the new engineering techniques that will come out of deep drilling.

If an ARD does become available it will have to be remodeled. In addition to the installation of a center well and all the drilling machinery, maneuvering propellers will be needed. Preliminary calculations indicate that the drag on an ARD hull and derrick broadside to a 60-knot wind and a 2-knot current—the maximum-design conditions—would be 130,000 pounds. Four 1250-horsepower Voith-Schneider propellers can deliver this much thrust and these could be installed in the floor of the dock.

To make certain that the hull will stand years of flexing caused by wave action, it may have to be stiffened with large structural-steel braces and transverse bulkheads. The stern gate will be welded closed and the open dock area will be roofed over at the level of the tops of the wing walls. This covering will greatly reduce the drag of the wind on the hull as well as protect the operations in the dock from the weather. A helicopter landing platform will be added.

The living quarters, the galley, and the recreational areas will be completely remodeled so that the men will be as happy as possible during their long stay at sea. And finally, a scientific area must be constructed where cores can be examined, instruments repaired, and thinking done.

This remodeling of an ARD will result in a satisfactory platform to hold our tools for digging through the crust. After testing it in increasingly difficult situations, we will finally put to sea to drill the Mohole.

Scientific Work

The many practical engineering problems of deep-sea drilling are apt to make one forget that the principal objective of the Mohole is to obtain scientific information. That information will come from four major sources: (1) continuous core samples of all the rocks penetrated; (2) logs made with geophysical surveying instruments; (3) oceanographic measurements; and (4) instruments left in the completed hole that will take records over a period of years.

The cores themselves will contain by far the largest part of the information and a great effort will be made to insure that undisturbed material is brought to the surface for study. When the hole is completed, the AMSOC scientists hope to have an essentially continuous rod-shaped core of rock about 2.5 inches (6 centimeters) in diameter and three miles (5 kilometers) long.

It will not be easy to obtain complete core recovery in the Mohole because as the bit penetrates the various layers it will pass from very soft to very hard rocks and back again. When these contacts are crossed, the driller may have to change coring techniques—perhaps trying a different bit, a different core barrel, or a different drilling speed—to get the best results. The project's success will depend largely on the material contained in the core barrel that the driller presents to the shipboard scientists.

The core barrels will be retrieved by a wire line equipped with a latching clip as described earlier. Wire-line latching clips are standard pieces of oil-well equipment but the one used in the Mohole will be especially equipped with a gyroscopic direction finder.

One of the objectives of drilling in the deep rocks is to obtain oriented cores from which the magnetic history of the earth can be worked out. This means that the direction of true north of the cored material while it is part of the deep rock must be known. To do this, one side of the vertical cylinder of core must be marked with a scratch that indicates some known direction; then the direction of that scratch must be determined. In the oil fields geologists commonly obtain core direction by photographing a magnetic compass that is incorporated into the core barrel. This is satisfactory for the purpose of mapping oil structures but not for the Mohole.

Very little is known about the meaning of compass direction deep in magnetic rocks; it may or may not point in the same direction as a compass on the surface above. Moreover, if an objective is to measure the direction of the magnetic field at depth, true north in the hole must be determined independently by a gyroscope.

Only a gyroscope expert can fully appreciate how difficult it will be to build an instrument that will meet the requirements of orienting cores in the Mohole. The gyro must measure direction precisely and transmit it to the surface; its temperature must not vary more than a degree even though the medium that surrounds it changes by 150° C; it must be contained in a case that can resist up to 15,000 psi; and the entire instrument must fit in a cylindrical package whose outside diameter is about three inches.

Happenstance brought two gyroscope experts together on the AMSOC staff: Dr. Jack McLelland, inventor of a precise mine-surveying gyroscope, and Phillip LaHue, an electronics engineer loaned to the project by the Minneapolis-Honeywell Regulator Company, largest makers of gyroscopes in the world. Together they showed that it is feasible to build an accurate core-orienting gyro and persuaded the Honeywell Company to start work on a prototype.

They plan to determine core orientation as follows: As the core enters the barrel, a diamond point on the core-catcher will mark one side of it with a scratch. After the core fills the barrel, but before the bottom of the core has been broken loose from the rock below, a wire line will be lowered to which is attached a combination latching device (to retrieve the core barrel) and a gyro orienter. The latcher, with its gyro direction finder, will only attach to the core barrel in one position. When the two are joined, the orientation of the core barrel will be reported to the surface. Thus when the barrel is brought back to the surface the direction of the scratch on the rock is known. In this manner core direction can be determined within the width of the scratch mark—about one degree.

The driller will turn the core barrel and all the data he has obtained pertaining to that piece of core over to the scientists; then he will pump another barrel down the hole and resume coring. The scientists will carry the core barrel back to the ship's laboratory and make a preliminary examination of its contents. Later on they will wrap and seal it carefully for shipment to laboratories ashore where a precise analysis can be made.

The shipboard scientists will begin by removing the core from the barrel with great care, making certain that no valuable fragments are lost and that the layered structure is undisturbed. The kind of rock should be apparent at a glance. Microbiologists will take sterile samples of the core's interior to find out if there is life deep in the rocks. Rock mechanics experts will make sheer strength tests of selected short segments of sediment. Those two groups must have the first chance at the uncontaminated core.

Then, if the core is sedimentary material, the paleontologists will look it over. A rapid inspection of its outer surface may locate foraminifera or other fossils revealing the geologic age of the strata to these experts. Cores of soft sediments may be sliced down the center and the two halves laid side by side. This may expose more fossils as well as making it easier to observe the stratification. There may be abrupt changes in color or texture from layer to layer but more often the boundaries are indistinct, a situation which may be attributed either to changes in oceanic sedimentation or to burrowing organisms that plow up the bottom. Or perhaps a long section will be uniform and barren of fossils as the red clays often are. The scientists at sea will not be looking for details. They will be satisfied to keep track of the major changes in rock type and age which may be of immediate importance in determining how to proceed.

Eventually, portions of the sedimentary cores will be distributed among paleontologists, stratigraphers, chemists, physicists, and biologists in laboratories ashore. Each looks at his little piece from a different point of view.

The paleontologist will want to examine the entire core minutely, looking for any clue about life in the past—its kind, its environment, its age. The stratigrapher is interested in the amount of compaction with depth and time. The chemist-mineralogist will analyze his portion spectrographically to determine what elements are present and in what proportion. From this he may learn something about the origins of the sedimentary particles and the changes they have undergone while on the sea floor. The radiochemist will "count" his part of the sample in an analyzer to determine what radioactive isotopes are present and in what quantity. He will try to discover if any of these are sufficiently abundant to produce a significant amount of heat and he may try to get radioactive dates at several depths. The physicist will want to determine the physical properties of the material—its density, the velocity at which it conducts sound, its thermal conductivity, its magnetic properties. The biologists will be looking for traces of living organisms found deep in the sedimentary rocks. It is possible that anaerobic bacteria or virus-sized creatures live there. The principal difficulty would be in preventing the cored material from becoming contaminated by surface life brought down by the drilling fluid.

As cores are obtained from deeper, older, more remote rocks, all of these specialists will be increasingly on the lookout for anything unusual that may reveal some unsuspected fact about the history of the earth.

At some time the drill will pass through the sedimentary rock into the igneous rocks below. Then the paleontologists and stratigraphers and biologists will lose all interest; in their place will appear the petrologists. These are the specialists in crystalline rocks, who will slice their portion into thin sections for examination under the polarizing microscope in order to determine the kinds of minerals that are present. The petrologists will then try to determine from the quantities and interrelationships of the minerals how the rock was formed. The physicists and chemists will continue to work with the cores of the deeper rocks, making measurements similar to those they made in the sediments. In the deep crust and in the mantle their findings will be of increasing interest to geodesists and seismologists, who will use the more refined information about rock density and seismic velocity to recompute the mass and thickness of the crust.

Occasionally little cubes of rock will be sliced out of the cores with a diamond saw. These cubes will be cut so that one flat side faces north and another one is horizontal—orientations derived from the position of the scratch on the core's side. These carefully prepared specimens will then be placed in a device which measures the magnetic orientation of the particles so that the former direction of the earth's magnetic poles can be determined.

The deep crust is likely to be a reasonably homogeneous rock and for many thousand feet there may be no important change in composition. If this appears to be the case after a thousand feet of it have been penetrated, the drillers may alternate coring bits with full-hole bits. If the drill is kept running without stopping to pull core barrels for as long as a turbine will operate and a diamond bit will stay sharp, the hole will deepen much more rapidly. No appreciable scientific information will be lost and the average drilling progress in the very hard rock below 20,000 feet might be substantially increased.

Eventually the Moho itself will be reached and cores of the mantle will be obtained. No one can say today how the Moho will be recognized. If it is a neat contact between two quite different kinds of rock as the first chapter suggested, then it may be easily identified. More likely there will be an almost imperceptible change in rock properties —the density will increase, the minerals will occur in new ratios, there will be a change in the water content. If this is the situation, then it will be necessary to drill well beyond the region of uncertainty and determine the Moho position by subsequent laboratory analyses. In any event the intention is to drill hundreds of feet into the mantle so that hundreds of pounds of core will be available for study.

Many scientists will want to study the cores from all levels in the various ways just described. Since there will be relatively little core material from some zones and many examinations to be made, AMSOC has set up a technical panel on Scientific Objectives and Measurements headed by Dr. Harry Ladd and Dr. James Balsley— paleontologist and geophysicist respectively of the U. S. Geological Survey—to decide how the work will be apportioned. The panel will determine priorities and decide which scientists or laboratories are best qualified to examine the cores. Eventually the work will be completed and reported on in the scientific journals; then the cores, or what remains of them, will go to the Smithsonian Institution in Washington, D.C.

The panel is also concerned with the "in-hole" measurements which are made by logging the characteristics of the rock in the walls of the hole with geophysical instruments. The logs will have two important purposes. They will give a record of layers from which complete cores may not have been obtained and they will measure properties of the rock in place—properties which may differ from those observed in the cores after pressure and temperature have been greatly reduced.

Some of the kinds of sondes, as the instrument packages are called, were described in the chapters on drilling. Lowered on multiconductor cables to the bottom of the hole, they are reeled in at a constant speed while information about the rock they are passing is recorded on the surface. In the experimental drilling the diameter of the sondes was limited to about three inches, but the Mohole will accommodate ones nearly twice that size. This opened new possibilities and Phillip LaHue, our electronics expert, was asked to review all the in-hole geophysical measurements that might be made, so that the panel could determine which would most effectively achieve AMSOC's objectives.

LaHue made a list of twenty measurements which might yield useful information. A number of these were rejected on the grounds that they would duplicate measurements more accurately made on the cores themselves, or that they would produce results of uncertain value, or that the development would be unacceptably expensive. But after careful screening, the list still included measurements of radioactivity, velocity of sound, density, intensity and direction of the magnetic field, and temperature.

Radioactive logging was described earlier but we might look briefly at how the other measurements will be made.

The velocity of sound in rock can be measured directly. A miniature transmitter at one end of the sonde sends out a series of pulsations. These sounds travel through the adjacent rock until they are picked up by two receivers at the other end of the sonde, one three feet farther from the transmitter than the other. Precise measurement of the difference in the time of the arrival at the two receivers gives the speed of sound—the seismic compression wave in rock.

Another method of measuring compression-wave velocity would be to lower geophones into the hole and make recordings while a ship several miles away on the surface sets off explosive charges. If this is repeated while the geophones are suspended opposite each major layer, the result will be similar to that of seismic-refraction work at sea but with the great advantage that the velocity of sound in each layer will be measured directly. With this method the velocities obtained will apply to a large area rather than to the rock immediately surrounding the hole as in the previous case.

The density of the rock in the hole walls can be determined by means of a "gamma-gamma" log. If a source of gamma radiation such as radioactive Cobalt 60 is mounted on one end of a sonde, the rays penetrate the rock in all directions. Some small part of these rays are reflected—back-scattered—in proportion to the density of the rock. If the other end of the sonde contains a Geiger counter shielded by a mass of lead from the direct radiations of the Cobalt-60 source, the change in amount of reflection can be measured and rock density determined.

Density might also be measured with a down-hole gravity meter. Several groups have worked on the development of such an instrument but none have announced successful completion as yet. With sufficient money and time the many formidable problems of holding a gravity meter rigidly, of leveling it, and of protecting the springs from temperature changes could be solved. However, AMSOC would be reluctant to try to develop this instrument.

Magnetic-field intensity and direction have not yet been measured in a hole but it probably is possible to do so. A proton precession magnetometer could be fitted into a sonde to make the intensity measurement. Direction could be determined by comparing photographs of a compass needle with the direction of true north as indicated by a gyroscope. This gyro would be the same instrument used to orient the cores.

The exact temperature of the rock at depth is a desirable piece of information but hard to obtain. The difficulty arises because the rock is warmed by the frictional heat of the drilling and cooled by the drilling fluid. The thermal conductivity of rock is so low that once its original temperature has been disturbed it may take months or years to reach equilibrium again. The temperature can be taken by means of an electrical thermometer lowered to the bottom of the hole and left there for an hour or so, but the results may not be accurate enough to determine heat flow. A more precise measurement would be time-consuming.

All the logging sondes must be able to stand pressures up to 20,000 psi, temperatures up to 200° C for a matter of hours, and they must be lowered on a special cable which can transmit their measurements back to the surface. One of the possible logging cables has six electrical conductors protected by a steel sheath made of two layers of armoring wire wound in opposite directions. This cable, with its diameter of less than half an inch and breaking strength of 18,000 pounds, has already been successfully used in oil wells of over 20,000 feet. If it is to go much deeper, step-tapering like that of the oceanographer's cables may be required to give it sufficient strength. The high temperatures and pressures in the deeper part of the hole could greatly reduce the electrical resistance of the insulation; if so, some other kind of cable or method of getting the information to the surface will be required. It is possible to log with a single conductor cable by electronically coding the data in the sonde and telemetering it up the wire. This requires more complicated electronics but the changes in the resistance of the conductor are not so important and the cable is simpler and cheaper.

Another unusual problem of logging from the Mohole ship will occur as the ship moves up and down with the tides and constantly changes its position with respect to the hole. The result will be that the depth of the layers may appear to change from log to log. Therefore, a method must be found so that logs taken at different times can be accurately marked for depth. One way is to use a system of reference marks.

We propose to use a side-wall gun to shoot radioactive slugs into the wall of the hole at intervals of about 600 feet. If all sondes are equipped with gamma-ray detectors which can identify these radioactive markers, it will be possible to compare exactly logs taken at different times, by matching up the gamma-ray signals.

A third group of scientific objectives of the Mohole project lie within the field of oceanography. Little is known about the motion of oceanic water masses but enough measurements have been made by ships moving from station to station to demonstrate that temperature, chemical content, and the direction and velocity of the deep currents are constantly changing. The patterns of change remain a mystery partly because not enough data has ever been taken at any one place to develop a continuous picture of the sequence of events.

It would be expensive to keep an oceanographic ship on one station for a year or more to make continuous records of all the changes at that spot and no scientific institution has felt that they could spare a ship and scientists for that length of time. However, the Moho drilling ship will have to remain on station for a long time anyway and if it is equipped to make certain oceanic measurements, it can make a substantial contribution to the understanding of the sea. The extra scientists, instruments, winches, and laboratory space needed for this work would be a minor addition to the total cost of the project and much of the data would be of direct value to the drilling operations.

Perhaps the most important information that could be obtained would be a continuous record of the velocity and direction of the currents at all depths for the duration of the drilling program. If the Moho ship can be held in position in all weather as we hope, it will offer a unique deep-sea platform for making current measurements. Oceanographers know in a general way the direction of motion of the ocean's huge water masses. Within these water masses there must be both horizontal and vertical turbulent eddies, the effect of which may be local reversal of current direction. There must also be zones of shear created when currents at different depths move in opposite

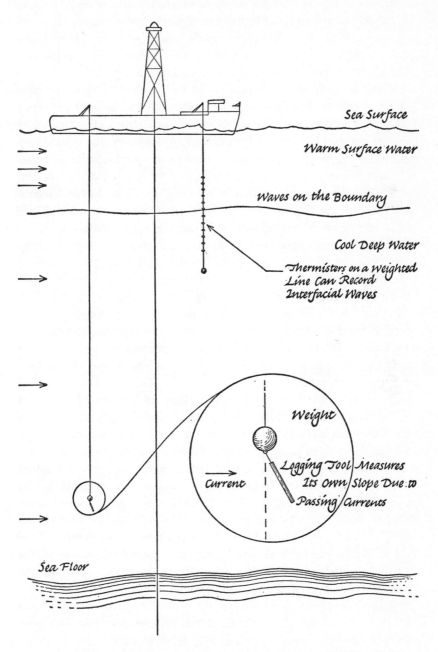

Sea Surface

Warm Surface Water

Waves on the Boundary

Cool Deep Water

Thermisters on a Weighted Line Can Record Interfacial Waves

Weight

Current

Logging Tool Measures Its Own Slope Due to Passing Currents

Sea Floor

Fig. XIV-5 Oceanographic Measurements from a Drilling Ship

319

directions or when there are large differences in velocity between layers of water moving in the same direction. There may be jetstreams within the ocean like those in the atmosphere. Unfortunately, the few measurements made to date give only the sketchiest indication of these motions. No one will know they exist until a continuous record has been made of the deep currents over an extended period.

Current-measuring instruments could be attached to the riser pipe but this would add to the already considerable problems of installing that pipe. Or currents could be measured by instruments attached to the deep-moored buoys used for positioning. However, the most direct method would be to make measurements from a multiconductor cable held taut between the ship and the sea floor. The lower end of the cable would be anchored with a heavy weight and the top end would be secured to the ship by an elastic line which would prevent the roll of the ship from disturbing the cable and the instruments.

Current meters capable of measuring currents of about 5 centimeters per second would be attached to the cable at regular distances, perhaps every 1000 feet. Their measurements would be continuously telemetered up the wire to the surface and recorded on the ship.

Another measurement which might be made from the ship is that of the interfacial waves moving along the surface of the thermocline. The thermocline is the boundary between the warm layer of surface water and the colder water below. Because of the temperature difference, there is a rather abrupt change in the density and waves travel along the interface. These interfacial waves are hard to measure and little is known about their velocity and wave length, or how and where they originate. But much could be learned if continuous records were made of them passing a fixed position in deep water. If a thermister cable, a string of electrical thermometers spaced at ten-foot intervals, were dangled from the ship, temperature changes in the zone of the thermocline resulting from the passage of these waves could be recorded. The rise and fall of the cold deep water on the string of thermisters would be analogous to the change in water level against a piling as surface waves pass. If a pair of thermister cables were suspended from the ship—one off the bow, the other off the stern—the direction of the waves might be determined.

These examples serve to indicate the possibility of making new and valuable oceanic measurements from a semipermanent scientific laboratory at sea. The oceanographers will think of many more.

Finally, when the Mohole is completed, it may be possible to install instruments in it that will continue to collect data for years. There are several valuable pieces of information that cannot be obtained until the drillers have left and quiet returns. One of these is precise rock temperature after it has returned to its original value. Another is the amount of deformation of the hole walls—essentially rock flow caused by pressure. Still another might be the collection of whatever gases and liquids may be flowing outward from the interior of the earth over a long period of time. It is not known how these measurements will be made or if they will be worthwhile; this lies beyond present planning.

However, one instrument will almost certainly be left in the completed Mohole. This is the in-hole seismograph.

Seismologists extract data from earthquake records by timing the arrival of the first waves. Using this travel time they then try to work out the rock pathways which the seismic waves have followed. Often the paths are very complex, involving several layers and several kinds of rock, each with a different velocity. For example, many earthquakes originate beneath the ocean and their waves travel to seismic observatories on land by "mixed paths"—partly in oceanic rocks and partly in continental rocks. This means that the seismologist obtains velocities that are the average of both rocks. He would like to make records of waves that have traveled by "pure" paths.

A seismograph in the Mohole, resting directly on the rock of the mantle, would have two major advantages over those on land. The background noise—the confused jiggles on the record caused by wind, running water, and the disturbances of civilization—would be small and there would be a direct pathway from the deep oceanic earthquake belts.

A small down-hole seismograph capable of withstanding the heat and pressure of the depths could be developed by the time the Mohole is ready for it. It would telemeter its information up a cable to a buoy at the ocean surface, where the data would be recorded or transmitted by radio to a receiver on shore.

But long before this seismograph is operating, the Moho ship and its crew will have returned to port—probably to go into dry dock immediately to be examined and refitted before it starts on another hole in another ocean.

After the data from the cores and logs and bottom instruments has been analyzed and interpreted by each of the subsciences, the initiative returns to the geophysical generalist again. His is the endless task of fitting the new information into the old, of reconciling the data of the space probes with the data of the earth probes, of improving the structural and historical description of the earth.

The new picture will be different in various ways. It will be more accurate and more complete; it will reinforce today's indirect knowledge with solid proof. But even as the generalist makes this advance he will outline new and more difficult problems whose solutions will make even greater demands on man's imagination and ingenuity.

Whether or not man's concept of the earth will undergo major revision cannot be foretold. But the goal of basic research—a better understanding of the earth for the sake of knowledge itself—will surely be fulfilled.

XV

The Future

This book has attempted to summarize man's ideas about the history, structure, and composition of the earth, for these form the conceptual foundation of the Mohole project. The product of 2500 years of scientific work is a framework of interlocking evidence like the structural-steel framework of a large building. Some day a towering edifice will exist; now the building is but a few stories high. Where the theoretical framework has been completed, routine collectors of data are busy compartmenting the floors into rooms. Where the construction is finished, commerce and industry have moved in and are making good use of the building. High above, scientists standing on the scaffolding of new hypotheses are using new evidence to rivet new theories solidly into place.

In man's great undertaking to gain complete knowledge of the universe, the Mohole project will play an important part. It will mark the beginning of explorations in the largest and least-known area on earth—the strata beneath the sea. The present Mohole project is only a beginning, but it will generate so much scientific excitement that deep-sea drilling will never stop. Other drilling ships will be fitted out by other countries. Before long they will become necessary scientific tools to be operated on a routine basis like radio telescopes, nuclear-particle accelerators, and satellites.

Virtually all of the earth remains to be explored in depth. In addition to the unknown ocean floor, there are vast areas of rock covered by tundra and jungle, ice sheets and wind-blown sand which have never been properly examined. Furthermore, the interior of the earth has myriad mysteries waiting to be unraveled.

Young people, searching for a career which combines intellectual excitement with travel, will do well to consider any of the earth sciences. Those who also want adventure on the high seas and a chance to join the age-old battle of man against the ocean will do well to consider oceanographic engineering. If they do and find a fraction of the stimulation, friends, and satisfaction in work that most of the AMSOC group have found, they will be well rewarded.

The Mohole project is a quest for fundamental scientific knowledge through basic research. It has no commercial or military reason to exist; its only aim is the fuller understanding of the earth. However, an experimental engineering project of these heroic proportions can hardly fail to have tremendous implications for those industries which use related technologies.

The petroleum industry will be influenced by the means employed for deep drilling and for drilling in deep water. The metals industries will see that it is possible to work on the ocean floor and recover the valuable mineral deposits awaiting exploitation. Naval engineers will discover that they need to hold ships in a fixed position in the deep sea and place heavy objects on the bottom precisely. Much of the future development of ocean resources will be traceable to the techniques first developed for the Mohole.

The United States is now competing for scientific and technical supremacy with the Soviet Union. The main battleground to date has been space and the main driving force has been the need for military know-how. But in addition to the military aspects of the space race, both sides are also interested in the exploration of the solar system by means of space ships. In the remote reaches of the solar system, space pioneers may make many valuable discoveries. However, if one disregards the romance and fun of landing on the moon or Mars and honestly answers the question: What is the best way to search for new evidence about the solar system?, drilling down will easily win over rocketing out.

In the field of drilling we would gladly engage the Soviets in a technological race, confident that United States deep-drilling technology and the capability for working in the ocean is well in the forefront. Perhaps, in the remoteness of the rocks beneath the sea, a scientific struggle will take place in which each side will see who can make the most discoveries first. It would be proper for two great nations to compete in this way, since mankind will surely profit from the results.

The earth scientist of today can count among his resources a century of modern geological thinking. He lives in an era of public understanding which will not condemn him for a radical theory; he can call on half a dozen related sciences for technical assistance; he can find massive financial support for projects too grand in scope to have been considered a generation ago. But still, he is wise to heed the words Nicholas Desmarest used 150 years ago to answer the geological theoreticians: "Go and see."

So the Mohole project will follow a classical pattern. We shall go and see for ourselves what the hidden rocks are like. Our trail will be marked by a series of holes in the bottom of the sea.

Appendix I

UNIT EQUIVALENTS

LINEAR

2.54 centimeters	= 1 inch 1 meter = 39.4 inches
1 kilometer	= 0.62 miles = 3281 feet = (about) ⅗ mile
30.5 centimeters	= 1 foot
1 knot (nautical mile)	= 1 minute of arc at the equator = 6080.20 feet
1 fathom	= 6 feet

SQUARE

1 square mile = 2.59 square kilometers

MASS

1 kilogram = 2.204 pounds
1 pound   = 0.453 kilograms

VELOCITY

1 kilometer/second = 3273 feet/second
8.2 kilometers/second
   (below Moho) = 26,838 feet/second

ACCELERATION

1 gal = 1 cm/sec^2 = 0.033 ft/sec^2
gravity at equatorial
   sea level = 978.05 gals or 32.27 ft/sec^2

PRESSURE

1 bar = 0.987 atmospheres = 14.5 psi
The pressure at the center of the earth = 3.9 million bars or 56.5 million psi
   earth = 3.9 million bars or 56.5 million psi

TEMPERATURE

To change Fahrenheit to Centigrade, subtract 32° and multiply by 5/9
To change Centigrade to Fahrenheit, multiply by 9/5 and add 32°.
Thus, 150° C = 302° F (approximate temperature of oceanic Moho)

Appendix II

BIBLIOGRAPHY

GEOLOGY-GEOPHYSICS

Bowen, R. N. C., *The Exploration of Time*. London: George Newnes, 1958.

Eiby, G. A. *About Earthquakes*. New York: Harper and Brothers, 1957.

Gamow, George. *One Two Three—Infinity*. New York: Mentor, 1954.

Gilluly, J., Waters, A. C., Woodford, A. O. *Principles of Geology*. San Francisco: W. H. Freeman & Co., 1953.

Gutenberg, Beno. *Internal Constitution of the Earth*. New York: Dover Publications, 1951.

Gutenberg, Beno, *The Physics of the Earth's Interior*, New York: Academic Press, 1959.

Holmes, Arthur. *Principles of Physical Geology*. New York: The Ronald Press, 1945.

Jacobs, J. A., Russell, R. D., Wilson, J. Tuzo. *Physics and Geology*. Toronto: McGraw-Hill, 1959.

Jakowsky, J. J. *Exploration Geophysics*. Los Angeles: Times Mirror Press, 1940.

Jeffreys, Harold. *Earthquakes and Mountains*, Cambridge, England: Cambridge University Press, 1952.

Moore, Ruth. *The Earth We Live On*. New York: Alfred A. Knopf, 1956.

The Planet Earth. New York: Scientific American Book, Simon and Schuster, 1957.

The Universe. New York: Scientific American Book, Simon and Schuster, 1957.

OCEANOGRAPHY

Kuenen, Ph. H. *Marine Geology*. New York: John Wiley & Sons, 1950.

Raitt, Helen. *Exploring the Deep Pacific*. New York: W. W. Norton, 1955.

Sverdrup, H., Johnson, M., Fleming, R. *The Oceans*. New York: Prentice-Hall, 1942.

HISTORICAL

Darwin, Charles. *The Voyage of the Beagle*. New York: Bantam Books, 1958.
Davidson, Charles. *The Founders of Seismology*. Cambridge, England: Cambridge University Press, 1927.
Gardner, Martin. *Fads and Fallacies in the Name of Science*. New York: Reinhart and Company, 1952.

REFERRED TO OR EXCERPTS USED IN THE TEXT

Burroughs, Edgar Rice. *Tarzan at the Earth's Core*. New York: Metropolitan Books, 1930.
Doyle, Arthur Conan. *The Complete Professor Challenger Stories*. London: John Murray, 1958.
Gonzales, Jenaro, and Foshag, William F. *The Birth of Paracutin*. Report of the Smithsonian Institution, 1946.
Mohorovičić, A., *The Earthquake of October 8, 1909*. Zagreb: Yearbook of the Meteorological Observatory Part IV, Section 1, 1909.
Plato. *Dialogues of Plato* (Jowett translation). New York: Pocket Books, 1950.
Verne, Jules. *Journey to the Center of the Earth*. Toronto: Blackie & Son.

OIL-WELL OPERATIONS

Ball, Max. *This Fascinating Oil Business*. Indianapolis: Bobbs-Merrill, 1940.
Uren, Lester C. *Petroleum Production Engineering*. New York: McGraw-Hill, 1956.
Introduction to Schlumberger Well Logging. Document No. 8, Schlumberger Well Surveying Corporation, 1958.
A Primer of Oil Well Drilling. Austin: Petroleum Extention Service, University of Texas, 1957.

MAGAZINE AND JOURNAL REFERENCES

Bascom, Willard. "The Mohole," *Scientific American*, April 1959.
Bascom, Willard. "Ocean Waves," *Scientific American*, August 1959.

Bauer, R. F., Field, A. J., and Stratton, Hal, "Offshore Drilling for Onshore Prices," *Oil and Gas Journal,* June 30, 1958.

Bingman, W. E. "The Status of Turbodrilling in the U.S.A.," American Petroleum Institute Paper No. 906-5-D, Southwestern District Meeting, Dallas, Texas, March 1960.

Elsasser, Walter M., "The Earth as a Dynamo," *Scientific American,* May 1958.

Gaskell, T. F. "A Borehole to the Earth's Mantle," *Nature,* Vol. 182, No. 4637, September 13, 1958.

Hess, H. H. "The Oceanic Crust," *Journal of Marine Research,* Vol. 14, No. 4, December 31, 1955.

Ladd, H. S., Tracey, J., Lill, G. G. "Drilling on Bikini Atoll, Marshall Islands," *Science,* January 16, 1948, Vol. 107, No. 2768, pp. 51.

Ladd, H. S., *et al.* "Drilling on Eniwetok Atoll, Marshall Islands," Bulletin of the American Association of Petroleum Geologists, Vol. 37, No. 10, October 1953.

Lill, G. G., and Bascom, W. "A Bore-Hole to the Earth's Mantle: AMSOC's Mohole, *Nature,* Vol. 184, July 18, 1959.

Lill, G. G., and Maxwell, A. E. "On Determining the Nature of the Earth's Mantle," *Science,* Vol. 129, No. 3360, May 22, 1959.

Pake, George. "Magnetic Resonance," *Scientific American,* August 1958.

Pettersson, Hans "Cosomic Spherules and Meteoritic Dust," *Scientific American,* February 1960.

Rubey, W. W. "Geologic History of Sea Water," *Bull of G.S.A.,* Vol. 62, September 1951.

Runcorn, S. K. "Rock Magnetism," *Science,* Vol. 129, No. 3355, April 1959.

Wager, L. R. "Beneath the Earth's Crust," *Advancement of Science,* No. 58, September 1958.

Wilson, Tuzo. "Geophysics and Continental Growth," *American Scientist,* Vol. 47, No. 1, March 1959.

Worzel, J. L., and Shurbet. "Gravity Anomalies of Continental Margins," *Proceedings of National Academy of Sciences,* Vol. 41, No. 7, 1955.

Zimmerman, R. M., Terrell, T. H., and Nagle, E. T., Jr. "The Drilling and Completion of the Richardson & Bass-Mecom-Freeport-Humble-LL&E-State 2414, Well No. 1L," American Petroleum Institute, Paper No. 926-2-K, Southern District, Shreveport, La., March 1957.

Appendix III

THE AMSOC COMMITTEE

CHAIRMAN: Gordon G. Lill, Office of Naval Research, Washington, D.C.

PROJECT DIRECTOR: Willard Bascom, National Academy of Sciences, Washington, D.C.

Dr. Maurice Ewing,* Lamont Geological Observatory, Palisades, New York

Dr. William B. Heroy, The Geotechnical Corporation, Dallas, Texas

Dr. Harry H. Hess, Princeton University, Princeton, New Jersey

Dr. Harry S. Ladd, U. S. Geological Survey, Washington, D.C.

Dr. Arthur E. Maxwell, Office of Naval Research, Washington, D.C.

Dr. Walter Munk, Scripps Institution of Oceanography, La Jolla, California

Dr. Roger Revelle, Scripps Institution of Oceanography, La Jolla, California

Dr. William W. Rubey, U. S. Geological Survey, Washington, D.C.

Dr. Joshua I. Tracey, U. S. Geological Survey, Washington, D.C.

Lt. Col. George Colchagoff, Air Force Office of Scientific Research, Washington, D.C. (Liaison representative)

Dr. Leonard S. Wilson, Army Research Office, Washington, D.C. (Liaison representative)

Mr. William Bates,† Shell Oil Co., Los Angeles, Calif.

Dr. J. B. Hersey,† Woods Hole Oceanographic Institution, Woods Hole, Mass.

Capt. Harold Saunders,† USN (ret.), Bureau of Ships, USN, Washington, D.C.

* resigned April 21, 1960
† added July 7, 1960

PANEL ON SCIENTIFIC OBJECTIVES AND MEASUREMENTS

CHAIRMAN: Dr. Harry S. Ladd, U. S. Geological Survey, Washington, D.C.

VICE-CHAIRMAN: Dr. James R. Balsley, Jr., U. S. Geological Survey, Washington, D.C.

Dr. Francis Birch, Harvard University, Cambridge, Massachusetts

Lt. Col. George Colchagoff, Air Force Office of Scientific Research, Washington, D.C.

Mr. Henri-Georges Doll, Schlumberger Well Surveying Corporation, Ridgefield, Connecticut

Mr. David Ericson, Lamont Geological Observatory, Palisades, New York

Dr. George V. Keller, U. S. Geological Survey, Denver, Colorado

Dr. John Lyman, National Science Foundation, Washington, D.C.

Dr. Arthur E. Maxwell, Office of Naval Research, Washington, D.C.

Dr. H. W. Menard, Scripps Institution of Oceanography, La Jolla, California

Dr. William T. Pecora, U. S. Geological Survey, Washington, D.C.

Dr. Hatten Yoder, Geophysical Laboratory, Carnegie Institution of Washington, Washington, D.C.

PANEL ON DRILLING TECHNIQUES

CHAIRMAN: Dr. William B. Heroy, The Geotechnical Corporation, Dallas, Texas

Dr. Paul P. Reichertz, Socony Mobil Oil Company, Dallas, Texas
(Alternate: Mr. Warren Brooks)

Mr. Douglas Ragland, Humble Oil and Refining Company, Houston, Texas
(Alternate: Mr. R. P. Knapp)

Mr. Arthur Lubinski, Pan American Petroleum Corporation, Tulsa, Oklahoma

Mr. E. M. Kipp, Standard Oil Company of California, San Francisco, California
(Alternate: Mr. Kenneth M. Nicolson)

Mr. W. A. Roberts, Phillips Petroleum Company, Los Angeles, California

Mr. C. Don Woodward, Texaco, Bellaire, Texas
(Alternate: Mr. Charles Wright)

PANEL ON SITE SELECTION

CHAIRMAN: Dr. Harry H. Hess, Department of Geology, Princeton University, Princeton, New Jersey

Dr. J. B. Hersey, Woods Hole Oceanographic Institution, Woods Hole, Massachusetts

Dr. John E. Nafe, Lamont Geological Observatory, Palisades, New York

Dr. Russell Raitt, Scripps Institution of Oceanography, La Jolla, California

Dr. George Shor, Scripps Institution of Oceanography, La Jolla, California

Staff Members of the National Science Foundation who are involved in the Mohole Project

Dr. Alan Waterman, Director

Dr. Richard H. Bolt, Associate Director (research)

Dr. Randal Robertson, Assistant Director, Division of Mathematical, Physical and Engineering Sciences

Dr. William Benson, Program Director, Earth Sciences Program

Dr. Roy Hanson, Associate Program Director, Earth Sciences Program

Personnel of the National Academy of Sciences-National Research Council who are involved in the Mohole Project

Dr. Detlev W. Bronk, President

Dr. S. Douglas Cornell, Executive Officer

Mr. G. D. Meid, Business Manager

Dr. John Adkins, Chairman, 1959–60, Earth Sciences Division

Dr. William R. Thurston, Executive Secretary, 1956–60, Earth Sciences Division

Dr. E. B. Espenshade, Jr., Chairman, 1960–61, Earth Sciences Division

Dr. Linn Hoover, Executive Secretary, 1960– , Earth Sciences Division

Staff Members of the AMSOC Committee

Mr. Willard Bascom	Director
Miss Sheila Walker	Secretary
Dr. John L. Mero*	Mining Engineer
Mr. Albert J. Milhomme*	Petroleum Engineer
Mr. Robert Taggart	Naval Architect
Dr. Jack I. McLelland	Mining Engineer (chief engineer on experimental drilling)
Mr. Philip M. LaHue*	Electronics Engineer (courtesy of Minneapolis-Honeywell Regulator Co.)
Mrs. Maria W. Krusos	Secretary
Mr. Edward E. Horton	Petroleum Engineer
Mr. Francois J. Lampietti	Mining Engineer
Mr. Peter A. Johnson	Naval Architect
Mr. Harold E. Ohanian	Electronics Engineer (Courtesy of Union Carbide Corporation)
Mr. Robert M. Snyder	Electronics Engineer
Mr. G. H. Savage	Geological Engineer
Mr. C. Don Woodward*	Petroleum Engineer (AMSOC drilling superintendent on experimental drilling) (Courtesy Texaco Inc.)
Mr. William R. Riedel*	Paleontologist (chief scientist on experimental drilling)

*temporary

Consultants to AMSOC Committee

Mr. John Marriner	Naval Architect
Mr. William J. Johnston	Legal Consultant
Mr. J. J. Leenderste	Civil Engineer
Mr. Hew D. Fanshawe	Petroleum Engineer
Dr. T. Vreeland, Jr.	Civil Engineer

Index

A

D

H

Holmes, Arthur, 110
Honolulu *Advertiser*, 42
Horizon, research vessel, 39
Horton, Edward, 277
Hudson Laboratory, 213
Hughes Tool Company, 282
Humble Oil Company, 245
Hutton, James, 75, 76
Hydrogen, 185
Hydrogen bomb, 39, 256

I

Igneous rocks, 74, 84, 85, 131, 139, 210, 314
Inside the earth, crank ideas, 62–65; MOLE, the, 65–66; science fiction, 57–62; speculation and theories, 67–68
Institute of Geophysics, UCLA, 176, 181
Intensity scale, earthquake, 124
International Drilling Machines, 298
International Flat Earth Society, 65
International Geophysical Year, 52
International Union of Geodesy and Geophysics (IUGG), 43, 49–50, 236
Ionium, 89, 91, 92
Isaacs, John, 31–33
Isostasy, 100–6
Isotopes, 89, 174
IUGG. *See* International Union of Geodesy and Geophysics

J

Jade, 186
Jaggar, T. A., 42–44
Jeffreys, Sir Harold, 79
Journey to the Center of the Earth, 57–59

K

Katz, Dr., 135
Kelvin, Lord, 26, 121

N

O

P

S